The Biology
of the Algae

The Biology of the Algae

Second Edition

F. E. ROUND, B.Sc., Ph.D., D.Sc.
Reader in Phycology, University of Bristol

ST. MARTIN'S PRESS   NEW YORK

Preface

The basic plan of the first edition and the balance of its content remain in this new edition for the same aims have been retained and the biology of the algae has not changed its emphasis in the last eight years. However, the opportunity has been taken to make many adjustments.

The first edition was a condensed account and thus some extensions have been made in a number of places throughout the book. Some new material has been incorporated taking into account recent work, but this has been very selective in order to keep the size of the book within reasonable bounds. In a number of cases illustrations have been amended and several new photographs have been added.

Most of the examples chosen are readily obtainable as teaching material but, since the approach is not that of the type methods used in many other books, other examples easily fit in with the text.

1973   F.E.R.

Preface to first edition

The aim of this book is to give a general account of the biology of the algae without undue emphasis on any one aspect. Thus early chapters on structure and reproduction have been reduced to proportions commensurate with an attempt to cover the algae in this wider biological sense—especially since excellent and detailed treatments are available in Fritsch's *Structure and Reproduction of the Algae*, in Smith's *Manual of Phycology*, in Fott's *Algenkunde*, in Chadefaud and Emberger's *Traite de Botanique*, and most recently in Christensen's *Alger*.

This approach has allowed more space to be devoted to cytology and especially ultrastructure, a field where considerable advances have been made, not only in detailed descriptive studies of the finer structure of algae but also in structure related to function and classification. Approximately half the book is devoted to the ecology and physiology of algae; I have attempted to present a wide picture of the role played by algae in their natural environments and to show how they have been used extensively to elucidate basic biochemical and physiological problems. In the latter context the intention has not been to write a physiological treatise but only to illustrate some of the physiological problems which have been investigated using algae as experimental organisms. This section commences with a discussion of cultural techniques which are the basis of much experimental work. Finally chapters on fossil, economic and classificatory aspects have been included. In the latter, simple descriptions of classes and simple keys to classes and orders are provided so that students may be enabled to place class material into a preliminary position, from which they may proceed using the appropriate detailed floras. Because most biologists work with visual images of organisms I have attempted to illustrate as many genera as possible within the space available—specific epithets have on the whole been avoided since identification to species is only possible with a full flora. Many of the drawings are from original material; the remainder are taken from standard texts and original papers and these have been acknowledged.

I wish to thank the many phycologists with whom I have discussed various aspects of this book. In particular I wish to thank Dr. J. W. G. Lund, F.R.S., who guided my early steps in phycology and who has encouraged my work ever since. He has now read and criticized the whole of this book. The chapters on physiology have been improved by discussions with Dr. B. F. Folkes who has also read and made numerous valuable suggestions to this section. I am greatly indebted to Professor R. D. Preston, F.R.S., Dr. G. F. Leedale, Dr. H. Canter-Lund and Dr. M. Parke for sending me copies of original electron-micrographs and photographs.

1965   F. E. R.

Contents

Introduction

The algae are a heterogeneous group of cryptogamic plants comprising thirteen large phyla and several smaller groups still incompletely studied. They have a long fossil history, some of them possibly extending back to the time of the origin of photosynthetic cellular plants. They are generally considered to be the group from which all the more complex Cryptogams and ultimately the Spermophyta arose. Morphologically they are cellular plants growing as single cells or aggregations of cells and sometimes even forming parenchymatous thalli, although these are still relatively undifferentiated into organs and only in the most complex genera are elementary conducting tissues found. Nevertheless the range of form is great, from minute cells a few micrometres in diameter up to the large seaweeds of the Antarctic which are many metres in length and weigh as much as a small tree. In many of the so-called simpler types of algae, organization of the cell is much more complex than that of any cell of a higher plant since more organelles are contained within its wall. Many possess the animal attribute of motility and in form grade into the Protozoa until no distinction between the two groups is possible.

Reproductive processes are almost as varied as the life forms and involve vegetative, asexual and sexual mechanisms, often characterized by the production of motile flagellate zoospores or gametes but also accompanied by evolution of oogamy in diverse groups. However, a multicellular wall around the sporangia or gametangia such as occurs in even the simplest Bryophyta is absent in the algae apart from the antheridium of the Charophyta. The gametangia are usually unprotected but in the more complex thalloid genera they may be borne on special structures and even embedded within the thallus which is differentiated around them. Many genera and even divisions are characterized by the development of morphologically identical (isomorphic) or morphologically dissimilar (heteromorphic) gametophyte and sporophyte plants and thus are said to exhibit a life history. In one group, the Rhodophyta, the production of accessory stages and spores in the life cycle is developed to an extreme degree leading to the most complex reproductive system in the plant kingdom, whilst at the other end of the scale in the Cyanophyta no sexual stages have been discovered and these plants are possibly the simplest in the plant kingdom apart from the Bacteria.

Despite the extreme morphological, cytological and reproductive variation in the groups of algae, the basic biochemical mechanisms and pathways appear to be similar to those of other plants. For example they all possess chlorophyll a and have a photosynthetic system working via this pigment. The basic nutrient requirements and the end products of assimilation, carbohydrates and proteins, are similar to those of higher plants even though the range of carbohydrates is greater. Both because of this similarity and because of the interest in investigating plants forming unfamiliar carbohydrates, the algae have been used in many basic physiological problems where the growth of the organism is facilitated by liquid culture. They are now proving equally valuable tools in studying metabolic pathways since many of the unicells, e.g. *Chlorella* and *Chlamydomonas* can be induced to form biochemical mutants.

Ecologically the algae are a world-wide group occurring on the land surface on all types of soil and on permanent ice and snowfields but having their major centre of distribution in the waters which cover 70 per cent of the earth's surface. Here they are the major primary producers of organic carbon compounds. They occur in the form of microscopic phytoplankton and as both microscopic and macroscopic growths along the boundary between land and water. In the ocean this littoral habitat is occupied by few plants other than algae. They are thus a fundamental but as yet only incompletely investigated part of the food chain leading to fish in most aquatic environments. Finally they have themselves been exploited as food and as a source of organic chemicals, although no longer of inorganic elements after their initial exploitation, following the discovery in the nineteenth century of iodine and bromine in seaweeds.

1   Morphology

Algae range in form from unicellular, through colonial, filamentous, siphonaceous, to the complex parenchymatous thalli of the larger seaweeds. The unicells may be sub-divided into non-motile (Protococcoidal), 'amoeba'-like (Rhizopodial) and motile cells (Flagellate). The colonial habit is achieved by the aggregation of the products of cell division within a mucilage mass (Tetrasporal), by juxtaposition of cells subsequent to division (Coenobial) or by the aggregation of motile cells (Flagellate coenobia). Filaments are formed by repeated transverse division of cells without separation of the daughter cells, and branching occurs by lateral outgrowth from cells and the formation of cross walls. The heterotrichous type of filamentous thallus is produced by the specialization of filaments into creeping and upright systems and is often associated with localization of cell division at the base of branches (trichothallic). Repeated nuclear division, without cross wall formation, is characteristic of the siphonaceous habit. Complex siphonaceous thalli are formed by the branching of the siphons and the aggregation of several siphons to form multiaxial types. Parenchymatous thalli are formed by the division of the cells of a filament in two or more planes. This is frequently accompanied by the localization of the meristem in either an apical or intercalary position. Complicated pseudo-parenchymatous thalli are also formed from the branching of a single central filament (Uniaxial), or from the branching of several central filaments (Multiaxial) in the Rhodophyta and some Phaeophyta.

UNICELLULAR ORGANIZATION

Simple isolated cells are found in all groups except the Charophyta and the Phaeophyta, whilst in some groups they are the only form represented e.g. Bacillariophyta. They are not necessarily the simplest cell forms, but are a convenient starting point, since they often exemplify, within a single cell, the morphological, cytological and physiological characteristics of the group. They are sometimes termed acellular rather than unicellular, since they function as a complete living unit without recourse to cellular differentiation.

Rhizopodial type

Rhizopodial cells lack rigid cell walls and form cytoplasmatic projections; they are found in the Chrysophyceae* (*Rhizochrysis* Fig. 1A), in the Xantho-

---

* For a synopsis of classification see Chapter 13.

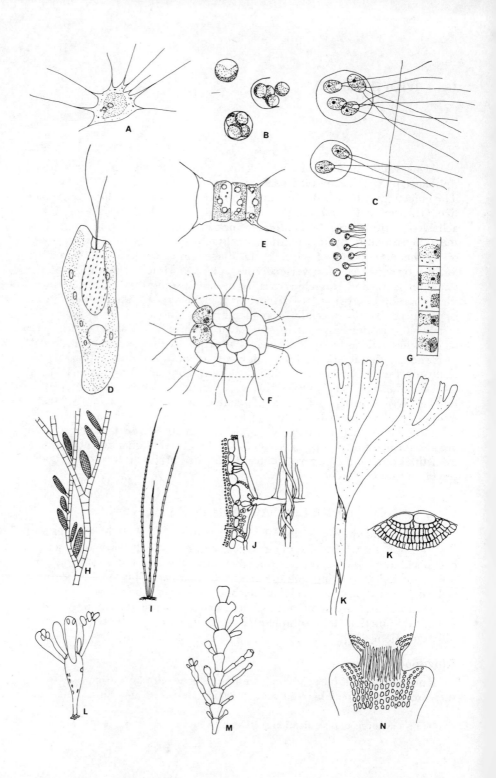

phyceae (*Rhizochloris* Fig. 2B) and in the Dinophyceae (*Dinamoebidium*). Rhizopodial forms also occur in which the cell is contained within a theca, from which cytoplasmic filaments extend, e.g. *Heliactis* in the Chrysophyceae and *Rhizolekane* in the Xanthophyceae (Fig. 2A and C).

Protococcoidal type

Some of the simplest non-motile genera are found in the Cyanophyta, e.g. *Synechococcus*, which lacks even an organized nucleus and plastids (see p. 45) whilst simple spherical cells with a nucleus and plastids containing the characteristic pigments of the group, occur in the Chlorophyceae (*Chlorella* Fig. 1B), Chrysophyceae (*Chrysosphaera*), Eustigmatophyceae (*Chlorobotrys*), Rhodophyta (*Porphyridium*), and Dinophyceae (*Cystodinium*). Not only are they distinguished by their coloration, but also by their form, e.g. in *Chlorella* there is a single bowl-shaped chromatophore, in *Chrysosphaera* the chromatophore is plate-like and in *Porphyridium* star-like.

The protococcoidal type of unicell may also be a circular or elongate box-like structure as in many diatoms (Bacillariophyta): triangular as in *Tetragonidium* (Cryptophyceae), *Goniochloris* (Xanthophyceae) and *Triceratium* (Bacillariophyceae): or elongate with a basal attachment disc, as in *Characium* (Chlorophyceae) and *Characiopsis* (Xanthophyceae). Two specialized and morphologically variable types of unicells are found in the Zygnemaphyceae and Bacillariophyceae. In the former the unicell may be rod-shaped and provided with two complex spiral chromatophores, e.g. *Spirotaenia*, with a plate-like chromatophore, *Mesotaenium*, or with two stellate chromatophores (*Cylindrocystis*); these are examples of Saccoderm Desmids in which the wall is composed of a single piece (Fig. 2). In the Placoderm Desmids the cell is composed of two halves, either fitting together without any constriction, e.g. the lunate shaped *Closterium*, or with a constriction (the sinus) between the two semi-cells which are then joined by the isthmus, e.g. *Cosmarium*, *Micrasterias* and *Staurastrum* (Fig. 2). In all these, not only is the cell wall ornamented with ribs, spines, warts, etc., but the chromatophores are complex, often lobed structures, one in each semi-cell. It is rarely possible to see that two half cells are involved, since the

---

FIG. 1. EXAMPLES OF MORPHOLOGICAL TYPES IN THE ALGAE.

A. Rhizopodial—*Rhizochrysis*; B. Protococcoidal—*Chlorella* single cell and formation of autospores; C. Tetrasporal—*Tetraspora*, part of mucilaginous colony and two groups of cells further magnified; D. Flagellate—*Cryptomonas*; E. Coenobial—*Scenedesmus*; F. Flagellate colony—*Pandorina*; G. Filamentous—*Ulothrix*; H. Filamentous—simple branching—*Ectocarpus*; I, J. Filamentous, uniaxial—*Lemanea*, whole plants and longitudinal section; K. Parenchymatous—*Dictyota*, part of plant and apex of branch; L. Siphonaceous—*Valonia*; M, N. Filamentous multiaxial—*Corallina*, part of plant and section through articulation.

(After Fott, Huber-Pestalozzi, Kjellman, Oltmanns, Smith and original.)

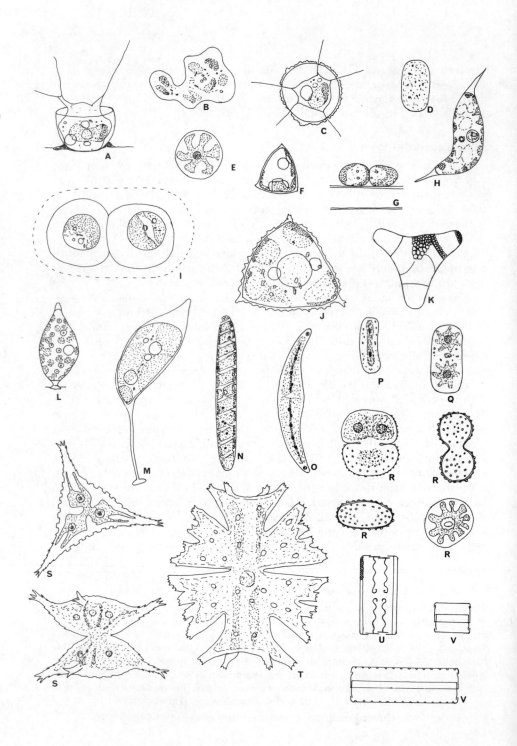

join by a bevelled edge is all but indistinguishable. The diatom (Bacillario-phyceae) cell again consists of two halves (thecae) joined together by girdle bands (hoops) (Fig. 2, Plate 12B). Wall structure is more complex than that found in any other group due to the poroid nature of the siliceous wall (see p. 40). Morphologically at least three types are recognizable: (*i*) the centric type in which the thecae are circular in outline, e.g. *Coscinodiscus* and *Cyclotella* (Plate 11B, C): (*ii*) a group in which the symmetry is based on 3, 4, or 5 equal axes, e.g. *Triceratium*: (*iii*) the pennate type which is elongated and bilaterally symmetrical, e.g. *Navicula*, *Gyrosigma* and *Pinnularia*. The brown chromatophores may be discoid, stellate or plate-like, often with complex lobing, whilst numerous discoid chromatophores are found in many of the Centrales and two parietal plates in some Pennales. Many pennate diatoms are actively motile and most Desmids produce copious mucilage sheaths, a few also being slightly motile.

Flagellate unicells

Motile vegetative cells, moving by means of flagella, are found in all groups except the Cyanophyta, Rhodophyta, Zygnemaphyceae, Phaeophyta, Charophyceae, Bryopsidophyceae and Bacillariophyceae. Motile gametes or zoospores occur however in all but the first three groups. With a few exceptions the structure of the flagellate vegetative cells, gametes and zoospores, of any group is remarkably constant and characteristic. Thus in the Chlorophyceae (Isokontae) the vegetative cells, the zoospores and the gametes, all have 2 equal flagella or multiples of 2, in the Dinophyceae there are 2 unequal flagella running in different planes, in the Xanthophyceae (Heterokontae) there are two unequal flagella in the same plane, in the Chrysophyceae one or two and in the pigmented Euglenophyta one long and, at least in some, one short (Figs. 3 and 4).

In the Euglenophyta the striate pellicle is either pliable, allowing change in shape of the cell (many *Euglena* spp.), or is firm and then often markedly striate (some *Euglena* and most *Phacus* spp.). The cell in *Euglena* is either radial or flattened and in Phacus the flattening is extreme and often accompanied by torsion of the cell. The flagellum passes into the cell through an anterior invagination at the base of which is the second shorter flagellum.

Fig. 2. Rhizopodial and Protococcoidal Cell Types.

A. *Rhizolekane*; B. *Rhizochloris*; C. *Heliactis*; D. *Synechococcus*; E. *Porphyridium*; F. *Tetragonidium*; G. *Chrysosphaera*; H. *Cystodinium*; I. *Chlorobotrys*; J. *Goniochloris*; K. *Triceratium*; L. *Characium*; M. *Characiopsis*; N. *Spirotaenia*; O. *Closterium*; P. *Mesotaenium*; Q. *Cylindrocystis*; R. *Cosmarium*, face, side and top view and stellate chromatophore; S. *Staurastrum*, side and top view; T. *Micrasterias*; U. *Grammato-phora*, girdle view showing girdle bands and septae; V. *Pinnularia*, side and end girdle view.

(After Beger, Carter, Ettl, Fott, Hustedt, Pascher, West and West, West and Carter and original.)

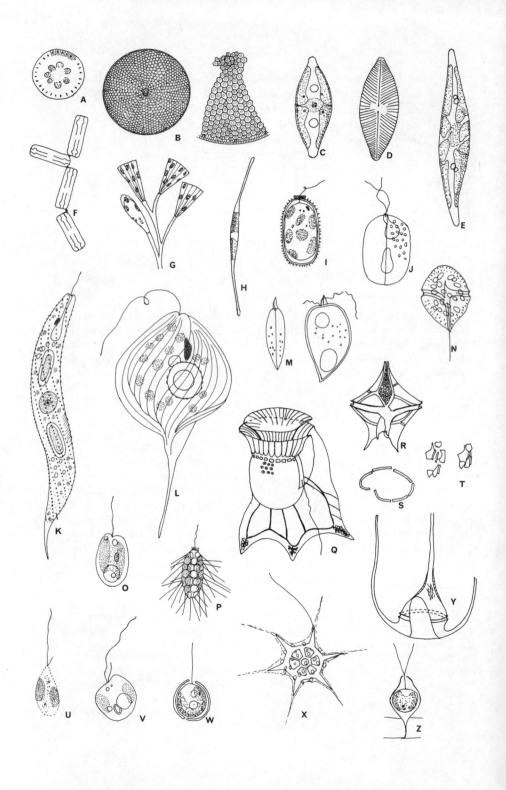

Around this region are found contractile vacuoles and frequently a red eye spot free in the cytoplasm. In *Trachelomonas* the long flagellum passes out through a pore surrounded by a collar at the anterior end of the theca. The theca itself is frequently ornamented with spines or warts and stained brown or black with iron and manganese compounds and encloses a typical euglenoid cell. Green chromatophores with pyrenoids are either discoid, band-shaped or stellate in this phylum.

In the Cryptophyceae (*Cryptomonas*, *Chroomonas*), the ovoid or elongate cell has a fine periplast with an apical depression, from which arise two almost equal flagella (Fig. 1). This depression is lined with trichocysts which shoot threads out when stimulated (cf. the Coelenterata). The cells contain one or two rather ill-defined parietal chromatophores, which may be olive green, brown, red or rarely blue in colour.

The Dinophyceae are a predominantly flagellate group, in which 2 main cell types may be recognized. The marine genera *Exuviaella* and *Prorocentrum* possess a rigid membrane, composed of two halves each like a watch-glass, joined at a suture in the anterior/posterior plane (Fig. 3 and Plate 10C of *Dinophysis*). The cells have two apical flagella, one of which is thread-like, whilst the other is band-shaped and undulates around the former. The second cell type, found in some Dinophysalidales and Dinophyceae, has one transverse and one longitudinal furrow; the band-shaped flagellum undulates within the transverse furrow, and the thread-like flagellum extends from the longitudinal furrow into the water. The two flagella emerge from pores on the longitudinal furrow in the Dinophysalidales, e.g. *Ornithocercus* and at the junction of the two furrows in the Dinophyceae, e.g. *Peridinium*. The latter group have either a fairly rigid periplast (e.g. *Gymnodinium*) or a rigid skeleton of cellulose plates joined at sutures, e.g. *Peridinium* and *Ceratium*. These plates are frequently ornamented with pores, warts, spines, etc., and in some instances are produced into ridges along the edges of the furrows (Plate 10). The plates are formed in vesicles (Plate 11A). The furrows themselves are lined with plates and the arrangement of these in the longitudinal furrow is complex and of importance in the classification of the

---

Fig. 3. Further Protococcoidal and Unicellular Flagellate Cell Types.

A. *Cyclotella*; B. *Coscinodiscus*, valve face and pores enlarged; C. *Navicula*, with cell contents; D. *Navicula*, showing markings on valve; E. *Gyrosigma*; F. Colony of *Grammatophora*; G. Colony of *Licmophora*; H. *Nitzschia*; I. *Trachelomonas*; J. *Exuviaella*; K. *Euglena*; L. *Phacus*; M. *Prorocentrum*, side and face view; N. *Gymnodinium*; O. *Chromulina*; P. *Mallomonas*; Q. *Ornithocercus*; R. *Peridinium*; S. Girdle plates of *Gonyaulax*; T. Plates in longitudinal furrow of *Peridinium*, expanded on left, unexpanded on right; U. *Heterochloris*; V. *Ochromonas*; W. *Chrysococcus*; X. *Dictyocha*; Y. *Ceratium*; Z. *Chrysopyxis*.

(After Bourelly, Cleve–Euler, Conrad, Ettl, Graham, Huber–Pestalozzi, Hustedt, Nygaard, Marshall, Pascher, Pochmann, Schütt, Stein and original.)

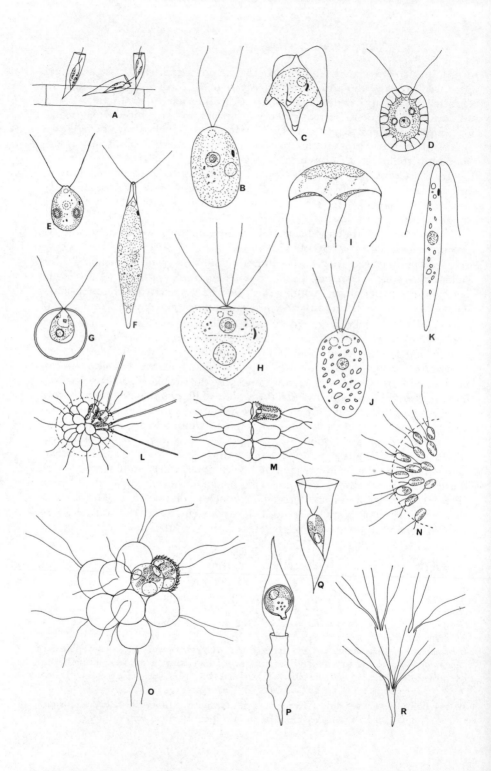

species (Fig. 3). Trichocysts are located beneath thin areas of the plates and when they release their threads they are extruded through the plate. The colour of the chromatophores is varied; brown is most common but yellow, red and blue also occur. They are generally discoid and embedded in the firm outer lining of cytoplasm.

In the Xanthophyceae the motile unicell is either a naked or encapsuled cell of simple structure. In *Heterochloris*, the cell is furnished with two unequal flagella and the characteristic vacuolate cytoplasm contains two or more chromatophores. The flagellate cell of the Chrysophyceae may have a single flagellum, e.g. *Chromulina*, *Dictyocha* and *Mallomonas*, or two unequal flagella, e.g. *Ochromonas*. A rudimentary second flagellum has been seen in some *Mallomonas* species. Some biflagellate Haptophyceae genera, e.g. *Chryso-chromulina*, have the two equal flagella and another organ, the haptonema (Fig. 14, p. 42); this organ, inserted between the flagella, resembles a flagellum, but has a different fine structure (see p. 50) and can coil or attach itself to substrata. Two brown parietal chromatophores are normally present, together with oil droplets and a reserve product, leucosin (chrysose, chrysolaminarin). The naked forms often exhibit rhizopodial development, whilst others, e.g. *Mallomonas*, have a pectin membrane on which small silicified scales occur, each with a delicate hinged silicified spine. In the Prymnesiales the cell membrane is covered by a layer of organic scales on which calcareous structures are deposited; the calcareous structures are known as coccoliths (see p. 41). In the Silicoflagellineae an internal skeleton of siliceous material is developed, forming a frame around which the cytoplasm extends; the brown chromatophores lodge in the outer zone of cytoplasm (Fig. 3). The flagellate cell of the Chrysophyceae may be surrounded by a theca, e.g. *Chrysococcus*. Encapsuled flagellate cells such as *Chrysopyxis* and *Epipyxis* (the single celled form resembling *Dinobryon*) are non-motile forms living epiphytically (Figs. 3 and 4).

The Chlorophycean flagellate cell has two or four equal flagella and the cell is either naked, e.g. *Dunaliella*, or enclosed in a cell wall, e.g. *Chlamydomonas*, or in a capsule, e.g. *Phacotus*. The flagella emerge from two canals through the cell wall; these canals are placed at 180° to one another on either side of the apical papilla. *Haematococcus* has a thick gelatinous wall penetrated by cytoplasmic strands whilst the cell of *Brachiomonas* is extended into several basal lobes. The quadriflagellate series are a parallel group of

---

Fig. 4. Further Unicellular and Colonial Flagellate Cell Types.

A. *Epipyxis*; B. *Dunaliella*; C. *Brachiomonas*; D. *Haematococcus*; E. *Chlamydomonas*; F. *Chlorogonium*; G. *Phacotus*; H. *Carteria*; I. *Medusochloris*; J. *Polytomella*; K. *Hyalogonium*; L. *Chrysosphaerella*; M. *Chlorodesmus*; N. *Uroglena*; O. *Synura*; P, Q, R. *Dinobryon*; Q. Theca and cell; P. Theca and cyst; R. Colony.

(After Arago, Beger, Bourelly, Droop, Ettl, Fott, Huber-Pestalozzi, Lauterborn, Matvienko, Phelps, and original.)

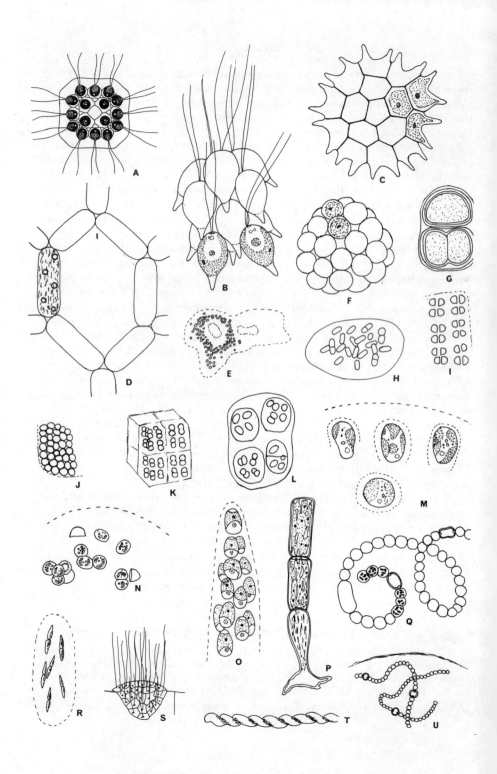

walled forms, e.g. *Carteria*. The unusual *Medusochloris* has four flagella produced from the corners of a cell shaped like a concave-convex lens. Contractile vacuoles and an eyespot are usually present, the latter being embedded in the chloroplast. The contractile vacuoles are precisely located beneath the apical papilla in *Chlamydomonas* but scattered throughout the cell in *Chlorogonium*. The chromatophore, although often of the basin-shaped chlamydomonad type, may be ridged, H-shaped, reticulate, etc. There are some colourless genera, e.g. the quadriflagellate *Polytomella* and the elongate biflagellate *Hyalogonium*. Pyrenoids are embedded in the chromatophores and starch, volutin and oil are also produced (Fig. 4).

COLONIAL ORGANIZATION

Flagellate colonies

Motile flagellate cells aggregate to form simple colonies in some species of *Gonyaulax* and *Ceratium* (Dinophyceae); in these the unmodified cells form into chains after division. In the Chrysophyceae clusters of cells, bearing siliceous scales or bristles are common, e.g. *Chrysosphaerella*, *Synura* and *Chlorodesmus*. In *Uroglena*, the cells are each attached to branching "mucilage" threads which join at a central point; the cells and threads are enclosed in mucilage with only the flagella projecting. Encapsuled cells of the *Epipyxis* type, form dendroid colonies in the genus *Dinobryon*. In the Chlorophyceae, aggregates of Chlamydomonad type cells, embedded in mucilage, form either plate-like colonies (e.g. *Gonium*) or spherical groups (e.g. *Pandorina*) or mucilage spheres in which the cells are arranged just below the surface and are interconnected by protoplasmic threads (e.g. *Volvox*). In *Spondylomorum* and *Pyrobotrys*, the cell aggregates are not enclosed in mucilage and are orientated in the same direction, the former having four flagella and the latter two per cell (Figs. 4 and 5).

Non-flagellate coenobia

Aggregations of non-motile cells, in which the cells are more or less fused together (as opposed to the Tetrasporal state, see below), are common only in the Chlorophyceae, e.g. the plates of cells of *Scenedesmus* and *Pediastrum*, the network of cells of *Hydrodictyon* and the spherical colonies of *Coelastrum* (Fig. 5).

FIG. 5. COLONIAL FLAGELLATES, COENOBIAL, TETRASPORAL AND FILAMENTOUS THALLI.

A. *Gonium*; B. *Pyrobotrys*; C. *Pediastrum*; D. *Hydrodictyon*; E. *Microcystis*; F. *Coelastrum*; G. *Chroococcus*; H. *Aphanothece*; I. *Merismopedia*; J. *Holopedia*; K. *Eucapsis*; L. *Gloeocapsa*; M. *Gloeochloris*; N. *Stichogloea*; O. *Hydrurus*; P. *Oedogonium*, base of filament; Q. *Anabaena*; R. *Elakatothrix*; S. *Chaetopeltis*; T. *Spirulina*; U. *Nostoc*.

(After Bourelly, Ettl, Fott, Geitler, Pascher, Skuia and original.)

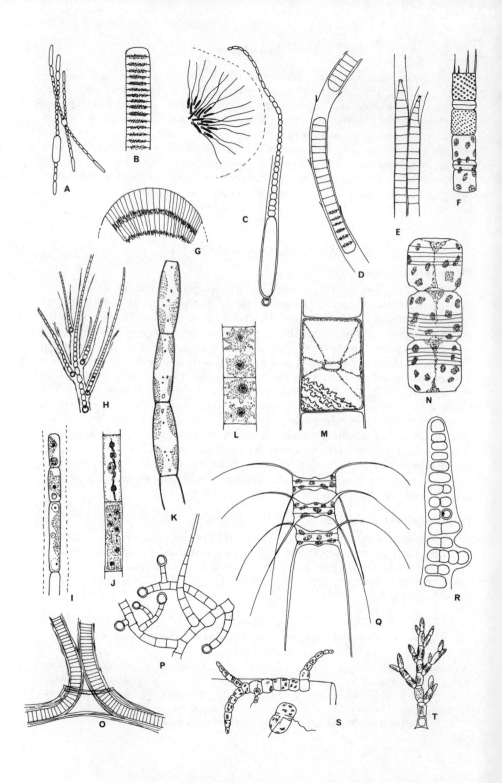

Tetrasporal forms

In most groups of algae, non-motile colonies are found in which the cells are embedded in mucilage; these are known as tetrasporal thalli. The name is unfortunate since in only a few genera are the cells grouped in fours and in no case is there any connection between these and the tetraspore plant of other groups (see p. 33). A tetrasporal type of morphology is found in the Cyanophyta; in *Microcystis* (=*Diplocystis*) and *Aphanothece*, the cells lie irregularly in the mucilage; in *Coelosphaerium* the cells lie in the peripheral mucilage of a sphere: in *Chroococcus* and *Gloeocapsa* they are in small packets surrounded by concentric zones of mucilage; in *Merismopedia* and *Holopedia* they are arranged regularly or irregularly in flat plates and in *Eucapsis* they lie in cubical masses formed by cell division in three planes. The Xantho-phycean genus *Gleochloris* is a planktonic tetrasporal form, whilst *Phaeocystis* and *Stichogloea* are parallel types in the Haptophyceae and Chrysophyceae (the unusual epiphytic mucilage colonies of *Hydrurus* are also tetrasporal). In the Chlorophyceae the tetrasporal genera are grouped into an order, the Tetrasporales, in which *Gloeocystis* and *Elakatothrix* are planktonic genera, whilst *Palmodictyon* and *Tetraspora* are epiphytic. In *Tetraspora* and *Chaetopeltis* the cells have mucilaginous pseudocilia (Fig. 5).

FILAMENTOUS ORGANIZATION

Unbranched filaments

Simple unbranched filaments are found in only a small number of algal groups; they may be either free-living (e.g. *Ulothrix*), attached at least initially (e.g. *Oedogonium*), or aggregated into colonies (e.g. *Nostoc* and *Aphanizomenon*). In the Cyanophyta the filament (trichome) is formed of simple vegetative cells (e.g. *Oscillatoria*, *Lyngbya* and *Phormidium*), the only modification being the development of the apical cell into a hooded or variously shaped cell. In *Spirulina* and sometimes in *Anabaena*, the filament is wound into a loose or close helix. These Cyanophyte genera are all motile, moving, sometimes very rapidly, in a sheath of mucilage. Sheets of trichomes often occur in which the outer mucilaginous sheaths coalesce whilst in *Gloeotrichia* the trichomes radiate from a central point. *Tribonema* in the Xanthophyceae is a simple filament, with cells composed of two overlapping

---

Fig. 6. SIMPLE AND BRANCHING FILAMENTOUS TYPES.

A. *Aphanizomenon*; B. *Oscillatoria*; C. *Gloeotrichia*, part of colony and one trichome, with basal heterocyst and akinete; D. *Lyngbya*; E. *Phormidium*; F. *Melosira*; G, H. *Rivularia*, part of colony and branching trichomes; I. *Geminella*; J. *Mougeotia*; K. *Tribonema*; L. *Zygnema*; M. *Spirogyra*; N. *Lauderia*; O. *Plectonema*; P. *Mastigocoleus*; Q. *Chaetoceros*; R. *Stigonema*; S. *Dinoclonium*, filament and zoospore; T. *Phaeothamnium*.

(After Bourelly, Conrad, Fott, Geitler, Hustedt, Pascher and original.)

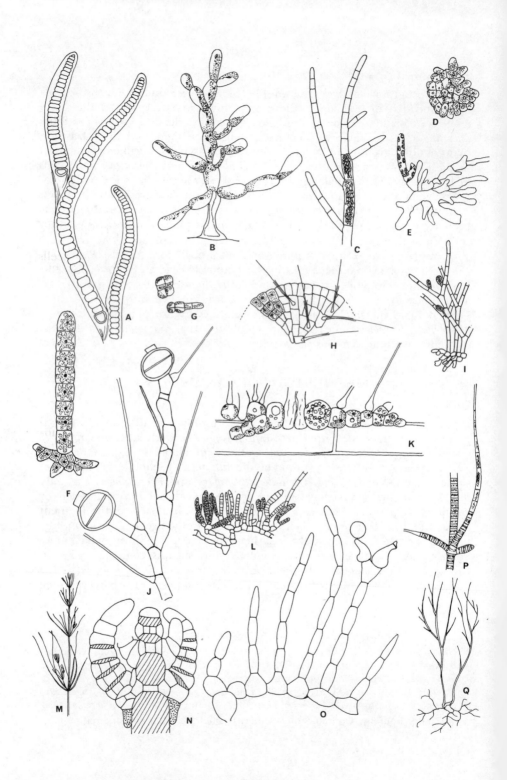

H pieces and containing numerous discoid chromatophores. In the Bacillariophyceae, filaments are formed by the non-separation of the daughter cells, e.g. *Chaetoceros, Melosira, Lauderia* and *Guinardia*. Three orders of the Chlorophyta include filamentous types. The simplest type is that of *Ulothrix* or *Stichococcus* where the cells each contain a single interrupted ribbon-shaped chromatophore. In the latter genus the filament readily fragments into groups each of a few cells. Some genera of the Ulotricales produce mucilage in which the filament is immersed and in others the individual cells of the filament are separated by the mucilage, e.g. *Geminella*. In the common genus *Oedogonium*, the basal cell secretes a small attachment disc. True filaments of the Zygnemaphyceae are easily recognized by their complex chromatophore structure. Three chromatophore types occur as in the Saccoderm desmids (see p. 5); flat plates with numerous pyrenoids are found in *Mougeotia*, one or more spirals in *Spirogyra* and two stellate chromatophores per cell in *Zygnema* (Fig. 6).

Branching filaments

There are three main types of thalli formed by branching filaments. (1) a simple branching system attached to the substratum by a basal disc secreted by the lowest cell. (2) the heterotrichous type with a basal attachment system of filaments giving rise to upright branches, and (3) a filamentous system of either a single or numerous central filaments, the final branches of which may aggregate to form pseudoparenchyma.

In the Cyanophyta the simplest systems occur in the genera with false branching; this is usually produced by the continued growth of the filament (trichome) beneath a heterocyst (an empty, often enlarged cell with prominent plugs at one or both ends) so that the latter is pushed to one side and forms with a row of cells above it, a false branch. In the species with fairly rigid sheaths these false branches remain attached to the main trichome and give the appearance of a much branched filamentous thallus (e.g. *Rivularia*) (Fig. 6). In other genera, branching occurs after the decay of an intercalary cell when one or both ends of the trichome adjacent to the dead cell push out of the parent sheath, e.g. *Plectonema*. In some species, one end grows out to form a branch, whilst the other forms a heterocyst (e.g.

FIG. 7. BRANCHING FILAMENTOUS THALLI.

A. *Tolypothrix*; B. *Heterodendron*; C. *Cladophora*; D. *Phaeodermatium*; E. *Heterococcus*, culture form; F. *Erythrotrichia*; G. *Desmococcus* (=*Pleurococcus*); H. *Coleochaete*; I. *Acrochaetium*; J. *Bulbochaete*; K. *Aphanochaete*; L. *Streblonema*; M. *Chara*, apical part of plant; N. *Chara*, apex of plant, internodal cells (cross hatched) and corticating filaments (stippled); O. *Trentepohlia*, filaments, empty gametangium and spore; P, Q. *Stigeoclonium*, heterotrichous branching system and portion of upright filament. (After Christensen, Fott, Geitler, Huber, Oltmanns, Pascher, Smith, Taylor and original.)

Tolypothrix). True branching and heterotrichy is found in the Stigonemati-nales, e.g. *Mastigocoleus* which forms branches growing from the centre of the cells of the filaments and which are produced into long hairs or end in heterocysts. The highest morphological differentiation of the Cyanophyta is found in this group in the genus *Stigonema*, in which a central row of cells is surrounded by, and joined by pit connections, to a ring of pericentral cells. Only at the apex of branches can the uniseriate system be observed. The cells which may undergo further radial and transverse divisions are enclosed in a mass of mucilage, which often takes up iron compounds and becomes so densely stained that the cell rows are difficult to distinguish.

In two genera of the Dinophyceae, very much reduced branched filaments are formed. Occasionally when cells of the filaments divide, the protoplast rounds off, forms furrows and a stigma and escapes as a zoospore of gymnodinioid form (e.g. *Dinothrix*). The filaments of *Dinoclonium* are weakly heterotrichous and produce definite *Gymnodinium*-like zoospores. Similarly in the Xanthophyceae and Chrysophyceae the branched filament is rare, occurring in the genus *Heterodendron* in the former group and in *Phaeothamnion* in the latter. Both these genera are attached by basal cells. The hetero-trichous habit is also present in both groups, e.g. *Heterococcus* and *Phaeoder-matium* (Fig. 7).

In *Bulbochaete* and *Cladophora* (Chlorophyta), a simple branched system is found with basal attachment cells. The branches of the former end in very characteristic hairs with bulbous bases and cell division is of the *Oedogonium* type. In *Cladophora* the branches arise immediately beneath the cross walls, the cell walls are thick, lamellate and non-mucilaginous and hence frequently covered with epiphytes. Heterotrichy abounds in the Chaetophorales (Fig. 7), where all stages in elaboration of the system are found. A typical central type is *Stigeoclonium*, which has both a well developed upright and creeping system of filaments, although in some species one or the other may be better developed. In *Draparnaldia* the upright system is elabo-rated at the expense of the creeping, with a central robust filament, giving off branches composed of short, thin cells which branch repeatedly to form clusters along the main axis. In some species rhizoidal filaments grow from the basal cells of the branches, forming a corticating layer around the main axis. One band-shaped chromatophore is usually present in each cell and occupies a narrow central region. The filaments are mucilaginous and in *Chaetophora* so much mucilage is produced that the branching systems form macroscopic colonies up to several mm in diameter. The branches are often drawn out into fine hairs and in some species growth is localized in a basal meristem. Only the basal branching system is present in some genera, e.g. the loose, slightly branching system of *Aphanochaete* and the compact pseudo-parenchymatous thalli of *Ulvella* and *Coleochaete scutata*. *Aphanochaete* is often found epiphytic on *Cladophora*; the filaments produce hairs with swollen bases, perched on the cells. Species of *Coleochaete* vary from branched upright systems (*C. divergens*) to the circular thalli of *C. scutata*; again hairs are produced on the thalli and these are of a peculiar type, bristle-like with a sheathing base. In the terrestrial genus *Trentepohlia*, there is both a prostrate and upright system and the thalli are frequently orange coloured due to haematochrome dissolved in oil globules in the cells. Another common epiphyte is *Desmococcus* (=*Pleurococcus*); this alga normally occurs as packets of cells growing on the bark of trees, but under moist conditions and in culture, short filaments are produced.

The heterotrichous habit is the simplest growth form in the Phaeophyta, where it is found in genera such as *Ectocarpus*, *Pylaiella* and *Tilopteris*, which closely parallel the *Stigeoclonium* type of the Chaetophorales (Fig. 7). Reduced forms with a basal system only are found in the lithophyte *Bodanella*, and in the endophytic *Streblonema*. Many genera of the Phaeophyta have a thallus derived from a heterotrichous filament or group of filaments, but these are not strictly filamentous forms. The gametophytes of Laminarians are microscopic branched filaments (Fig. 9, p. 24).

In the Rhodophyta, apart from a few genera of the Bangiophycidae, the simplest structures are heterotrichous, e.g. *Erythrotrichia* and *Acrochaetium*, the branching of the latter being similar to that in *Cladophora*. Branched systems similar to *Draparnaldia* are found in *Batrachospermum*, but with the addition of downward growing filaments (corticating threads) clothing the central filament except in the apical region (Fig. 8).

The Charales have a complex branching system derived from apical cells which cut off segments at the base which then form nodal and internodal cells. The internodal cells do not divide but enlarge to form oblong cells; the nodal cells divide, cutting off pericentral cells from which arise whorls of branches each growing in the same way as the main axis. In *Chara* but not in *Nitella*, cells at the bases of the branches grow downward and often coil round the internodal cell forming a corticating system (Fig. 7).

SIPHONACEOUS ORGANIZATION

This type of thallus is confined to a few genera in the Xanthophyceae and the Bryopsidophyceae. The simplest organization is that of a small unbranched vesicle containing a central vacuole and peripheral cytoplasm in which the chloroplasts and nuclei are located and anchored by branching rhizoids (*Botrydium*). An irregular branching system with rhizoids or haptera and occasional cell walls cutting off old empty siphons is found in *Vaucheria*. In *Valonia* the initial vesicle is divided by cell walls into a number of multinucleate portions. In some Bryopsidophyceae the siphon branches in a relatively simple pinnate manner, e.g. *Bryopsis* or in a more complex radial manner in *Dasycladus*, whilst in *Codium* a large number of central siphons form the core of the thallus giving off lateral branches which bend outwards and form a packed layer of assimilating cells. Most of the tropical, siphonaceous genera are calcified and thus large thalli can be elaborated without the formation of cell walls, e.g. *Halimeda* (Fig. 8).

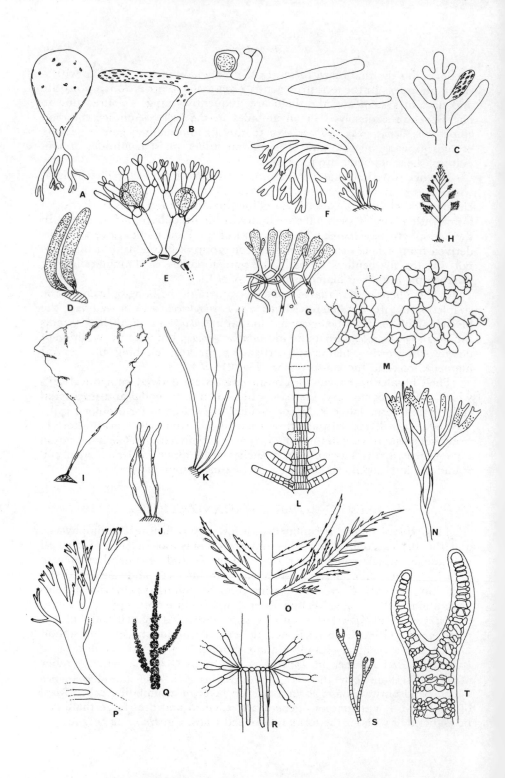

PARENCHYMATOUS ORGANIZATION

Flat foliose or tubular thalli are formed by the septation of a filament in two or three planes in the Chlorophyceae, e.g. *Ulva* (flat) and *Entero-morpha* (tubular) and in the Phaeophyta, *Scytosiphon* (tubular) (Fig. 8). The most complex types are found only in the Phaeophyta. One of the most striking and easily observed is that of *Sphacelaria* where the derivation of segments from the dome-shaped apical cell and subsequent formation of walls at right angles to the basal wall of the apical cell, leads to a parenchymatous thallus. The lateral cells, of alternate rows, form branch apical cells giving rise to a branch system of similar form to the main axis. Apical growth is admirably illustrated by *Dictyota*, in which it gives rise to a dichotomously branched parenchymatous thallus which is formed of large inner cells sandwiched between outer small cells (Fig. 1). In certain groups the growth may be by intercalary or by trichothallic meristems. For instance growth may be localized at the base of hairs as in *Cutleria* and *Desmarestia*. The formation of complicated sporophytic thalli with intercalary meristems, reaches its peak in the Laminariales. The young plants are monostromatic, consisting of a layer of cells attached by a basal group of rhizoids. By the formation of periclinal walls the thallus becomes polystromatic and gradually differentiates into holdfast, stipe and lamina, with the meristem ultimately localized at the junction of stipe and lamina. Growth in a transverse plane is then continued by the division of the superficial cells (meristoderm). In the Fucales, initial growth is from a single apical meristematic cell which is responsible for growth in length and branching of the thallus, whilst the increase in diameter is achieved by the continued meristematic activity of the surface layer of cells, the meristoderm. In some genera, cavities (cryptostomata), are formed in the cortex, from which tufts of hairs grow, and in the fertile regions of the plant these are converted into conceptacles in which the antheridia and oogonia arise. The apparently complex parenchymatous thalli of the Rhodophyta are built up from the aggregation of filaments all capable of apical growth and only rarely do divisions occur in an intercalary, or surface, position. The simplest types are derived from a single central filament system (uniaxial), e.g. *Batrachospermum* (Fig. 8) and *Ceramium* (Fig. 12, p. 33) which gives rise to laterals of limited

---

FIG. 8. SIPHONACEOUS AND PARENCHYMATOUS THALLI.

A. *Botrydium*; B. *Vaucheria*; C. Apex of *Bryopsis*; D. Two plants of *Dasycladus*; E. Cross section of *Dasycladus* showing sporangia and calcified region, thick black; F. *Codium*; G. Assimilators and siphons of *Codium*; H. *Bryopsis*; I. *Ulva*; J. *Enteromorpha*; K. *Scytosiphon*; L. *Sphacelaria*; M. *Halimeda*; N. *Pelvetia*; O. Fragment of *Desmarestia* frond; P. *Cutleria*; Q. *Batrachospermum*, apex of plant; R. *Batrachospermum*, nodal region showing side branches and corticating filaments; S. *Ceramium*; T. Apex or *Ceramium*, showing central and pericentral cells.

(After Oltmanns, Sauvageau, Taylor and original.)

growth. Others produce laterals which divide profusely and ultimately fuse to form an outer pseudoparenchymatous sheath, e.g. *Lemanea*. The aggregation of numerous filaments into a multiaxial system (fountain type) is easily seen after decalcification in *Corallina*. Some of these multiaxial types are hollow and in a few families growth is more diffuse and the axial system is difficult to distinguish. Although dealt with here since the overall impression is of a flat or segmented and apparently parenchymatous thallus there is no doubt about their basic filamentous nature and indeed they are the most complex filamentous plants known.

2 Reproduction and life history

Vegetative reproduction is widespread in the algae; in many species it is related to increase in cell or colony size and therefore associated with normal growth processes, whilst in other species, portions or specializations of the thallus are detached and the parent plant continues growth.

In unicellular flagellates (e.g. *Euglena*), in the desmids and diatoms, increase in size is controlled within fairly narrow limits. Division of the cell occurs when a set size is reached, e.g. in the desmids, where this size is related to the basic morphology of the cell. In diatoms, vegetative division is initiated after a period of increase in cell volume, accompanied by a growth and sliding apart of the girdle bands; the valves do not increase in size, and thus cell division is accompanied by a progressive reduction in cell size. Some diatoms are capable of laying down new valves of similar size to the parent valves and in these growth takes place without any reduction in cell size. This phenomenon is probably due to the pliability of the girdle bands which expand sufficiently to allow the new valves to form without any restriction. The time lapse between vegetative divisions in desmids and diatoms is controlled to some extent by the time taken to complete the new half cell. In flagellates, vegetative reproduction is brought about by the longitudinal fission of the cell and the reformation of organelles which have not divided, e.g. the eyespot. Fission usually commences at the anterior end and progresses downward (Fig. 9A). Some *Euglena* spp. and other flagellates, e.g. *Cryptomonas*, become enclosed in a mucilage sheath prior to division and may then divide repeatedly to form palmelloid stages.

The simplest methods of vegetative reproduction are those in which division of the protoplast is not directly involved, but where the individual cells or cell-aggregates are separated. In some colonial forms, e.g. *Dictyosphaerium* and *Symura*, the colonies tend to become elongate and constricted, eventually breaking into two separate colonies. In the Cyanophyta, Ulotrichales and filamentous Zygnemaphyceae, fragmentation of filaments occurs. In the first group, sections of trichomes are cut off by the occurrence of simple breaks in the filaments or after the formation of intercalary cells (necridia and separation discs). The short lengths of trichome thus released are known as hormogonia and are often more actively motile than the parent filament. In *Fischerella* cells of the filaments grow out at right angles, divide and form short homogonia (Fig. 9E). *Ulothrix* and *Hormidium* become fragmented into short lengths of cells by dissolution of the cross walls at intervals along the filaments. In the Zygnemaphyceae the end walls of the cell invaginate, and then changes in turgor pressure within adjacent cells tend to set up shearing strains between the two cross walls and after evagination of

23

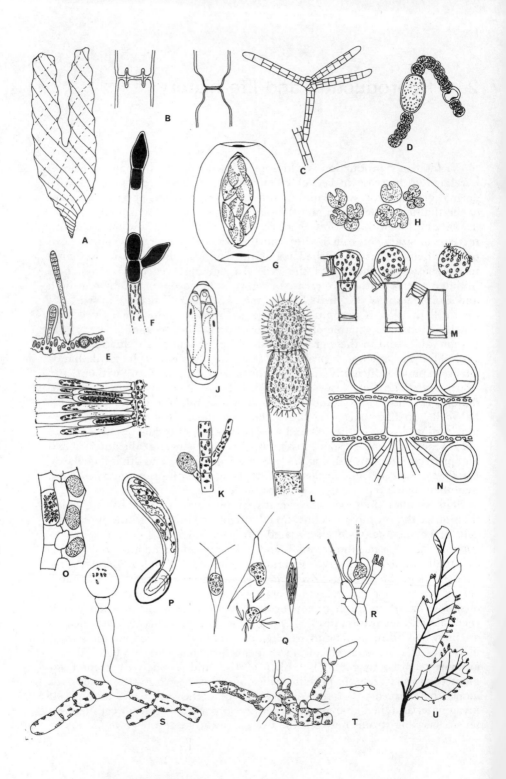

the replicate end walls, fragmentation occurs (Fig. 9B). In the larger thalloid algae there is often a formation of adventitious thalli, e.g. in *Dictyota* and *Fucus* or of bulbils, e.g. *Sphacelaria* (Fig. 9C). The formation of thick walled cells containing copious food reserves is another form of vegetative reproduction; structures such as these are termed akinetes and are often found in *Pithophora* (Fig. 9F) and in some filamentous Cyanophyta, e.g. *Anabaena* (Fig. 9D).

Asexual reproduction

In some aspects this is very similar to certain forms of vegetative reproduction, particularly in the flagellate groups. In general it is a process whereby the protoplast(s) is released from the algal cell and germinates to form a new plant. The protoplast(s) may be released as a motile zoospore or as a non-motile aplanospore which, when it has a thick cell wall is termed a hypnospore.[5] In a few genera the aplanospores have the form of the autospores (Fig. 9G, H).

In unicellular algae which form zoospores, each cell is usually capable of being transformed into zoospores, similarly in multicellular species, most cells of the thallus are fertile except in Phaeophyta and Rhodophyta, where special sporangia are produced. In general the production of asexual spores is preceded by mitotic division of the nuclei and followed by partition of the protoplasts, e.g. in *Chlamydomonas*, where 2, 4, or 8 zoospores are formed by longitudinal cleavage within the parent cell wall. In this case the whole cell acts as a (zoo)sporangium (Fig. 9J). The number of zoospores produced per cell varies from genus to genus e.g. in *Oedogonium* a single zoospore is produced, and is exceptional in having a ring of paired flagella (see Fig. 9M). In *Vaucheria* the single zoospore is a compound structure with numerous paired unequal flagella (synzoospore), whilst in the Ulothricales a small

---

FIG. 9.

A. Dividing *Euglena*; B. Fragmentation mechanism of *Spirogyra* filaments; C. Vegetative propagation of *Sphacelaria*; D. Akinete and heterocyst in filament of *Anabaena*; E. Hormogonia of *Fischerella*; F. Akinetes of *Pithophora*; G. Autospores of *Oocystis*; H. Autospores of *Kirchneriella*; I. Unilocular sporangia of *Laminaria*; J. Zoospores of *Chlamydomonas*; K. Unilocular sporangium of *Ectocarpus*; L. Synzoospore of *Vaucheria*; M. Release of zoospore of *Oedogonium*; N. Tetrasporangium of *Dictyota*; O. Conjugation and zygospores of *Zygnema*; P. Germination of the zygospore of *Spirogyra*; Q. Formation and release of oogonia and male gametes of *Chlorogonium*; R. Oogonium, and antheridia of *Coleochaete*; S. Female gametophyte of *Desmarestia* with egg cell attached to the wall of the oogonium; T. Male gametophyte and gamete of *Laminaria*; U. Part of tetraspore plant of *Phycodrys*, tetraspores in small marginal branchlets.

(After Ettl, Fritsch, Fott, Geitler, Hirn, Kanada, Komarek, Oltmanns, Pascher, Pochmann, Pringsheim, Sauvageau, Schreiber, Skuja, Smith, Thuret and Bornet, West and original.)

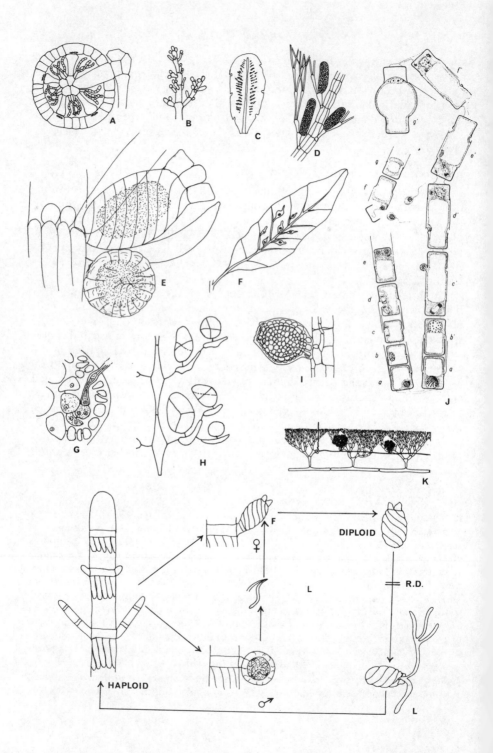

number, 1–4 zoospores are formed, and in some species of *Ulothrix*, the zoospores differ in size. In the Cladophorales and in *Volvox*, large numbers of zoospores are formed from a single cell; in the latter, the individual zoospores form a sphere with the anterior flagellate ends directed inwards; inversion then occurs through a pore in the sphere so that the flagella come to lie on the outside of the colony. In the Phaeophyta special zoosporangia are delimited in which cross walls segment the sporangium into compartments in which single zoospores are formed, e.g. *Ectocarpus* (plurilocular sporangia, Fig. 1H).

The morphology of the zoospore is characteristic for each group of algae and in general is a small version of the flagellate vegetative cell type of that group (e.g. equally bi- or quadri-flagellate in the Chlorophyceae, laterally inserted and unequally biflagellate in the Phaeophyta etc.).

Spores are formed not only as a means of asexual reproduction of the haploid or diploid plant, but often also after meiosis; e.g. the tetraspores of the Rhodophyta and some Phaeophyta (*Dictyota*, Fig. 9N) and the zoospores formed on the germination of a *Chlamydomonas* zygote. The two types of (zoo)spore formation are quite distinct, since in one, the (zoo)spores (haploid or diploid) are merely an accessory mechanism for the reproduction and dispersal of the haploid or diploid plant, whilst in the other they are the products of reduction division, and therefore haploid, although formed on the diploid plant. At its simplest, the meiotic formation of zoospores is seen in the production of four (eight or sixteen in some species) zoospores, e.g. from the zygospore of *Chlamydomonas*. In the Phaeophyta these zoospores are formed in specialized sporangia devoid of cross walls, i.e. unilocular sporangia —*Ectocarpus* and *Laminaria*; here, after the meiotic divisions, the zooids continue to divide to produce a larger number of zoospores. The tetrasporangia of the Rhodophyta are produced on quite separate 'tetraspore plants'. They are often cut off from the filaments as one-celled laterals which then divide to form the four spores. In the more massive thalloid forms they are often embedded in the thallus and variously arranged as linear rows, cruciate or tetrahedral groups. This (zoo)spore stage, terminating the diploid phase, may of course be regarded as a final stage of sexual reproduction and not one of asexual reproduction.

FIG. 10.

A. Section of antheridium of *Chara*; B. Spermatia of *Rhodochorton*; C. Spermatial sori of *Apoglossum*; D. Male gametangia of *Polysiphonia*; E. Antheridium and oogonium of *Chara*; F. Cystocarps arising as branches from the veins of *Phycodrys*; G. Procarp of *Plocamium*; H. Tetraspores of *Caloglossa*, Embedded in thallus: surface cells not shown; I. Pericarp of *Polysiphonia*; J. Diagram of life history of *Melosira*, a–g formation of male gametes, a^1–g^1 formation of egg cell, fertilization and enlargement to form an auxospore; K. Carpogonial branch and formation of carpospores on carposporophyte of *Platoma*; L. Diagram of life history of *Chara*.

(After Drew, Kylin, Smith, Papenfuss, Taylor, von Stosch in Fott and original.)

Sexual reproduction

This is not a universal feature in the algae; it has never been demonstrated in the Cyanophyta and in many genera of the Chrysophyta and Bacillariophyta it has rarely been observed, although it is probably a feature of the life history of most of the species.

Sexual reproduction involves the combination of nuclear material and frequently cytoplasm, from two organisms of the same species. The commonest mechanism is the union of two morphologically identical gametes (isogamy). The gametes may be motile and similar in form to the flagellate vegetative cells of the group although usually devoid of a rigid cell wall, or they may be relatively immobile masses of cytoplasm brought together by the prior juxtaposition of the parent thalli, e.g. Zygnemaphyceae and Bacillariophyta. In some species the gametes differ in size or in motility (anisogamous), and in these the larger or less active gamete generally absorbs the other. The oogamous state is achieved when one gamete becomes immobile; this egg cell may be released (e.g. *Fucus*), or retained within the parent cell wall, e.g. Rhodophyta. Oogamy occurs even in relatively simple groups, e.g. the Volvocales (*Chlorogonium* and *Volvox*), but is more widespread in the highly differentiated Phaeophyta and Rhodophyta. Another type of fusion is illustrated by some diatoms in which daughter nuclei fuse without release from the parent cell (autogamy).

Gametes are formed within gametangia, which may be unmodified parent cells, as in some isogamous and oogamous *Chlamydomonas* species. The cells may release the whole protoplast as a gamete or the female plant may merely loose its flagella, whilst in other species the protoplast cleaves to give rise to the gametes. In multicellular algae the individual cells may function as gametangia giving rise to a single gamete, e.g. filamentous Zygnemaphyceae, or by cleavage of the protoplast giving numerous gametes, e.g. *Ulothrix* and *Cladophora*. In some genera, although the vegetative cells act as gametangia, they are localized within the thallus, e.g. in the colonial flagellates *Eudorina* and *Pleodorina*. The Dasycladales have specialized gametangia in the form of swollen, often spherical 'branches', cut off from the remainder of the plant by a cross wall; within these, isogamous or anisogamous gametes are produced by free nuclear division followed by cleavage of the protoplast (Fig. 8E). The male gametangia of *Ectocarpus* and *Dictyota* are multicellular and each cell produces a gamete. In the Rhodophyta (Figs. 10 and 12) the male and female gametes are both formed in single celled gametangia, the former in small branch cells (antheridia or spermatangia), each producing a single non-motile male gamete (spermatium), and the latter, forming as a single celled structure (carpogonium) containing the female nucleus and drawn out into a long beak (trichogyne), down which the male nucleus passes (Figs. 10G and 12). In some genera the antheridia are borne on special branches (e.g. *Polysiphonia*, Fig. 10D), in others on special leaflets (e.g. *Chondria*) and in others in sori on the thallus (e.g. *Apoglossum*, Fig. 10C). The female gametangium is borne on a cell (supporting cell) or group of cells forming a short branch system (carpogonial branch). After fertilization the vegetative tissue surrounding this system, may grow to form an urn-shaped protective structure known as the pericarp (Fig. 10I). Morphologically similar structures occur in *Coleochaete* in the Chlorophyceae (Fig. 9R), but the female gametangium is not associated with a special branch system. Perhaps the most complex gametangia are found in the Charophyta (Fig. 10), where the oogonia are formed as short branches at the nodes and are protected by enveloping filaments growing from the supporting cells; these twist round the developing oogonia and end in special pointed cells (coronae), between which the sperm pass to fertilize the oogonium. This then falls from the plant still enclosed in these corticating filaments. The antheridia are likewise borne at the nodes and formed of eight segments (shields) making up the octants of the more or less spherical antheridium. The shield cells have infolded walls so that they appear multicellular in section and they cut off two internal segments, the one adjacent to the shield forming the manubrium and the inner the capitula. This latter further divides forming secondary capitula, from each of which develop long antheridial threads forking twice at the base. At maturity these threads fill the interior of the antheridium and each is made up of numerous rectangular cells in each of which a vermiform biflagellate male gamete forms (Fig. 10A).

In all groups the product of fusion of the male and female gametes is the zygote. This may continue to move, often swimming away from light (i.e. it is negatively phototactic) before attaching to a substratum by the flagella end. In others there may be a brief period of motility or this may be omitted and a thick walled zygospore is formed. In oogamous species a thick wall is also laid down around the zygote to form an oospore. Species which are haploid in the vegetative state, e.g. *Chlamydomonas* and *Ulothrix*, produce four cells on germination of the zygote, during which meiotic division occurs. The cells so produced in *Chlamydomonas* are normal vegetative cells, whilst those of forms such as *Ulothrix* swim for a time and then settle, usually attaching themselves to the substratum by their flagella ends, and then developing into vegetative plants. In the Zygnemaphyceae the germination of the zygote results in four haploid nuclei, three of which disintegrate, e.g. in *Spirogyra*, whilst the fourth passes into the germ tube and continues division to initiate a new filament (Fig. 9P). Genera which are normally diploid, e.g. Bryopsidophyceae, form the vegetative plant from the direct germination of the zygote. In plants with haploid and diploid vegetative phases, e.g. *Cladophora* and *Dictyota*, the zygote, on coming to rest, germinates to form a single diploid plant and the reduction division is delayed until zoosporangia, often formed as tetrasporangia, are initiated on this diploid plant.

Life histories

The union of male and female gametes results in the formation of a zygote and a doubling of the chromosomal complement to give the diploid state. Before sexual reproduction can occur again the chromosome number must be halved. In some groups this is achieved by meiotic division of the zygote nucleus, and subsequent germination to give the haploid stage (e.g. Zygnemaphyceae); in other algae the zygotic nucleus divides mitotically and the resulting cells form a diploid phase, which later produces cells capable of meiotic division. The common nuclear cycle of higher plants is a simple one, the mature plant being diploid bearing gametangia called anthers and carpels, in which the meiotic division results in haploid 'gametes.' Fusion results in a zygote, which is at first morphologically simple (embryonic) and subsequently develops into a complex plant. This basic cycle can also be found in the algae, e.g. in the centric diatom *Melosira varians* (Fig. 10), where the vegetative cells are diploid (sporophytic) and some cells act as male gametangia producing four uniflagellate male gametes by meiotic division. These are released and penetrate a cell (female gametangium), in which meiotic division of the nucleus has proceeded, but with a degeneration of one nucleus after each division, resulting in the formation of a single egg cell. Fusion of the male gamete with the egg cell results in a zygote, which on germination forms the vegetative diploid stage. All diatoms are diploid, but usually they produce non-flagellate gametes which fuse in the mass of cytoplasm released when the valves come apart. The resulting zygote(s) are termed auxospores and inside these the new cells (frustules) are formed.

In the Charophyta a superficially similar life history occurs, and the analogy with the Angiosperms appears even closer, since in some species the male and female gametangia (antheridia and oogonia) are formed on the same plant (monoecious) and in others on different plants (dioecious). However, here the vegetative plant is haploid and the gametes are formed by mitotic division in complex gametangia. The biflagellate male gamete fuses with the egg cell to form a zygote, which during germination undergoes meiosis, thus producing the haploid plant (Fig. 10). In *Fucus* a similar cycle exists, but the vegetative plant is diploid and the only gametophyte stages are the gametes.

The fundamental distinction in these life histories is the point at which reduction (i.e. meiotic) division occurs. In *Melosira* and *Fucus* this is delayed until gametangia are initiated and the vegetative phase is diploid, whilst in Charophyta and Zygnemaphyceae meiosis occurs immediately on germination of the zygote nucleus and therefore the vegetative phase is haploid. In the algae the presence of free haploid and diploid stages and also often, of free gametes, leads to an alternation of generations, comparable to those in the Bryophyta and Pteridophyta. Thus although the algae are less conspicuous and morphologically less complex than higher groups, they conform in having a basic alternation of haploid and diploid phases. However, this basic similarity is often obscured by the exceptional degree of variation in the life histories of algae, resulting in a multiplicity of types unknown in other plant groups.

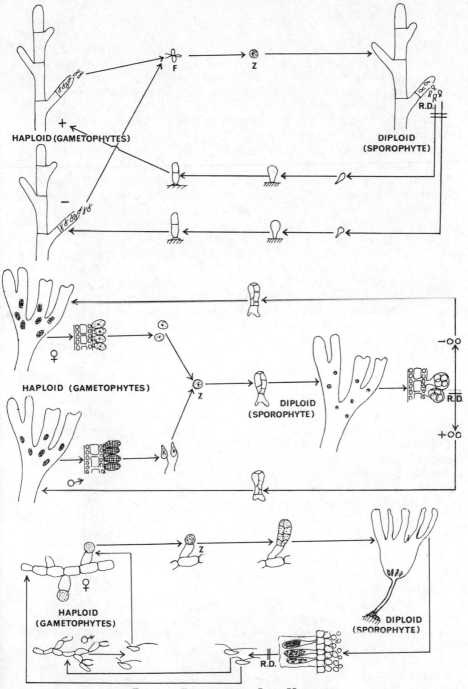

Fig. 11. Diagrams of Life Histories.

Cladophora; (upper), some species only, others have heteromorphic life histories *Dictyota* (middle) and *Laminaria* (lower).

These complexities arise from the prolongation of the vegetative phases both in the haploid and diploid state; they reach their height in the Rhodophyta, with the formation of additional phases and spores. A further complication is the development of morphologically similar (isomorphic) or dissimilar (heteromorphic) haploid and diploid vegetative stages in the life history. The following examples will suffice to illustrate some of these points. Certain *Cladophora* species (Fig. 11) have an isomorphic alternation of generations, coupled with heterothallism in the haploid stage, which results in the formation of two identical gametophytic plants, producing morphologically identical gametes (isogamous) of different strains. Fusion only occurs between gametes of opposite strain, leading to two zygotic phases, initially a large biflagellate cell, which later becomes non-motile and germinates to give the diploid, vegetative, sporophytic plant. This sporophyte (morphologically identical with the gametophytes) produces (zoo)sporangia, similar in form to the gametangia of the haploid plants, in which biflagellate zoospores arise from a meiotic division. At the reduction division in the (zoo)sporangium, the genetic distinction into strains occurs and the zoospores so formed give haploid plants of the two strains.

A similar state is found in *Dictyota* (Fig. 11), but here there is a difference in cell size between the gametophytes and sporophyte, and also the male and female gametophytes can be distinguished when fruiting, since the male gametangia form numerous uniflagellate gametes* whilst the female produce single eggs; both types of gametangia are produced in clusters (sori) on the surface of the thallus. Likewise the sporophyte produces tetraspores in tetrasporangia on the surface of the thallus.

In the Laminariales (Fig. 11) the life history is basically similar, but the haploid (gametophytic) generation consists of minute filaments producing gametes, whilst the diploid sporophyte is a large macroscopic plant bearing (zoo)sporangia in which reduction division occurs. This group is oogamous and the egg cell and zygote are retained at the mouth of the oogonium where a small embryo develops; this then separates from the gametophyte, forms rhizoids for attachment and develops into the mature sporophyte. The gametophyte and sporophyte generations are heteromorphic and there is also slight heteromorphism of the male and female gametophytes, in that cell size and degree of branching vary.

In the subclass Florideophycidae of the Rhodophyta the simplest type of life history is in the Nemaliales (Fig. 12), where after fusion between the male cell (spermatium) and the trichogyne of the carpogonium, the male nucleus migrates inwards and fuses with the carpogonial nucleus. This diploid nucleus then undergoes a meiotic division and the haploid nuclei are transferred to filaments (gonimoblast filaments) growing out of the carpogonium. This filamentous structure is termed the carposporophyte, and in this instance

---

* The gametes are normally biflagellate in the Phaeophyta but in *Dictyota* the second flagellum is reduced to a small vestigial structure.

is haploid, and gives rise to the haploid carpospores. In the simpler Bangio-phycidae the carpospores arise within the carpogonium. On germination the carpospores form the gametophyte plant (Fig. 12). In most genera of the remaining orders of the Florideophycidae the meiotic division is delayed and occurs on the tetrasporophyte—a plant which is usually morphologically identical with the gametophyte but bears tetrasporangia in which meiosis

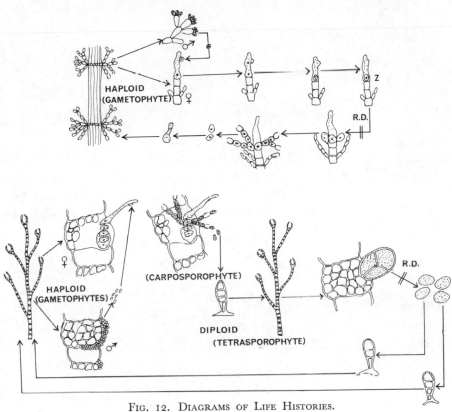

FIG. 12. DIAGRAMS OF LIFE HISTORIES.
(*Batrachospermum* (upper) and *Ceramium* (lower).
(Adapted from drawings in Dixon, Taylor and original.)

occurs; these form on the surfaces, on special branches, in cushions or in conceptacles. However, between the gametophyte and the tetrasporophyte, there is intercalated a third somatic phase—the carposporophyte which is thus diploid. It is formed of filaments growing either from the carpogonium or from the auxiliary cells after the diploid nuclei have been transmitted to these cells, either directly if the auxiliary cell is adjacent to the carpogonium, or via the connecting filaments (e.g. *Platoma*). Short filaments (gonimoblast filaments), arise from the auxiliary cells and these may lie free amongst the cells of the parent thallus or be compacted. The terminal cells or all the cells of these filaments produce single celled carpospores which are diploid. These are released and on germination form the tetrasporophyte (Fig. 12). This latter type of life history is termed diplobiontic and that of the Nemaliales type is haplobiontic.

3   Cytology and genetics

The details of algal cytology have increased enormously during the last two decades largely from electron microscope studies of cell walls, flagella and cytoplasmic organelles, but considerable cytological detail is obvious in routine light microscopic examinations of algae and has long been considered important in the taxonomy of certain groups. The correlation of the data, from the light and electron microscopic approaches, is yielding fascinating insights into structural details; the relationships between these, and the physiological functions, is only more slowly being elucidated. The ultra-structural studies are also proving invaluable in solving problems of classification and inter-relationships of groups.

Cell walls

A bounding layer of relatively inert material is present in the majority of algal cells; it is composed of relatively pure or mixed carbohydrates but may be impregnated or layered with inorganic substances, e.g. silica, calcium or magnesium carbonate.

In many flagellates, zoospores and gametes the enclosing membrane is merely the outermost layer of the cytoplasm (pellicle, periplast). In some algae it is quite flexible, allowing amoeboid or rhizopodial motion, whilst in others it has a more definite form owing to underlying structural elements, e.g. *Euglena*. Even in the latter genus there is often considerable change in cell shape (metaboly) appearing as an inflation passing up and down the cell. In spite of the cytoplasmic nature of this type of cell membrane, it may have extremely complex striations, be produced into wings (e.g. some *Phacus* species), or be ornamented with a spiral system of nodules (e.g. *Euglena spirogyra*).

In most non-motile, unicellular and all the multicellular species the cytoplasm is bounded by a definite cell wall; it is rarely composed of a single substance and usually has a layered structure. The outer layer is often mucilaginous or is a thick envelope of mucilage, not normally visible, but made so by running dilute Indian ink under the cover-glass, when the particles stop at the outermost layer. The mucilage of some Desmids is arranged in prisms, arising from pores, in the membrane; it is striate and there is also an internal mucilage mass penetrating into the cytoplasm[82] (Fig. 13).

Some algal cell walls are composed of a non-crystalline matrix and a dispersed crystalline, often fibrillar phase, both being polysaccharide. A common constituent of algal cell walls is pectin, which is a polyuronide, composed of galacturonic acid residues (e.g. most Xanthophyceae), but it is

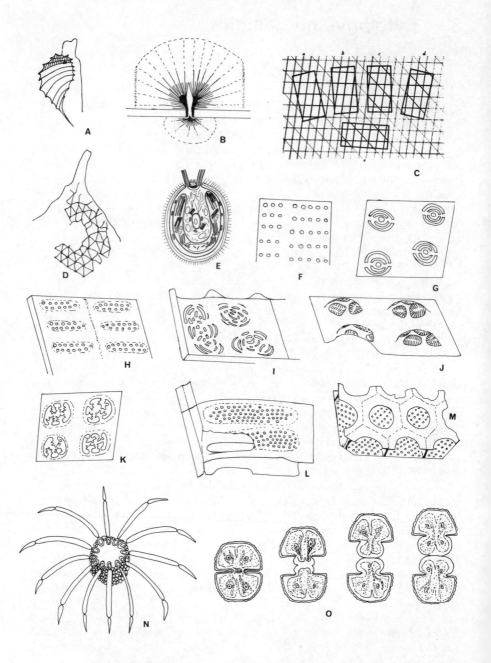

more frequently mixed with cellulose (Chlorophyceae, Dinophyta, Phaeo-phyta, Rhondophyta), with xylose and/or mannose (Bryopsidophyceae) or with silica (Bacillariophyta). In some algae, notably Prymnesiales (Cocco-lithineae), Dasycladales and coralline Rhodophyta, the wall is strengthened with plates or an encrusting and even penetrating deposit of calcium car-bonate. Variations in the amounts of substances present are quite large and few generalizations are possible. In some groups additional compounds are present in the wall layers, e.g. hemicellulose, alginic acid, fucoidin and fucin in Phacophyta, geloses in Rhodophyta and chitin as a thin outer investment, e.g. in *Cladophora* and *Oedogonium* (cf. the prolific growth of epiphytes on these genera and their relative absence on species producing large amounts of mucilaginous polysaccharides, e.g. Zygnemaphyceae and many Rhodophyta and Phaeophyta). In some algae there is a surface deposit of clay minerals, which gives an X-ray diagram similar to that of cellulose II and this has led to misinterpretation of their wall structure.[112]

Microfibrillar walls

The commonest microfibrillar component is cellulose, usually laid down in the form of lamellae running in two directions almost at right angles (Plate I), or with a third lamellae in which the fibrils run in the obtuse angle between the other two (Fig. 13), e.g. *Cladophora rupestris, C. prolifera, Chaetomorpha melagonium, C. princeps* and *Valonia ventricosa*, or in a random arrangement of microfibrils in an amorphous matrix, e.g. *Ulva lactuca, Enteromorpha* sp., *Halidrys siliquosa, Fucus serratus, Himanthalia elongata, Ascophyllum nodosum, Pelvetia canaliculata, Laminaria saccharina, L. digitata, Ptilota plumosa, Griffithsia flosculosa, Rhodymenia palmata* and *Porphyra* sp.[73, 111, 112] Desmid walls have also been shown to have a lamellate fibrillar structure.[82] The percentage of microfibrillar material is high in *Cladophora* and *Chaetomorpha* (28·5 per cent and 41 per cent) and lower in the other algae, becoming

---

FIG. 13.

A. Striate membrane in *Phacus*; B. The mucilage prisms on the outer and inner face of the wall in *Micrasterias*; C. Diagram of the orientation of microfibrils in (*a*) *Chaetomorpha melagonium*, (*b*) *Cladophora rupestris*, (*c*) *Chaetomorpha princeps*, (*d*) *Clado-phora prolifera*, and (*e*) *Valonia ventricosa*. The longer edge of each rectangle represents the long axis of the cells. Double lines are the direction of the two major orientations of the microfibrils and the single line the third orientation; D. Pattern on the cell wall of *Pediastrum* as seen with the electron microscope; E. A reconstruction of a *Chlamydomonas* cell from electron micrographs; F, G, H, I, J, K, L, M. Patterns of pores in the silica wall of diatoms seen with the electron microscope. *Synedra fulgens, Raphoneis amphiceros, Synedra ulna, Achnanthes brevipes, Cocconeis stauroneiformis, Didymosphenia geminata, Pinnularia* and *Stephanopyxis* respectively; N. Cell of *Michael-sarsia* showing two types of coccoliths; O. Four stages in the cell division of *Cosmarium*.

(After Bretschneider in Pochmann, Christensen, Drawert and Mix, Frei and Preston Fritsch, Hendey, and Moner.)

as small as 1·5 per cent in *Pelvetia*. *Porphyra* differs from all others in that glucose is apparently replaced by xylose as the basic unit in the microfibrils; there is in addition, a cuticle composed of mannose which led to earlier erroneous reports that mannose was the principal polysaccharide. The complexity and variability in the chemical make-up of the wall constituents (fibrils and matrix) is shown in Table 1. The Bryopsidophyceae form an interesting group in that *Halicystis*, the haploid stage of *Derbesia*, yields, on hydrolysis, a mixture of glucose and xylose (cf. the wall structure of *Hydrodictyon* of the Chlorococcales which is also composed of two sugars, glucose and mannose), whilst others (*Bryopsis*, *Udotea*, *Halimeda* and *Caulerpa*) have a microfibrillar wall composed of β-1, 3 linked xylans with encrusting glucans.[112] Other Bryopsidophyceae (*Codium*, *Acetabularia*, *Dasycladus* and *Batophora*) have walls composed mainly of mannose deposited as short fibrillar bodies; traces of glucose and galactose are also found in these walls. The orientation of the microfibrils in the green algae so far investigated, show that only in *Cladophora* and *Chaetomorpha*, is there any resemblance to

Table 1. The polysaccharide composition of some algal cell walls
(From Cronshaw *et al.*, 1958) [73]

	Cladophora rupestris	*Enteromorpha* sp.	*Halidrys siliquosa* and all *Fucales*	*Ptilota plumosa*
Water-soluble fraction	S Uronic acid S Galactose S Glucose M Arabinose W Xylose	S Glucose M Uronic acid M Galactose W Xylose	S Uronic acid M Galactose M Glucose M Xylose M Fucose	S Galactose M Uronic acid M Glucose M Xylose M Ribose W Arabinose
Hemicellulose		S Xylose S Rhamnose M Glucose	S Xylose S Fucose	S Xylose
a-cellulose before chlorite treatment	S Glucose M Galactose M Arabinose W Xylose	S Glucose M Xylose M Rhamnose	S Glucose M Xylose M Fucose	S Glucose S Galactose M Xylose
a-cellulose after chlorite treatment	S Glucose	S Glucose M Xylose M Rhamnose	S Glucose W Xylose W Fucose	S Glucose W Galactose W Xylose

(S, M or W refer to strong, moderate and weak intensity of the spots in the chromatographic method used for these sugar analyses)

that of higher plants. Earlier work[293] indicated that the type of cellulose (I or native cellulose, or II, a less polymerized cellulose with more fractions consisting of irregularly disposed molecules) is not constant throughout the Chlorophyta, e.g. in the Cladophorales cellulose I is present in all *Cladophora* spp., *Chaetomorpha* spp. and *Rhizoclonium* spp., whereas it is replaced by cellulose II in all *Spongomorpha* species. In the Oedogoniophyceae and Zygnemaphyceae, neither kind of cellulose has been detected by X-ray defraction studies, but chemical methods may yet show them to be present, since later work suggests that X-ray analysis is not completely reliable for the identification of cellulose, particularly in algae having a large amount of non-cellulosic material in the wall. It is of interest to note that the famous early phycologists Agardh and Naegeli, observed striations in algal walls (*Valonia*, *Microdictyon* and *Chamaedoris*) and in the mid-nineteenth century Correns observed them in *Cladophora*. The latter worker separated the lamellae by maceration and studied their birefringence and showed that the cellulose micellae were orientated in the direction of the striations and the two main sets of lamellae lay at an angle of nearly 90° to one another. The presence of lamellae composed of microfibrils running in slow, steep and third spirals in the walls of *Cladophora*, *Chaetomorpha* and *Valonia*, poses the fascinating question of their origin; the third spiral is not always present, and then the wall is a two lamellae repeat; even more intriguing is the fact that microfibrils are interwoven between different lamellae. Frei and Preston[111] showed that the microfibrils of the side walls are continuous with those of the cross walls. The fibrils are arranged randomly in the cross walls (Plate 1) and in apical cells of *Cladophora prolifera* the microfibrils also pass over the apex through a random patch at the tip. The set of microfibrils are also deposited in the same order even in the sporelings, the first making a small angle to the transverse axis of the cell, followed by the second at a greater angle, and finally the third when this is present. The rhythm of deposition is retained by daughter cells through several cell divisions so that adjacent cells in a filament have the innermost lamellae lying in the same direction although eventually they do get out of step. The regions of the wall where perforations appear during sporulation have been investigated and it is shown that a cytoplasmic plug is pushed into the wall layers disturbing the orientation of the microfibrils. Wall formation continues, but in the region of the future perforation the microfibrils are laid down at random. This extremely complex and exact system of wall formation suggests that deposition is under very precise control and that the production and orientation of microfibrils is a function of the outermost layer of the cytoplasm. In *Chaetomorpha* the outer layers of the wall are cemented together by encrusting material, whereas the inner lamellae are relatively free of such material; in this alga the encrusting material may have an affinity to protein (there are no pectic compounds in the wall of this genus).[111] In the genus *Pediastrum* a network pattern, sometimes joining globules, is often observable under the ordinary light microscope and this has also been photographed under the electron microscope, but it has been impossible to decide whether this is on, within or inside the fine continuous wall membrane[287] (Fig. 13). A fibrillar layered cellulose wall has been deduced for *Chlamydomonas reinhardtii*, but details are lacking.[355] In this species there is an outer capsule containing polysaccharides (20–60 nm thick) appearing as a fibrillar felt with a frayed outer surface. This capsular material is continually diffusing into the medium.

Silica walls

The electron microscope has not revealed any structural components in diatom cell walls, so that details of its crystal structure and its mode of deposition are still unknown. It has however been shown that the siliceous components are laid down in large vesicles just beneath the plasmalemma (see Plate 12C, D). It has, also, revealed the finer details of pore and raphe structure, some of which had already been detected by the use of the light microscope. Basically the diatom cell wall consists of either a simple or perforate lamina (Plate 11 B, C), or a loculate system consisting of inner and outer laminae, separated by vertical walls. The perforations may be open or occluded by thin siliceous perforated plates, which are seldom visible under the light microscope.[169] A smooth lamina with no perforations is rare and found in *Guinardia blavyana*. The simplest type of perforate laminate wall is seen in *Synedra fulgens* (see Fig. 13), in which rows of simple perforations form the striae of the cell as seen in the light microscope. The other types of lamina walls have occluded punctae, e.g. *Synedra ulna*, in which the 'striae' seen under the light microscope are really elongated structures closed by a perforate plate. Four other types of perforation are illustrated, reticulate (*Achnanthes longipes*), incised (*Cocconeis stauroneiformis*), concentric plates (*Raphoneis amphiceros*) and dendriform (*Didymosphaenia geminata*). Additional wall markings in the laminate type may be due to thickening of the wall to form ribs, costae, reticulae, etc., in between the pore system. The loculate wall is a double structure with vertical partitions between upper and lower lamina, often hexagonal in shape, giving a single honeycomb structure. The vertical walls may themselves have pores connecting the loculae laterally. The scanning electron microscope is an enormous help in understanding the structure of diatom walls. The loculae have outer and inner closing plates, one of which usually has an occluding plate with a large pore (foramena) in it, and the other is of the occluded type with a perforate plate (cribrum). Such a loculate type has been known for many years in the genus *Pinnularia*, but only with the electron microscope is it possible to see that the outer membrane is a perforate plate, and the inner a simple plate with an elliptical pore readily seen under the light microscope (Fig. 13). An example of the opposite type is *Stephanopyxis palmeriana* with a simple pore in the outer layer and a perforate plate on the inner lamina. The basic siliceous framework of many diatoms appears to be formed of ribs between which porous plates are suspended; these ribs extend beneath the raphe in some genera e.g. *Hantzschia* and *Nitzschia* (Plate 7). It has been shown that the silica wall has a membrane potential, and will adsorb positively charged, but not negatively charged, particles. This potential must have a profound influence on the absorption processes of the cells and other physiological activities, e.g. it was found that the absorption of positively charged particles reduced motility of *Pinnularia* and *Nitzschia* sp.[118]

The use of submicroscopic detail will probably not change the concept of the majority of diatom genera or species, but it is of value in deciding doubtful affinities, e.g. the classic example of *Nitzschia closterium*. f. *minutissima* alias *Phaeodactylum tricornutum*, which has now been shown to possess *Cymbella*-like markings on one valve only, in the oval stage of this pleomorphic organism.[243]

Periplasts

Many of the so-called 'naked' flagellates have an outer membrane (periplast or pellicle), which is differentiated from the rest of the cytoplasm but is not so obvious as the cellulose and silica walls just discussed. 'Naked' is in fact a comparative term used to distinguish the organisms without cellulose or silica walls. However the periplast is visible under the electron microscope as a differentiated layer and in many Euglenoids is produced into warts, ridges, etc., with definite rigidity and sculpturing (see Plate 5). In addition in the Chrysomonadales, there are scales or discs of silica or organic materials associated with the periplast which have an intricate structure under the electron microscope.

One of the simplest algal cells examined in detail with the electron microscope is *Micromonas pusilla* (=*Chromulina pusilla*) in which the bounding membrane consists of three layers, the outer and inner being electron dense and the mid a translucent layer. This is almost certainly comparable with the cytoplasmic membrane of other flagellates, e.g. in *Chlamydomonas reinhardtii*, Sager and Palade[355] record a continuous membrane 100 Å in thickness, stratified into two dense layers ≈3 nm thick separated by a light layer. In both *Micromonas* and *Chlamydomonas*, the flagellar membrane is continuous with the former and with the cytoplasmic membrane of the latter genus, suggesting that these membranes are homologous. Therefore *Micromonas* is a 'naked' flagellate and *Chlamydomonas* is 'clothed' in a cell wall.

The pellicle of *Euglena* differs from the above in that it appears under the electron microscope as a series of semi-rigid rings alternating with strips of pliable material.[421] These rings are articulated one to another (Plate 5).

Coccoliths

The scales and coccoliths of the Prymnesiales (a section of the Haptophyceae), are often so small and so intricate, that only electron micrographs reveal the full detail. There are two main types of coccolith. (1) Holococcoliths composed of submicroscopic crystals, e.g. the crystalloliths of *Crystallolithus hyalinus* (Plate 2), which has now been shown to be the motile stage in

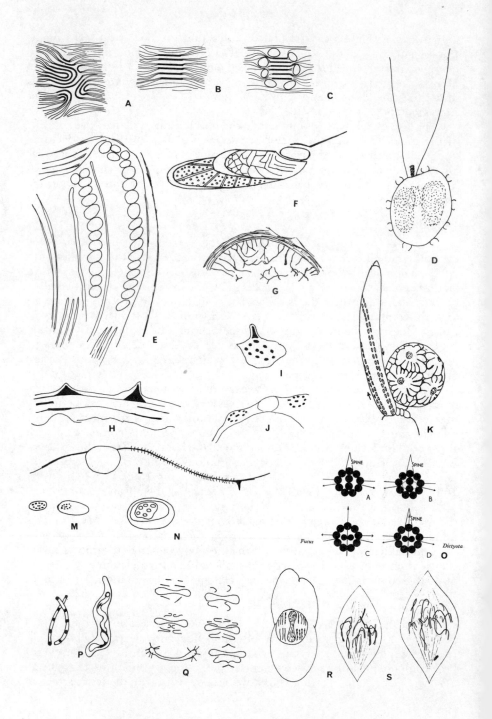

the life history of *Coccolithus pelagicus*.[310] These crystals appear to be rhomboidal calcite and they completely cover the cell body. They are borne on very delicate sculptured scales embedded in an outer hyaline region of the periplast. A distinct inner layer of the periplast gave a doubtful cellulose reaction, but the chemistry of the hyaline layer is unknown. There may be more than one layer of scales bearing crystalloliths on their outer surfaces and embedded in the hyaline layer. The crystals can be built up into most complex forms, e.g. *Homozygosphaera* (Plate 2). (2) Heterococcoliths (Placoliths). These are the larger, more obvious coccoliths built up of plates, ribs, girdles, etc., to form a complex amorphous structure.[142] Two cells bearing such complex coccoliths are featured on Plate 9.

The possession of either holococcoliths or heterococcoliths may in some instances be a valid taxonomic criterion; however, the study of *Coccolithus pelagicus* bearing heterococcoliths in the non-motile phase and holococcoliths in the motile phase (*Crystallolithus hyalinus*), shows the dangers inherent in placing genera on coccolith structure alone.[310] In some genera the heterococcoliths are dimorphic, e.g. *Michaelsarsia* (Fig. 13), with its crown of spine-like coccoliths and elliptical body 'discoliths' (numerous names have been given to the differently shaped and constructed heterococcoliths). The mechanism of coccolith formation is not yet completely understood but there is evidence that in *Coccolithus* and *Cricosphaera* the unmineralized scales and the calcareous coccoliths arise within the cisternae of the Golgi body.[277a] The function of these complex calcareous plates is unknown. Superficially it would appear that this 'heavy exoskeleton' would be detrimental to floating organisms.

FIG. 14.

A, B. Pyrenoids with lamellae passing into them in *Closterium* and *Spirogyra*; C. Simple pyrenoid with starch grains; D. Cell of *Chrysochromulina chiton*. Note the coiled haptonema; E. Eye-spot of *Chlamydomonas reinhardtii*; F. Diagram of scale of *Mallomonas*; G. Part of transverse section of *Caulerpa* coenocyte; H, I, J. Diagrams of flagellum of *Dictyota*; H, I. Longitudinal and transverse sections showing spines; J. Flagellum coiled beneath surface membrane and cut transversely; K. Cytoplasmic streaming in *Nitella* cell; L. Flagella on *Himanthalia*; M. The two flagella of *Synura*, cut transversely; N. Transverse section of *Chrysochromulina strobilus* haptonema; O. Diagram of the arrangement of "flimmer" and spines in *Dictyota*, and *Fucus*. Lateral lines indicate alternate positions of "flimmer"; A. *Dictyota*; B. Showing alternative positions of the two central strands; C. Front flagellum of *Fucus*; D. *Dictyota* as finally resolved. Arrow heads indicating the probable position of organs at different times during the investigation of the organisms; P. Chromosomes of *Spirogyra* in mid-prophase and coiled within matrix; Q. Shape of chromatids and dividing endosome of Euglenoids during mitotic anaphase; R. Anaphase of *Oxyrrhis*; S. Elongated chromosomes of *Oedogonium*.

(After Dodge, Godward, Harris, Kretschmer, Leyon, Manton, Parke, Manton and Clarke, Manton, Clarke and Greenwood, Sachs, Sager and Palade and original.)

Scales of other flagellates

At least two other scale types occur, thin oval plates of unknown composition, just visible under the light microscope and thicker and more complex siliceous scales with characteristic markings comparable to those of the diatom frustule. The former are found in flagellates of the genus *Chrysochromulina* associated with the delicate periplast. They are often dimorphic, the smaller scales being roundish or oval with a thickened rim and a radiating series of ridges (see Plate 3), the larger often oval and striate, with a ridge running round the scale cutting off an outer rim (see Fig. 14), e.g. in *C. chiton*.[311] In *C. strobilus* the small scales are present as a single layer beneath the outer layer of larger cup-shaped scales (see Plate 3),[312] whilst in *C. ericina*, there are small scales with radiating markings on the inner face and a mesh-work of markings on the outer face, together with hollow spines with an enlarged base closed by a flat plate.[276] Thus these scales are double structures and in the spinous type, the spine is produced by the outward extension of the outer face of the scale; this is shown by the mesh-like markings on the base of the spine and the radiating markings on the base plate. The scales of *Chrysochromulina* seem to have a fibrous structure and may possibly be formed in vesicles beneath the outer membrane. Manton and Parke[278] found that the scales of *Micromonas squamata* (a genus of the Prasinophyceae), were formed in definite vesicles beneath the cell surface; it is now known that this mode of formation is widespread in several algal groups. The scales on the flagellum of this species are probably formed from a cluster of vesicles around the base of the flagellum (Plate 3).

In the Prasinophyta there are scales on both the flagella and on the body of the motile cells e.g. *Pyramimonas*. There are many rows of small scales next to the flagellar membrane, and on top of these, nine rows of larger scales with central spines. On the body three layers of differently shaped scales occur.[277b] More recently scales of a rather simple type have been discovered on the flagella and body of the male gametes of *Chara* thus adding yet another highly distinctive feature to the Charophyta.[286a]

The siliceous scales of *Mallomonas* species (see Fig. 14 and Plate 3) are not only complex in their ornamentation but furnished with spines. Only one type of scale is present, but in some species the spines may occur only on the apical scales (e.g. *M. tonsurata*), whilst the remaining scales on a single cell may vary in size, often becoming smaller towards the base, although retaining the basic pattern of the species. The spine of *Mallomonas* fits onto the 'dome'-shaped apical end of the scale, probably held by cytoplasm and it is this mounting which makes the spine movable.[148] Fig. 14F is a reconstruction of this arrangement.[148, 149] The form of the scales is clearly a taxonomic character, with some *Mallomonas* species having a simpler type of scale. The structure of the scales in *Synura spinosa* is similar to that of *Mallomonas* but the scale in section shows a raised 'crown,' the apex of which may be slightly extended to form a short spine (Plate 3) whilst the basal scales are of simpler form.

Cytoplasm

The cytoplasm of algal cells tends to be viscous and granules other than plastids and reserve products are generally very small. It is rare, except in the Xanthophyceae and Chrysophyceae, to find a highly vacuolate cytoplasm, although in most algal cells vacuoles are present; large vacuoles occur in *Spirogyra* and *Sphacelaria*, and are traversed by cytoplasmic threads, whilst in others, e.g. many Bryopsidophyceae and Charales there is a large central vacuole. The vacuole is traversed by strands of thickening (callose and pectin) in some Bryopsidophyceae, e.g. *Caulerpa*. In the Charales streaming of the cytoplasm carries the plastids with it. Ettl [96] has recently emphasized the importance of contractile vacuoles in the taxonomy of the Volvocales which either have two situated adjacent to the flagellar bases, e.g. *Chlamydomonas*, or several scattered throughout the cell, e.g. *Chlorogonium*. They appear to be highly characteristic and constant in occurrence in various genera and species. Specialized vacuoles occur in the Cyanophyta, appearing black under the microscope; these are the gas vacuoles containing nitrogen. In the Phaeophyta small vacuoles, containing fucosan and known as physodes or fucosan vesicles are found, often clustered round the nucleus. In some algae the vacuolar sap is coloured, e.g. purplish in *Zygnema* and *Zygogonium* (Zygnemaphyceae).

The most obvious feature of algal cells is the chromatophore (plastid), the form of which is a useful criterion of taxonomic affinity when combined with other features, e.g. discoid chromatophores are common in centric diatoms, Bryopsidophyceae, Charophyceae, many Dinophyceae and some Euglenophyceae. Parietal plates are found in Ulotrichales, Chaetophorales, most Pennate diatoms, many Chrysophyceae, Phaeophyta and Rhodophyta and may be simple or lobed. Complex chromatophores are found in the Volvocales (basin shaped and often ribbed), Oedogoniales (reticulate), Zygnemaphyceae (ribbon-like, simple or spiral, stellate and branched, e.g. in *Cosmarium*). Early work using polarized light suggested that the chromatophore was a lamellate structure since it showed form birefringence. Electron microscopic studies show a chromatophore membrane of unit membrane structure (deduced from earlier osmotic studies on chromatophores). Inside the chromatophore membrane further stacks of membranes occur, each of which is a paired structure, joined at the ends to form thylakoids, with a less dense region inside (see Plate 12E). Between the thylakoids is the matrix (previously called the stroma) and this, the stacks of thylakoids and the membrane, form the algal chromatophore. In most algae there are no grana comparable to those of the higher plants, but in the desmid. *Micrasterias*, very pronounced grana-like areas are present in the chromatophore.[82] The thylakoids are the chlorophyll containing structures and granules, lipid droplets and starch grains are found in the matrix. In most algae the eyespots and pyrenoids are associated with the chromatophores. Figures 4E and 13E show *Chlamydomonas* as seen by the light and electron microscopes and reveal the wealth of detail hidden from the light microscopist. Work on

Euglena and *Poteriochromonas*, demonstrated that the stacks of thylakoids were ≈20 nm in thickness, with denser edges ≈5 nm and less dense interspaces of 20–50 nm. It was concluded that the cross sectional area occupied by the chlorophyll molecules would be ≈225 Å²; from estimates of the chlorophyll content, this allows all the interfaces to be covered by chlorophyll molecules.[421] A yellow mutant strain of *Chlamydomonas*, in which carotenoid pigment was present contained no thylakoids, although the chromatophore was still recognizable, this suggests that thylokoids are only associated with the chlorophyll containing part of the chromatophore. If these yellow mutants are transferred to light, chlorophyll appears in the cells preceding thylakoid formation,[355] presumably this is the light sensitive chlorophyll synthesis reaction from protochlorophyll, which can occur without thylakoid formation. In view of the wide use of *Chlorella* in physiological studies, the structure of its chromatophore is of great interest. The cup-shaped chromatophore has 4–8 concentric electron dense layers, each of which is made up of 4 laminae. Olsen and Engel[304] devised a neat method for photographing live *Chlorella* cells and intact chromatophores using light from the mercury line at 435 nm, which corresponds with the blue *in vivo* chlorophyll absorption peak. The layers containing chlorophyll absorb this energy and the regions between do not, so that a photograph of the lamella is possible. These are not so clear as electron microscope photographs, but they do show the presence of at least 4 chlorophyll absorbing concentric layers, corresponding to the electron dense layers. This technique also shows that the wavy pattern of the lamellae, which appears in electron micrographs, is not an artefact. In order to see the lamellae within the 4 concentric layers, the chloroplasts were extracted and transferred to 0·1 M KCl solution in which the lamellae separated so that they could then be photographed using the above technique. These results indicate that there are about 16 laminae per chloroplast, giving 32 monolayers of chlorophyll which agrees with calculated and observed data on chlorophyll content of *Chlorella*.

Recent work has shown that ultramicroscopic structures are also present in the chromatoplasm of the Cyanophyta. Calvin and Lynch[51] separated a green sediment from a blue suspension when broken cells of *Synechococcus cedorum* were centrifuged at 36 000 g/min. The green sediment gave an absorption curve for chlorophyll and carotene and the blue solution a curve for phycocyanin. The sediment was granular of the order of 222 nm diameter and it was suggested that these granules were homologous with the grana of green plants. Sections of *Phormidium uncinatum*, under the electron microscope show thylakoids in the chromatoplasm and later work has shown similar structures in all the Cyanophyta investigated.[184] In *Oscillatoria chalybea*, the thylakoids consisting of two layers and similar to those of the Chlorophyceae and higher plants, run longitudinally in the cells with the cross walls appearing to 'cut' them[284] (see Plate 4). In *Nostoc muscorum* the lamellae tend to form spirals, whilst in an unknown genus a network of lamellae was seen.

Inclusions in the chromatophore such as starch are found within the matrix and appear as light, structureless bodies in electron micrographs. The pyrenoid however is penetrated by tubules which are derived from the thylakoids (see Plate 12E); in some phyla starch is laid down in plates around the pyrenoid and between these plates the tubules run out and connect with the thylakoids of the chloroplast. Thylakoids also pass into the pyrenoid of *Closterium, Spirogyra* and *Mougeotia*[247] (Fig. 14). In the Rhodophyta the grains of Floridian starch are scattered in the cytoplasm. In the Phaeophyta, Bacillariphyta and Chrysophyta, polysaccharides, laminarin, volutin and leucosin are formed. It is probable that these are all only slight variations of the same polysaccharide, and the names chrysose and chrysolaminarin have been suggested as more suitable terms (see p. 180 for the chemical nature of these compounds). In all three groups, oil droplets are frequent and in the diatoms often occupy constant positions in the cell. Oil, stained yellow or red with carotenoid pigments is often very abundant in the Dinophyceae. Some of the most distinctive reserve compounds occur in the Euglenophyceae, these are the colourless carbohydrate masses known as paramylum; this substance is formed as characteristic discs, rods, rings, etc., the form being fairly constant for the species and thus being used as a taxonomic criterion.

The eyespot of some flagellates is situated immediately beneath the chromatophore membrane, e.g. in *Chlamydomonas reinhardtii* where it consists of two parallel rows of granules. Between the two rows are two thylakoids, running longitudinally through the eyespot and into the thylakoid system of the chromatophore (Fig. 14). The eyespot of *Euglena* is not within the chromatophore, a feature which can be seen by light microscopy. It consists of clusters of granules each surrounded by a membrane, located immediately adjacent to the membrane of the reservoir (a chamber with smooth walls that terminates the ridged canal,[423] (see Plate 5). The granules besides containing carotenoids, also possess a special pigment, astaxanthin (a dehydroxydiketo derivative of β-carotin), which is a pigment occurring in several animals, and thus this *Euglena* possesses pigments characteristic of both plants and animals.

A most striking eyespot is present in the *Fucus* spermatozoid, consisting of some 50–70 pigment chambers spread in a single layer on the outside of the chromatophore below the chromatophore membrane[274] (see Plate 4).

Flagella

Although considerable detail of the flagella structure has been revealed by careful cytological technique and observation with the light microscope, it is only with the use of the electron microscope that the fine structure has been elucidated. Flagella are either acronematic (smooth) or pleuronematic, i.e. bear fine hairs ('flimmer' or mastigonemata). In section, two central tubules can be seen surrounded by nine peripheral tubules all enclosed in a membrane; this is the basic pattern of plant and animal flagella. Even in mutant strains of *Chlamydomonas*, in which the flagella are paralysed, this tubular structure is identical to that of the wild type strains.

The outer membrane is continuous with the plasma membrane in *Chlamydomonas reinhardtii*[355] and *Fucus*.[271] This membrane is nothing more than the uplifted plasma membrane as is shown by the superb studies of the spermatozoid of *Dictyota dichotoma*,[272] and *Micromonas pusilla*.[273] In *Dictyota* the single flagellum (the second flagellum of the Phaeophyta is present only as a residual base), is coiled round the young spermatozoid several times and

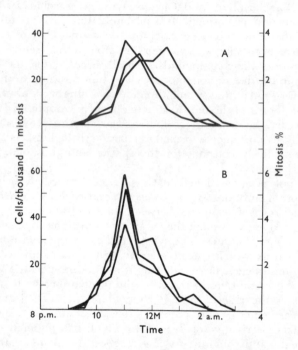

FIG. 15.

The relationship between frequency of mitoses and time in *Euglena spirogyra* (A) and *Euglena viridis* (B).

(From Leedale, 1959.)

in section the 9 + 2 tubules can be seen beneath the body membrane but without any membrane of their own. After release of the spermatozoid the flagellum uncoils and in doing so lifts up the body membrane, which at this stage must be in a very labile state (Fig. 14). In *Micromonas pusilla* (=*Chromulina pusilla*) the developing flagellum is formed in the body of the flagellate and in its emergence raises the body membrane. The *Dictyota* flagellum has 'flimmer' and also a row of spines attached to one of the outer fibrils; the spines themselves are covered by the flagellar membrane. A study of these, in relation to the symmetry of the flagellum, showed it to be a bilaterally symmetrical structure with the plane of symmetry passing between the central strands and with the lateral hairs at slightly more than a right angle to this in *Dictyota*. In *Fucus* the hairs are at right angles to this plane (lines with arrows in Fig. 14O). In the biflagellate sperm of other Phaeophyta it is the front flagellum which is pleuronematic. In *Fucus*, *Ascophyllum* and *Pelvetia* this flagellum is the shorter of the two and in these genera there is a striate proboscis at the front (Fig. 14), which is extended backwards along the body of the sperm as a strand of fibrils visible as such.[275] The front flagellum of *Himanthalia* differs from the above in being the longer of the two (as in *Pylaiella*, *Laminaria* and *Scytosiphon*) and in bearing 'flimmer', which stop about one-quarter of the distance from the apex where a single conspicuous spine occurs attached to a single fibril of the peripheral series. In the *Fucus* spermatozoid the 'flimmer' also cease some distance below the apex, which ends as a whiplash. The hind flagellum of all these spermatozoids is of the whiplash type. In *Fucus* this flagellum loops back onto the body of the sperm and is attached in the region of the eyespot. Here the sheath of the flagellum is enlarged so that the eleven strands lie in a corner (Fig. 14A).

Pleuronematic flagella are now known to be characteristic of *Euglena*, *Phacus*, *Synura*, *Ochromonas*, *Mallomonas*, *Cryptomonas*, *Vaucheria* (spermatozoid but not zoospores), *Chlorosaccus*, *Botrydium* and *Tribonema*. The second flagellum, when present, is always of the acronematic type, except in *Cryptomonas*, which has two pleuronematic flagella. The second acronematic flagellum is reduced in some genera, e.g. *Mallomonas*, where it persists as a photoreceptor, whilst in *Chromulina* it has completely disappeared or remains as a short internal flagellum.[309] A short second flagellum is also present in *Euglena* species but does not usually extend beyond the apical invagination. The arrangement of hairs on the flagellum is not constant; the double row in species of the Phaeophyta has already been mentioned and other types are those of certain Chrysophyceae, e.g. *Ochronomonas malhamensis*, which has hairs arising in tufts and also another layer of hairs close to the axis, and of Euglenoids which have a one-sided arrangement (see Plate 5). These hairs are now known to be formed in vesicles inside the cells of some flagellates, and one presumes that this may be a fairly general method of formation. In *Euglena* there is a large swollen structure at the base of the long flagellum which is believed to function as the photoreceptor (see Plate 5). The flagellar membranes vary, e.g. relatively loose structures are found, as in the pleuronematic flagellum of *Synura*, whilst the acronematic flagellum has a closer fitting sheath (Fig. 14M),[270] and in *Euglena* it is striate.[422]

The type of flagellum appears to be characteristic of taxonomic groups and constant throughout the group, e.g. one acronematic and on pleuronematic in the Phaeophyta and Xanthophyta and two acronematic in the Chlorophyta. In the Chrysophyta the flagella bear flimmer (e.g. *Synura* and *Mallomonas*) whilst those of the Haptophyta are smooth.

Surprisingly few flagella of Chlorophyta have been studied. Early workers did not regularly find eleven tubules, e.g. in the flagella of *Chlamy-domonas moewusii* or *C. reinhardtii*, although they did note that each was a paired structure; this has since been demonstrated in other flagella. Certain treatments result in the rapid loss of the central tubules and later work shows that *Chlamydomonas* does not differ from the general pattern. Preparation tends to pull the tubules, together with their basal bodies, out of the cytoplasm in preparations of some Chaetophorales;[272a] the tubules of each flagellum can then be seen to be joined in a ring by fibrous connections, whilst the 'roots,' arising between the basal bodies, are connected to the latter by fibrils.

Micromonas is a most interesting genus of small flagellates, belonging to the phylum Haptophyla although previously its taxonomic position was uncertain. In *M. squamata* the single flagellum (supernumerary flagella may be present in some stages) is covered by a coating of fine, imbricated circular scales with a spider's web pattern on them. These are also present on the cell, and transverse sections show them to be outside the cell membrane. In addition there are also fine hairs on the flagellum and a tuft of hairs at the tip, which may merely be a few microfibrils which are longer than others. In *M. pusilla* the single flagellum is of the normal type in the basal region (roughly 0·5 μm in length), and then tapers to a hair point, which consists of the flagellar membrane and the two central fibrils.

The flagella end in the cell, in hollow basal bodies separated from the flagellum by a diaphragm, but with the nine outer tubules continued into its wall whilst the two centre tubules stop short at the diaphragm. In the spermatozoid of *Dictyota*, the basal bodies both possess nine tubules in the walls; only one bears a flagellum which has a strap-shaped fibrous root[272] arising at the inner end of the basal body and running through the cell without touching the nucleus, although in other algae, e.g. *Micromonas squamata*, it runs on to the surface of the nucleus. In *Pedinomonas tuberculata* the single flagellum enters the cell and forms a normal base to which is attached a cruciform series of four fibrous roots with conspicuous striate membranous coverings (cf. similar striation in *Synura* roots). In *Fucus* spermatozoids, the hollow flagellar bases are joined, pointing in opposite directions and separated from the flagellum proper by a membrane at the level of the cell membrane (see Plate 4). There appear to be fibrous connections from the base of the front flagellum to the nucleus.

The violent metaboly of dividing *Euglena* cells sometimes results in anucleate cells which, possessing flagella, move normally and respond to light and other stimuli; thus the presence of a nucleus is not necessary for control of flagellar action.[233a]

In some mainly marine flagellates, e.g. *Chrysochromulina*, there is in addition to the flagella, a structure known as the haptonema, which is similar in length to the flagella or in some species much longer and often with a swollen tip; it is capable of being coiled to varying degrees, even right up to the body in the form of a solenoid (Fig. 14D), is thinner than the flagella and can serve to anchor the flagellate. In *C. strobilus*, it consists of three concentric membranes enclosing a ring of six tubules,[312] the outer is three-layered, each layer being approximately 3 nm thick, whilst the inner are thinner and their structure is not discernible (Plate 4). In *C. chiton* the tubules (7 in this species) tend to lie close to the inner membrane, appearing almost as ridges on it.[311] The variation in the number of tubules in haptonemata is in distinct contrast to the fixed number in flagella.

Mitochondria

These are conspicuous in electron micrographs of flagellates and the species of *Micromonas* are exceptional in having but a single mitochondrion per cell. As yet there is only a small amount of data on the form and distribution of these minute organelles. However, all the evidence to date suggests that they are basically similar in all groups, and certainly function similarly as sites of enzyme action in glycolysis, amino acid interconversion and protein synthesis. They are bounded by a double membrane, the inner produced into folds (cristae mitochondriales), projecting into the lumen which contains a structureless or slightly granular matrix. Those of the Chlorophyta, e.g. *Chlamydomonas reinhardtii* have a few flat plate-like 'cristae' leaving much of the lumen free and appearing in section as separate small elongated sacs unattached to the wall; in serial sections these are seen to be long extensions of the inner membrane. The Chrysophyta, Phaeophyta and Xanthophyta, all have mitochondria with 'cristae' appearing as closely crowded finger-like microvilli which tend to occupy more of the lumen than those of the Chlorophyta. In certain cells the number of mitochondria appears to be relatively constant, e.g. four in *Fucus* spermatozoid. In the zoospore of *Vaucheria* they are associated with the chloroplasts and with the Golgi bodies. Cells of Cyanophyta do not possess mitochondria.

Golgi bodies (Dictyosomes)

These are present in all algal cells except Cyanophyta and are fairly easily recognizable in sections under the electron microscope. They may be found in the region of the nucleus (e.g. in *Chlamydomonas*) or associated with the flagellar bases (e.g. in *Chrysochromulina* and *Pedinomonas*), and are composed of stacks of flat vesicles (cisternal elements), the ends of which may be dilated. They are frequently accompanied by smooth, circular or oval vesicles which form at the edges of the dictyosome (see Plate 5). In *Chlamydomonas*,[355] there are no large vesicles associated with the lamellae (cf. the dictyosomes of some invertebrates and protozoa), but in *Chrysochromulina*, large vesicles are very evident.[312] Very conspicuous dictyosomes are found along the periphery of the chloroplast in some desmids.[82] The dictyosomes of diatoms produce vesicles which are involved in wall formation (Plate 12D).

Endoplasmic reticulum

The ground substance of all algal cells is traversed by endoplasmic reticulum. This interconnecting system does not penetrate the chloroplast or pyrenoid. Most striking are oblique sections which show a deposit of fine granules on the reticulum and in some surface views, these appear as 'paired linear arrays of particles.' Similar particles are found free in the cytoplasm.

Nucleus

The nucleus is frequently visible in algal cells appearing as a greyish body often enclosing a darker region, the nucleolus. It is sometimes suspended in the centre of the cell by cytoplasmic threads, e.g. *Spirogyra*, or in a cytoplasmic bridge, e.g. most Naviculoid diatoms, whilst in others the nucleus lies alongside the wall. In the multinucleate genera the nuclei are generally found in the cytoplasm between the vacuole and the plastids; this condition is widespread, occurring in certain genera of the Chlorococcales and Xanthophyta and in the Bryopsidophyceae, Gelidiales, Rhodymeniales and Ceramiales. Whereas in most algae, the nucleus is a discrete spherical or ellipsoidal structure, in the Cyanophyta the chromatinic material forms a diffuse central region of the cytoplasm unbounded by a nuclear membrane. The size of the nucleus varies from less than a micron in some algae to 80 μm in the primary nucleus of *Acetabularia*; large nuclei also occur in the rhizoids of Charophytes. The algal nucleus can be stained by the usual methods showing the nucleoplasm to be slightly granular during interphase except in the Dinophyceae, where the chromosomes are always stainable.[78]

Electron micrographs of sections of algae, reveal a nuclear membrane consisting of two layers separated by a narrow space and perforated by pores. In *Chlamydomonas* the outer membrane bears dense particles (10–15 nm diameter) attached to the outer surface, the inner being smooth. In places this membrane appears to be continuous with the endoplasmic reticulum. The nucleoplasm is composed of fine granular material, whilst the nucleolus consists of granules 10–15 nm in diameter, with some finer particles in the centre. The particles on the outer membrane of the nucleolus are smaller than the pores in the *Chlamydomonas* nuclear membrane ($\approx$50 nm), thus allowing the possibility of transport of these into the cytoplasm as has been suggested for some organisms.

One or more nucleoli (endosomes) are often clearly visible in algal nuclei. Four types of nucleolar structure have been noted in desmids,[210] (a) a single nucleolus per nucleus, (b) two or more unassociated nucleoli per nucleus, (c) a complex nucleolar mass (in some *Closterium* spp.) and, (d) a linear association of a large number of small nucleoli (in some *Micrasterias* spp.). Vacuolar-like structures were also visible in the larger nucleoli. The nucleolus in *Spirogyra* and in desmids produces material which is released during mitosis and concentrates round the metaphase plate, either as a loose mass of 'nucleolar substance' or as a coating on the chromatids;[120] it is also distributed generally throughout the nucleus. The chromatids then carry this substance to the poles at anaphase or in some species it moves to the poles independently. At telophase the chromosomes are embedded in a mass of 'nucleolar substance,' which then breaks up and is assembled by the 'nucleolar organizing' chromosomes, into a new nucleolus.[128] In both the Euglenophyta and Dinophyta, the nucleolus persists throughout mitosis dividing as a unit distinct from the chromosomes and at least in Euglenophyta retaining its ribonucleic acid.[232]

There is evidence that the nucleus is separated from the cytoplasm, not only by its double membrane, but also by a perinuclear space, which may be bridged at intervals. In some flagellates, e.g. *Paraphysomonas*,[277] fibres from the flagellar bases pass down the sides of the nucleus and hold it in some way; this close relationship is seen in other flagellates, e.g. *Ochromonas* and in the synzoospore of *Vaucheria*. It is not however a universal mode of attachment, for in many other genera these fibres are attached to plastids or to the cell wall.

There is a wide range of chromosome morphology in the algae from small almost spherical chromosomes in some desmids, through the common elongate type, to thread-like structures in some *Oedogonium* spp. Chromosomes with a single median or subterminal centromere are common in the Siphonocladales and many diatoms, whilst in some Zygnemaphyceae, the single centromere is terminal or subterminal. In the desmids,[211] *Spirogyra*,[129] Euglenophyta[232] and Dinophyta,[79] there is no conspicuous centromere (cf. *Luzula* in the Angiosperms); these chromosomes may be interpreted as having a 'diffuse centromere' or a polycentric structure. In *Oedogonium* there appears to be a row of chromomeres along the chromosome. The chromosomes of the Zygnemaphyceae are surrounded by a sticky material (matrix) (Fig. 14S). In *Spirogyra* centromeres are absent from the nucleolar organizing region of the nucleolar organizing chromosomes. This part of the chromosome drags behind when the chromatids separate at anaphase. The 'nucleolar organizing' region passes into the nucleoli along 'organizer tracks,' which are visible in the resting nucleus in the form of unstained bands. Such nucleolar organizing chromosomes and tracks also occur in *Zygnema*, *Closterium* and other desmids.

Some of the smallest chromosomes are 0·25 μm or less in length, e.g. in some species of Ulotrichales,[356] whilst the average chromosome is a few μm in length. Measurements however are difficult to present, since, as in other organisms, the chromosomes contract during the early stages of mitosis.

Spiral structure is clearly seen in chromosomes of *Spirogyra*, and in addition chromatids are seen to spiral around one another.[129] These spirals condense between prophase and metaphase, at which stage the densely staining short spiral is immersed in the matrix (Fig. 14P). At telophase the expanded chromosome is stainable only in certain regions; this is also seen in some desmids. The stained regions are termed chromocentres and during prophase can be seen as irregular twisted regions, which gradually contract as the chromosome spiral condenses.

Chromosome numbers in algae are sometimes difficult to determine. In some groups, e.g. desmids, the difficulty is due to the large number of small chromosomes, in others, e.g. Dinophyta, it is due to the entanglement of numerous thread-like chromosomes, whilst in many Phaeophyta, large amounts of mucilage and other substances interfere with fixing and staining techniques. In spite of these difficulties the numbers are rapidly being ascertained and the following is a summary of some of the data. In the Volvocales haploid numbers vary from 5 in some *Volvox* species through 12, 13, 14, 15, and 16 to 22. *Chlamydomonas reinhardtii, C. moewusii, C. eugametos* and *C. chlamydogama* have 8[234] although 16, 18, 34, 38, etc., were earlier reported. In the Ulotrichales the chromosome counts tend to be 5 (or multiples, e.g. 10, 20) or 8 (or multiples, e.g. 16, 24, 32, 48), in the Clado-phoraceae the number in *Cladophora* is basically 12 but multiples of this occur, some of which is due to polyploidy, in *Chaetomorpha* 18 or 36 whilst in *Rhizoclonium* 12, 18, 24, 36, 48 are recorded. In the desmids numbers may be of a similar order, but in many species counts of 112, 182 and even 592 have been recorded.[209] In the Phaeophyta, the Ectocarpales often have 8 chromosomes, the Cutleriales 24, the Sphacelariales and Dictyotales 16, the Fucales 32, whilst the Laminariales seem to have three orders of magnitude 8, 13 or 27–31, with all three recorded for *Laminaria digitata* by three different workers.[291] In the Dinophyta[78] one group of species has about 30 and another about 60, but accurate counts are very difficult to make at the moment.

Polyploidy is recorded in some species of *Cladophora* and in *Chlamydomonas reinhardtii* triploids occur when 3 gametes fuse. Colchicine treatment induces increase in cell diameter and nuclear mass in *Chlamydomonas*, and nuclei appear polyploid, but when transferred back to colchicine-free medium, there is a reduction to the normal haploid state. It has also been shown that in *Chlamydomonas*, light intensity of 8610 lux induces temporary poly-ploidy, whilst early stages of mitosis often show a large number of chromatin bodies, which then condense to form eight chromosomes. The number 8 is borne out by genetic analysis of linkage groups.[234a]

In the desmids different clones of a species may have different chromo-some numbers and even in a single clone differences have been recorded.[211] Variation of this type (aneuploidy) is apparently common in organisms with a non-localized type centromere in which fragmentation of chromosomes can occur without the loss of the fragments. Irradiation of dinoflagellate nuclei also fragments chromosomes which pass into the daughter nuclei; also possible because of the absence of centromeres.

Mitosis

In many algae mitosis proceeds as in other plants but some deviations occur. In the Euglenophyta the mitosis occurs within the nuclear membrane, and there are no organized fibrillar spindles, centrioles, centrosomes, centromeres or polycentromeres.[232] Likewise in the Dinophyta spindles and centromeres are absent. In both these groups the chromatids pass to the poles orientated at right angles to the metaphase plate. In Euglenophyta the separation and anaphase movement of the chromatids is staggered and the nuclear membrane becomes stretched, finally meeting between the daughter groups to reconstitute the new nuclei. In some species of *Spirogyra* and desmids there is parallel separation of the chromatids at anaphase, 'no part of the chromatid preceding any other part of the pole, as a general rule.'[129] In these chromosomes there is no localized centromere and from the early metaphase stage chromatids are completely separated from one another. Mitosis exhibits periodicity in many algae, e.g. in *Euglena* it begins one to two hours after the onset of darkness[233] (Fig. 15, p. 48).

Meiosis

Few detailed studies have been made, but the data suggest that the process is very similar to that in other organisms. The difficulty of observing the stages is illustrated by the fact that meiosis in *Spirogyra* was first recorded in the first decade of this century and has not been reinvestigated until recently.[131] In the absence of centromeres in *S. crassa*, some other mechanism is involved in movement of the chromatids, and terminalization of chiasmata in this species is accomplished without the aid of centromeres. At metaphase I, the four chromatids are visible, held together by a sticky matrix. At anaphase I the pairs of chromatids are associated at their ends, forming rings; since the two anaphase plates show identical 'half bivalents' it is deduced that separation of sister chromatids occurs at this stage.

Genetic analysis

Although the first tetrad analysis on any organism was carried out almost half a century ago by Pascher using *Chlamydomonas*, there has been little subsequent work until recently. Details of techniques using *Chlamydomonas reinhardtii* are given on p. 149. Mutants may be produced spontaneously or by ultraviolet or x-radiation, and these may be non-photosynthetic, have paralysed flagella, eyespots absent, form unusual colony growths, be resistant to changes in pH or streptomycin, require organic nutrients such as thiamin or p-aminobenzoic acid, etc. Many of these characters are determined by a single pair of alleles, are segregated in a 2:2 ratio and result from single gene mutations. Genetic analysis of the above and many other mutant strains, has yielded data for the mapping of these markers, together with distances from the centromeres and the presence of linkage groups.[234a] Aberrant segregation ratios (3:1 or 4:0) result if irradiated gametes of one mating type are crossed with unirradiated gametes. These may also in some instances arise from triple fusions giving a triploid zygote followed by meiosis.

Cytoplasmic inheritance has been investigated in a *Chlamydomonas reinhardtii* mutant. which is resistant to streptomycin. This was obtained in the plus mating type, which when crossed with wild type ('streptomycin sensitive'), gave rise to streptomycin resistant tetrads. These tetrads segregated in a 2:2 ratio and the plus progeny conferred resistance when crossed with sensitive strains, whilst the minus strain did not. This was thought to be associated with a non-chromosomal factor linked with the plus mating type.

Interactions between cytoplasm and nucleus have been studied using the siphonaceous algá *Acetabularia* (see Fig. 47, p. 135).[144] This has a single large nucleus situate in the branched rhizoid, whilst the stalk and cap are devoid of nuclei until spore formation, when the single nucleus divides and the products move into the cap. *Acetabularia* is capable of regeneration from either the nucleate rhizoidal part, or the anucleate stalk. Anucleate pieces from the stalk can regenerate new caps and less frequently new rhizoids, providing a certain minimum of cytoplasm is present in the anucleate segment. The morphogenetic capacity of any segment differs according to its position, segments from the upper region having a greater regenerative capacity than those from the base. Nucleated segments possess full regenerative power. These experiments show that morphogenesis can proceed in the absence of the nucleus, provided that sufficient cytoplasm is present.

Grafts between nucleate rhizoidal segments and anucleate apical segments of *Acetabularia* are viable and further grafting can be achieved, thus increasing the nuclear complement. Experiments have shown that the divisions of the primary nucleus do not commence until the cap has reached a certain size—i.e. nuclear division is dependent on some nutritional/cytoplasmic factors. Removal of the cap prevents division of the nucleus until a new cap is formed. Likewise rhizoidal regions grafted onto almost mature cap-bearing apical segments are induced into premature nuclear division. Whatever the cytoplasmic factors are, they are not species specific, for the same result can be obtained by grafting between two different species. Grafts between nucleated and anucleated parts of different species always form caps whose structure is that of the nucleated portion, that is, the nucleus of *A. mediterranea* can influence cytoplasm of a different species, e.g. *A. crenulata* to form *A. mediterranea* type caps and *vice versa*. Binucleate grafts with nuclei derived from different species form intermediate type caps, whilst trinucleate grafts form caps which are closest in form to those of the type formed by the species contributing two of the nuclei.

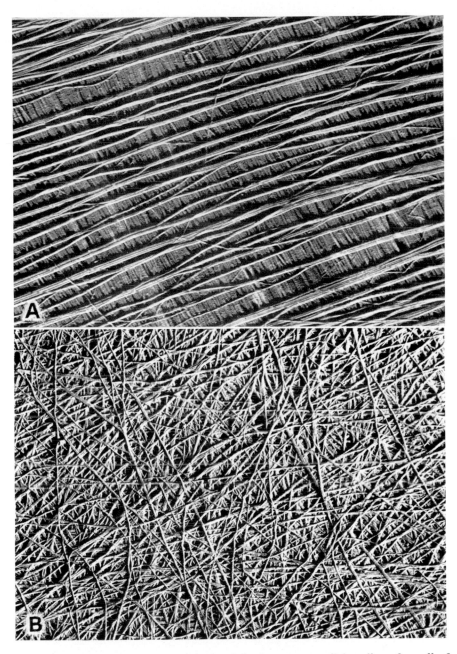

PLATE 1. **A:** An electron-micrograph of the innermost wall lamellae of a cell of *Chaetomorpha melagonium* viewed from the inside. Each lamella consists of microfibrils about 200 Å wide and the two sets cross at an angle rather less than 90°. **B:** Random arrangement of microfibrils in cross wall lamellae of *Chaetomorpha melagonium*. (×15,500.) (Electron-micrographs kindly supplied by Professor R. D. Preston, from *Proc. Roy. Soc.*, B, **155**, 1961.)

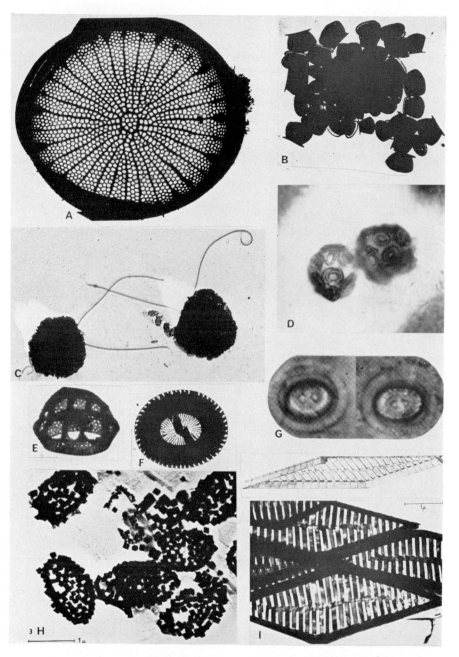

PLATE 2. **A:** Electron-micrograph of the frustule of a centric diatom (*Stephanodiscus*) showing the intricate nature of the pores (cf. Fig. 13). **B:** *Anthosphaera:* group of coccoliths surrounding a disintegrating cell. **C:** Two cells of *Crystallolithus* completely covered by crystalloliths. **D:** Division stage of a *Coccolithus pelagicus* cell showing placoliths. **E:** *Homozygosphaera* coccolith showing micro-crystals. **F:** *Gephyrocapsa* coccolith. **G:** Two placoliths from the *Coccolithus pelagicus* phase. **H:** Scales and crystalloliths from the motile *Crystallolithus* phase. **I:** *Anoplosolenia* coccoliths and a model of a single coccolith. (B, E, F & I from Halldal and Markali; C, D, G & H from Parke and Adams.)

4   Ecology: freshwater

Algae are abundant everywhere except in sandy desert regions and on permanent snow and ice fields, and even in these inhospitable regions specialized algal floras can be found in favourable habitats. The aquatic environment comprises some 70 per cent of the earth's surface and here the algae are important as primary producers of elaborated organic materials, and thus play a critical role in the economy of the seas and freshwaters. On the land they are important constituents of the flora of soils, moist rocks and stone surfaces. Along the coasts at the boundary between land and sea an extremely rich flora is found and here the large macrophytic forms reach their greatest abundance and diversity. The study of the algae in all these environments is the prime object of algal ecology; some important aspects are the recognition, delimitation and classification of the algal habitats within the environments; a study of the composition of the flora within each habitat; the relationship between these floras and the biological, physical and chemical factors operating directly or indirectly in the habitat; the study of individual species within the populations and of the factors controlling their growth; the productivity of the populations and of individual species. These approaches start with a consideration of the physical and chemical factors of the environment and lead ultimately to experiments on selected species within the environment or under controlled environmental conditions. The study of the flora is dependent upon a knowledge of the classification of the groups, the data for which are largely obtained from the morphological approach outlined in the previous chapters, and the ultimate stages are dependent on progress in algal physiology.

Snow and ice flora (Kryoflora)

Algae are found in these habitats only where the surface is stable for some length of time, e.g. on the polar ice caps and on permanent snow fields in mountains. A freshwater and a marine flora exists; both are relatively little known. The species are usually unicellular and at least in the freshwater habitat are confined to a few genera mainly of the Chlorophyta, e.g. species of *Chlamydomonas*, *Chlorella*, *Ankistrodesmus*, *Raphidonema*, *Stichococcus*, *Scotiella* and *Hormidium*. *Chlamydomonas nivalis* is most frequently recorded and owing to the presence of carotenoids in the cytoplasm of the cells and particularly of the resting spores, produces a red coloration on the snow. The species composition of the kryoflora varies according to the pH of the ice or snow and this in turn is affected by the fine rock dust which settles on the permanent snow and penetrates into it.[218] The Antarctic and Arctic appear to have a different series of species.

Aerial epiphytic algae

These are algal communities dependent directly upon rain water or high humidity for their water supply. They may thus be subject either to extreme dessication, e.g. the coating of *Desmococcus* (=*'Pleurococcus'**) on tree bark in temperate climates or maintained throughout most of the year in high humidity, e.g. the epiphytic, Cyanophyte flora on tree bark and leaves of plants in tropical mist forest. Some of these algae are semi-parasitic; *Stomatochroon*, a member of the Trentepohliaceae, penetrates into the stomata of tropical plants, *Cephaleuros virescens* grows on many economic plants, e.g. citrus fruits, avocado and tea bushes and is known in India as 'red rust,' whilst *Phycopeltis epiphyton* (Chaetophorales) occurs on leaves of tropical trees and is even found in Europe on *Abies, Hedera* and *Rubus*. Algae are also reported on the pileus of some genera of Basidiomycetes and even penetrate into the superficial tissues, e.g. *Stichococcus bacillaris, Keratococcus caudatus, Chlorella ellipsoidea* and species of *Chlamydomonas* and *Coccomyxa* have been recorded on Polyporaceae.[109] The aerial epiphytic habitat is characterized by the absence of nutrients other than those in rain and those obtained by solution of dust or material on or from the host plant tissues. This factor rather than desiccation is probably more important in the restriction of the flora to a few species. Desiccation of soils may be equally extreme but here the floras are often rich in species.

A little investigated algal flora is that epiphytic on Bryophyta. The flora depends on the degree of dampness amongst the leaves; in dry situations a few diatoms such as *Pinnularia borealis, Navicula mutica* and *Hantzschia amphioxys* occur whilst in moist clumps the number of diatom species increases and coccoid Cyanophyta (*Aphanocapsa*-like forms, *Nostoc* and *Oscillatoria*) and Chlorophyta occur (Desmids and mucilaginous masses which are often palmelloid stages of *Chlamydomonas*, etc.).

Aerial epilithic algae

Rock and stone surfaces which are relatively stable, are often coated with algae. On rocks which receive only atmospheric moisture the flora is similar to that on tree bark: *Desmococcus* and *Trentepohlia* are common and mucilaginous masses containing *Mesotaenium, Cylindrocystis* and other coccoid green algae occur. However, many rock surfaces receive seepage water from overlying soils and hence a rich nutrient supply is available. On acidic rocks a rich growth of blackish, mucilaginous Cyanophyta, consisting of *Chroococcus, Gloeocapsa, Stigonema* and *Calothrix*, also greenish mucilaginous masses of desmids such as *Cylindorocystis* and *Cosmarium* and brown streaks of diatoms such as *Tabellaria, Diatoma, Eunotia, Frustulia* and *Pinnularia* are frequently found. This flora greatly resembles that of peat soils, although the mucilage forming Cyanophyta and the non-motile diatoms on the rocks tend to be more conspicuous than on the soils.

* The classification of *'Pleurococcus'*—like forms is in a state of flux.

The soil flora

The surface of most soils supports a rich algal flora. Spores and fragments of algae are washed to greater depths and remain viable for long periods, but actively growing algae are probably confined to within a mm or so of the surface. Species growing in this habitat are either motile, e.g. *Euglena*, *Chlamydomonas*, *Oscillatoria*, *Lyngbya*, *Phormidium* and numerous species of diatoms, particularly of *Caloneis*, *Stauroneis*, *Navicula*, *Pinnularia*, *Hantzschia* and *Nitzschia* or are non-motile, e.g. *Stichococcus*, *Hormidium*, *Anabaena* and *Chroococcus*. The most advanced morphological stage found is that of a heterotrichous filament, e.g. *Fritschiella*. The genus *Nostoc* forms large macroscopic, mucilaginous colonies clearly visible to the naked eye, especially on wet tropical soils.

The distribution of many of the common species of soil algae is almost world wide, although more detailed observations on the less common species may reveal distribution patterns. Many of the species are taxonomically difficult, e.g. the diatoms tend to be extremely small and indeed where the same species occurs in another habitat the soil form always tends to be the smaller; others need to be cultured for identification, e.g. flagellates and coccoid algae and in the Cyanophyta there are a multiplicity of 'species' with few adequate characters to separate them.

Methods of studying the soil algae may lead to diverse results; some authors report as many as one million algae in one gram of soil but many of these must exist as spores. Addition of soil to culture solutions, although of great value to obtain sufficient cells for correct identification and for examination of life cycles, will not yield an accurate picture of the soil flora. This is because many terrestrial species may not flourish in liquid media, species will be selected according to the composition of the culture solution, its pH, etc., the balance of species will undoubtedly be upset, and spores of non-terrestrial species may germinate when under normal soil conditions they would not grow. Plating techniques in which soil or soil solutions are spread over agar in petri dishes and the algae allowed to multiply, are of limited value, open to the same objections as liquid culture, although again of value in separating species for subsequent culture and for obtaining large numbers of cells of the species which grow on agar. A distorted picture of the actual flora may be obtained.

What is usually of importance to the ecologist is the actively growing flora of the soil at any one moment and hence some method of extracting the growing algae is necessary. Direct observation of the surface soil mixed with water on a slide and observed under the microscope rarely yields more than a few individuals and leads to the usually inaccurate impression of a poor flora. Soil placed in petri dishes, moistened with distilled water, develops a rich algal flora on its surface. Coverglasses, or pieces of lens cleaning tissue, placed on the surface of the soil and removed after varying periods of time will have adhering to them, many if not all of the activity growing soil species. The author has found that in general the dominant species appear in the first few days and remain dominant on the soil surface for some months, although there are undoubtedly minor fluctuations of the flora. Some of the Cyanophyta which form skin-like growths are underestimated by this method and need to be removed from the soil surface by means of a scalpel. Lund[249a] devised this technique but used a 0·05 per cent Benecke solution to moisten and enrich the soil. On many soils, diatoms are extremely abundant and often dominant; some can be identified directly in the living state but most only after careful comparison of the live cells with frustules cleaned in acid, since almost all the taxonomic characters are based on markings on the frustule.

The soil algal flora does not consist of species which are entirely confined to this habitat, many extend their range into other terrestrial habitats (amongst mosses and liverworts, on wet rock surfaces, etc.), and frequently into small or temporary waters and even into the littoral zone of lakes. However in these latter habitats they are usually rare in the flora and it is obvious that they attain their greatest growth on the soil surface. Many species are world-wide in distribution, e.g. *Nostoc* spp. and *Hantzschia amphioxys*, whilst others are confined by specific soil characteristics, e.g. the flora of moorlands, of saline soils. The ease of dispersal, either as spores or fragments, or within the soil itself by animals, or by wind and water, results in an almost universal possibility of distribution. That the soil flora is neither geographically uniform nor uniform on individual soil types, is a clear indication of the operation of selective factors. Indeed within a few square centimetres of exposed soil, one may find a mosaic of dominant species together with their accompanying species. On soils of the Lizard Peninsular in Cornwall the author has observed discrete blackish communities of *Scytonema* growing radially from a central point, rather like a fungus culture on an agar plate, and nearby, pale green films of *Mesotaenium* and globular colonies of *Rivularia* and *Nostoc*. These may form almost pure stands covering a centimetre square or more, whilst in between them a less dense algal community of filamentous Cyanophyta, diatoms and desmids may occur. In other places green patches of soil are found to be dominated by species of *Euglena*, whilst other patches appear as purplish felts composed of filaments of *Zygogonium* (which has a purple pigment in the vacuole) and yet others appear as a black paper-like covering to the soil, due to the confluence of the sheaths of filamentous blue green algae such as *Phormidium* and *Microcoleus*. On many soils these communities are difficult to recognize, since their coloration is similar to that of the soil. This mosaic of soil algae with its dominant and associated species, has received little attention since most studies have been made from bulk samples of soil. Nevertheless the gross examination of soil of a definite physico-chemical structure, irrespective of the surface pattern of communities, yields the fundamental data on species composition. Extreme examples are the studies of moorland soils of low pH, or of base rich loams of high pH, or of sands of high base status and low organic content. These studies have revealed soil floras of great diversity. The

algal flora of peat soils is characterized by the abundance and often dominance of desmids, e.g. *Mesotaenium, Cylindrocystis, Penium, Zygogonium*, etc., of
Cyanophyta, particularly *Chroococcus turgidus* and *Gloeocapsa*, and of diatoms
such as *Frustulia*. On base rich loams these algae are extremely rare or absent,
and are replaced by green coccoid algae, filaments of *Stichococcus, Hormidium*
and *Ulothrix*, Cyanophyta such as *Oscillatoria, Phormidium, Aphanothece* and
Nostoc and the diatoms *Caloneis* and *Amphora*. These floras can be recognized
with little difficulty on many soils and thus related to soil characteristics
such as pH or base status, although these may not in themselves be the
selective factor(s) determining the flora.

Soils are not permanent structures; they have an origin and undergo
changes in which the algae are involved. New soils exposed by land slips,
agricultural techniques, burning, etc., are rapidly colonized by algae. Algae
are usually, with the bacteria and fungi, the primary colonizers. As in the
open sea it is the algae of the new soil surface which are the primary energy
fixers (with the exception of a few bacteria). The colonization by algae is
rapid; they may be derived from spores and fragments in the soil, or may
be wind blown. The effects of this first algal colonization have not been
fully studied, but it undoubtedly has a profound influence on the soil surface;
the organic matter content is increased as the algae multiply, the soil surface
is aerated, whilst the lower layers may become sealed off by a coating of
mucilaginous algae. Beneath this surface layer the carbon dioxide concentration may be reduced and oxygen increased, water may be absorbed and
water loss from lower layers reduced, the soil particles may be bound together
since the algae are often copious mucilage producers and therefore stabilize
the soil. Soil erosion is often prevented by algal stabilization, although on
some soils drying produces cracking and the stabilized surface can be seen
to curl up in polygonal patches and be blown away. As colonization proceeds, the algal flora changes, e.g. in heath litter on peat soils, the soil algae
have mainly disappeared and an association dominated by the diatom *Eunotia*
occurs.

Soil algae not only derive nutrients from the soil water, but also add
chemicals to the soil either on their death or by diffusion from the cells.
Well-known examples are some genera of the Cyanophyta which fix atmospheric nitrogen and thus increase the nitrogen content of the soil. Cyanophyta and Chlorophyta have been shown to release polysaccharides and/or
polypeptides into culture media and it is probable that this also occurs in
nature. Many algae have been shown to produce growth substances and
antibiotics which almost certainly affect the soil flora and may be responsible
for the development of mosaics of algal associations. It is noteworthy that
actively growing colonies of algae tend to exclude or seriously limit the
growth of others. This may be related to competition for space; mucilage
forming Cyanophyta and desmids tend to blanket the ground and prevent
other algae growing (sometimes other taxa may grow on or in the mucilage),
whilst others are not so dense in growth and may compete in more subtle

ways. There may also be a certain degree of seasonal growth; in the Bristol area *Euglena* and diatoms are abundant in spring and Cyanophyceae in summer and autumn.

The soil algal community is subject to greater extremes of climate than those of submerged habitats. Broadly speaking there are two classes of soil algae, the ephemerals which appear at random and multiply rapidly when conditions are suitable, e.g. *Chlamydomonas*, *Euglena*, *Phacus* and *Trachelomonas* species which develop in waterlogged patches, and the perennial desmids Cyanophyta and diatoms which must be able to withstand submergence during heavy rain, drought and heat in summer, freezing in winter and be able to survive as fragments or spores when washed below the soil surface and unable to photosynthesize. Many soil algae have a thick protective mucilage sheath around the cells, e.g. *Nostoc*, *Phormidium*, *Chroococcus*, *Aphanocapsa*, *Mesotaenium* and *Cylindrocystis*. On the other hand the diatoms are very thinly coated with mucilage, although *Mastogloia* has been found on sand-dune soils with a large striated mucilage envelope. They are not very resistant to heat, but unlike the Cyanophyta and desmids, they are actively motile so that movement to lower, wetter parts of the soil is possible; they are also much smaller and may easily live in the film of moisture around the soil particles. Motility must be a valuable asset for the soil flora which is often disturbed. It is noteworthy that few of the soil algae are non-motile attached species, even coccoid genera such as *Cylindrocystis*, *Chroococcus*, *Stichococcus*, etc., probably have limited powers of movement within their mucilage and the whole colony may move in the water film on soil particles. The movement of soil algae is made use of in the determination of the flora by the coverglass method.

Competition between algal species has been mentioned above and in addition the soil flora is subject to grazing by soil protozoa and rotifers. Little is known of this phenomenon, which may easily be a factor in the maintenance or periodicity of the flora. Examination of coverglasses in the estimation of the flora shows that there is extensive feeding on the smaller coccoid forms particularly of genera such as *Chlorococcum*, *Stichococcus*, *Navicula*, *Pinnularia* and *Nitzschia*. In addition some protozoa are selective, taking either Chlorophyta or diatoms, whilst grazing of Cyanophyta is less common. Another factor which may well influence the soil flora is the incidence of fungal diseases caused by Chytridiaceous and other Phycomycetous fungi. These infestations have long been recognized, attacking particularly the diatoms and desmids.

Springs, streams and rivers

The algae of running waters have received much less attention than those of other habitats since the measurement of variables such as rate of flow, temperature, nutrient status, etc., is more complicated in a habitat which changes rapidly in both time and space. However in springs these factors remain more constant than in relatively static bodies of water such as lakes.

Before the algae of these habitats or those of ponds, lakes and oceans can be considered, it is necessary to define the habitats within these waters. The habitats in large bodies of water tend to be fairly well defined, e.g. the floating and swimming algal community of open waters, phytoplankton, is easily recognizable, and mixing only occurs at the boundaries between communities. In streams and rivers a floating community may or may not occur depending on the size of the river and the rate of flow. An analysis of the phytoplankton in small bodies of water is often impossible without a knowledge of the other communities since these often provide many casuals. These other communities are associated with solid substrata and are often referred to as the benthos, however, strictly this term should be used only to refer to those communities growing on the bottom of the stream, river, lake or sea but it tends to be extended to the epiphytic communities living on plants; it is useful to have a term to embrace the communities associated with underwater surfaces as opposed to those free floating i.e. planktonic. These benthic algae may grow on mud or sand (epipelic) on rock surfaces (epilithic) or attached to sand grains (epipsammic) and often form distinct communities. The epiphytic algal communities grow on microscopic or macroscopic plants, which may be algae (seaweeds, *Chara*, *Cladophora*, etc.), Bryophyta, Pteridophyta or Angiosperms growing in or on the water. Another attached community of algae grows on animals (epizooic), for example on hydroid colonies, Copepods, fish or even on whales. Only amongst the attached communities (i.e. the epilithic, epiphytic and epizooic) is there a tendency for the same species to occur abundantly on different substrata; the epipelic and planktonic are quite distinct from one another and from the attached community.

a) Springs

Underground water forced to the surface tends to be fairly constant in physical and chemical properties, though these rapidly equilibrate with the surroundings. Temperature is usually constant either at about 9°C in cold springs or at various temperatures between 18°C and 90°C in hot springs. The cold springs support an algal flora on any solid, sandy, silty or living substratum in the water and most of the species are also found in other habitats, in particular those of running water since the spring is often the beginning of the lenitic (running water) habitats. Many soil species have also been reported in springs but these may be contaminants. Most cold springs have a high concentration of Ca^{++} and HCO_3^- ions, resulting in an alkaliphilic flora. The only common macroscopic alga which is widely reported from springs is *Batrachospermum*, which often grows anchored in the fine sand around underwater springs (limnocrenes) and may itself be coated with diatoms, e.g. *Achnanthes lanceolata*, *A. lanceolata* v. *elliptica*, and *Denticula tenuis*.[344] The sediment flora is composed mainly of diatoms plus a few cells of desmids. Filamentous diatom species are found, e.g. *Fragilaria construens*, *F. leptostauron*, *F. pinnata* and *Meridion circulare*, which are presumably attached to sand grains since they are non-motile and would otherwise be washed away; other common attached species are *Achnanthes minutissima* v. *cryptocephala* and *Achnanthes lanceolata*.

Of eight springs arising at the bottom of small ponds in the Malham Tarn region, all had either *Fragilaria* or *Achnanthes* spp. as the dominants.[344] The other species in these communities were motile diatoms such as are common on pond, lake and river sediments, e.g. *Neidium dubium, Stauroneis smithii, Navicula pupula* v. *capitata, N. cryptocephala, N. radiosa, Amphora ovalis* and *Campylodiscus noricus* v. *hibernica*. Underwater springs may also emerge in ponds, lakes and rivers but these are generally less obvious and their flora has not been studied in detail. They often have a deposit of calcareous tufa around them, partially formed by physical precipitation of calcium salts in the spring water and partially by biogenic precipitation on the cells and in the sheaths of algae.

Hot springs are mostly of volcanic origin and in addition to their high temperature, usually have a high concentration of dissolved salts. Throughout the world the most frequent algae of hot springs are the Cyanophyta; many are recorded at temperatures of up to $85°C$, although it is doubtful whether growth can occur at these temperatures. Recent work using the uptake of radioactive phosphorus into nucleic acid as an indicator of survival, has however shown that survival is possible for some algae from hot springs up to temperatures just above $70°C$ (Fig. 16). On Sunda (Indonesia) 3 species were found growing at temperatures above $60°C$, viz. *Synechococcus elongatus* f. *thermalis, Synechocystis aquatilis* and *Phormidium laminosum*. These three, plus *Onconema thermale, O. compactum, Phormidium tenue, P. cebennense* f. *thermale* and *Mastigocladus laminosus*, grew between $55–60°C$. *M. laminosus* and *P. laminosum* maintained optimum growth between $45–55°C$ and *Pleurocapsa fluviatilis, Plectonema notatum* v. *africanum* and *Scytonema coactile* v. *thermale* were also found at this temperature. Most of the hot springs are alkaline and it appears that the tolerance of extreme temperatures is associated with this factor.[352] In acid hot springs only the doubtful Cyanophycean, *Cyanidium caldarium* has been recorded. Of the other algal groups occurring in hot springs, only the diatoms have received much attention but no diatoms are characteristic of hot springs and none occur above $40°C$.

b) Streams and rivers

Streams and rivers provide habitats which are very different from those in springs, for they are subject to changes along their length associated with depth, rate of flow, geology of the land surface and of the stream bed, salt concentration (in some changing from freshwater to saline), turbidity, etc.; all these being further complicated by seasonal changes. Thus a multitude of habitats are available and most are colonized by algae, although comparative studies are difficult except between approximately comparable stretches. Streams may arise from springs or standing waters; the former are simpler since there is no large source of algal inoculum and the algal flora is actively growing in the microhabitats of the stream, whereas the latter may contain much algal detritus from the ponds or lakes. Thus in streams arising from springs, there is never a floating community of actively growing algae. This 'phytoplankton' community does however exist in streams and rivers outflowing from standing waters, but in most cases is only a hetero- geneous collection of standing water species which maintain themselves for a variable time in the flowing water. Much of the literature on this so-called potamoplankton, merely lists benthic and lake planktonic species washed

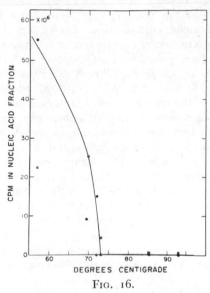

FIG. 16.

The incorporation of radioactive phosphorus into the nucleic acid fraction of algal growths taken from a hot spring and incubated for 48 h. at temperatures up to 93°C with P⁰⁹ labelled H_3PO_4.

(From Kempner.)

into the flowing water. In a study of streams around Malham Tarn, it was found that much of the lake plankton, e.g. *Asterionella formosa* and *Diatoma elongatum*, was deposited on the sediments in the first few metres of the outflow stream. The problems of maintaining a floating population in a stream or river are enormous since the products of division are continuously being transported downstream. A rapid development of a potamoplankton may occur, but is rarely maintained over a long period; indeed only in slow flowing rivers can a true potamoplankton be developed, e.g. in the Thames in 1902/3 a true plankton was recorded throughout the year with *Pediastrum boryanum*, *Melosira moniliformis*, *M. varians*, *Campylodiscus noricus*, *Surirella* spp., *Fragilaria virescens*, *Synedra ulna*, *Nitzschia sigmoidea* and *Pleurosigma* (*Gyrosigma*) *attenuatum*. However, in this list none of the species are confined to the river; many of them were in fact recorded in the backwaters and some of them, e.g. *N. sigmoidea* and *P. attenuatum* are sediment living species. All algal communities tend to contain a proportion of casual species, but in most it is possible to detect the constant species and to recognize their suitability and adaption to their microhabitat. Flowing water would appear to afford a highly characteristic habit in which one might expect to find species adapted to this habitat and no other. Are there then, amidst the conglomeration of detrital species in the 'potamoplankton' any which are confined to or overwhelmingly abundant in this habitat? In a detailed study of the diatoms of the Weser,[189] 31 forms were listed, which were regarded as autochthonous, euplanktonic species, i.e. true phytoplankton. Of these the following are common, at one or more stations around Bremen, *Actinocyclus normanii, Bacillaria paradoxa, Chaetoceros mulleri, Cyclotella atomus, C. meneghiniana, C. nana, C. pseudostelligera, C. striata, Nitzschia acicularis, Stephanodiscus astreae, S. hantzschii, S. subtilis, S. tenuis* and *Thalassiosira fluviatilis.* These, with the exception of *B. paradoxa* and *N. acicularis* which are known to grow on sediments, are all non-motile spp. of the Centrales and are also recorded from the littoral zone of the Weser. The Centrales and the non-motile species of the section Araphidineae, also form the bulk of the diatom phytoplankton in lakes and oceans—see later. This community in the Weser is probably developed because the rate of flow is reduced by tidal pressure and the species can reproduce in the water before being washed out to sea. In the Nile the phytoplankton is reduced considerably during flood periods, and it has been suggested that prior to the control of water flow by dams, there was little phytoplankton in the waters.[353] Thus it would seem that a true phytoplanktonic community, maintaining itself by active reproduction of cells, is only possible in slow flowing rivers.

Epilithic communities

The algae of rock surfaces are adapted to swiftly flowing water by being either encrusting or basally attached, but flexible and streaming in the current. In some reaches of rivers, current flow and subsequent movement of the stones is so severe that an algal flora cannot establish itself. Although water flow may appear fast, there is a surface effect, which greatly reduces the rate of flow in the region immediately above the rock surface; in this particular region, the attachment of many unicellular, or encrusting parenchymatous algae or sporelings of filamentous forms is possible. In addition the irregular nature of many rocky or stony stream bottoms increases the turbulence and completely changes the rate of flow in the vicinity of the substratum. A further characteristic of this habitat is the constant high concentration of gases and nutrients in the water; many of the algae therefore grow abundantly at all seasons of the year and the fluctuations which may be recorded, are related to physical reduction of the flora at times of flood. Some algae do however show a seasonal preference, e.g. some of the larger green algae tend to be summer forms. The epilithic flora may be contaminated with species filtered out of the water, and where the rate of flow is reduced, silt tends to become trapped amongst the epilithic algae and a flora intermediate between the epilithic and epipelic type develops. Numerous studies have shown the effect of current pressure on the colonization of stones, e.g. *Lithoderma fluviatilis* grows on the side facing the current and not at all on the leeside, whilst *Cocconeis placentula* was shown to grow on experimental spheres suspended in a stream, on the side exposed to the current and in the current shadow, but not on the sides where the water shears past.[121] Hydrodynamically it can be shown that at the point of an object facing the current there is a reduced rate of flow, whilst behind the object the flow is often reversed and complicated currents arise according to the shape of the object.

Four groups of algae are found frequently in the epilithic flora, *viz.* encrusting and filamentous Cyanophyta, Chlorophyta and Rhodophyta and encrusting Bacillariophyta. It is a characteristic of the habitat that relatively pure stands of species develop, e.g. the red encrusting growths of *Hildenbrandia rivularis*, the blackish/blue mucilaginous crusts of *Chamaesiphon* spp. the brownish patches of *Heribaudiella* (*Lithoderma*) *fluviatilis*, a prostrate 'parenchymatous' thallus a few cells thick. Also relatively pure stands of the mucilaginous globular thalli of *Rivularia* spp. and *Chaetophora* spp. occur. All these have a few associated epiphytic algae, in particular small *Achnanthes* spp. and *Gomphonema* spp. Encrusting algae are often associated with species of the lichen genus *Verrucaria*, e.g. an association of *Hildenbrandia rivularis* and *Verrucaria rheithrophila* (with occasional *V. aquatilis*) is widespread in European rivers.[260] Following the naming of higher plant associations, this is termed the *Rheithropilo-hildenbrandietum* and very few other species occur in the association, e.g. at a station in south Finland it is mixed with *Chamaesiphon geitleri*, at Swedish and Swiss stations with *Heribaudiella fluviatilis* and in Denmark mixed with flocs of the diatom *Cocconeis placentula*. This association is also found along lake sides, where there is flow of water over the stones, and in Fennoscandinavia appears in electrolyte rich waters of neutral or alkaline reaction and avoids extreme calcareous or acid waters. Epilithic diatom associations of rivers of the Ardenne are characterized by the dominants *Diatoma vulgare/Melosira varians*, *Navicula viridula*, *Cymbella ventricosa*, *Diatoma hiemale/ Meridion circulare*;[386] to these associations could be added those with *Achnanthes minutissima* dominant, e.g. in streams around Malham Tarm,[344] *Achnanthes minutissima/A. minutissima* v. *cryptocephala/A. microcephala/A. linearis* in streams in the English Lake District.[81a] The latter stream had as subdominants *Gomphonema* spp. (*G. parvulum* and varieties, *G. intricatum* v. *pumilla*, *G. olivaceoides*) and *Synedra* spp. (*S. vaucheriae*, *S. vaucheriae* v. *capitellata*, *S. rumpens S. amphicephala*). This *Achnanthes/Gomphonema/Synedra* group is probably associated with acidic, nutrient poor waters in rapidly flowing streams, whereas in larger rivers *Fragilaria* spp. or *Tabellaria flocculosa* may be dominant, e.g. in the river running from Kilpisjärvi to the Gulf of Bothnia between Finland and Sweden.[343] The *Diatoma/Melosira varians/Meridion circulare*

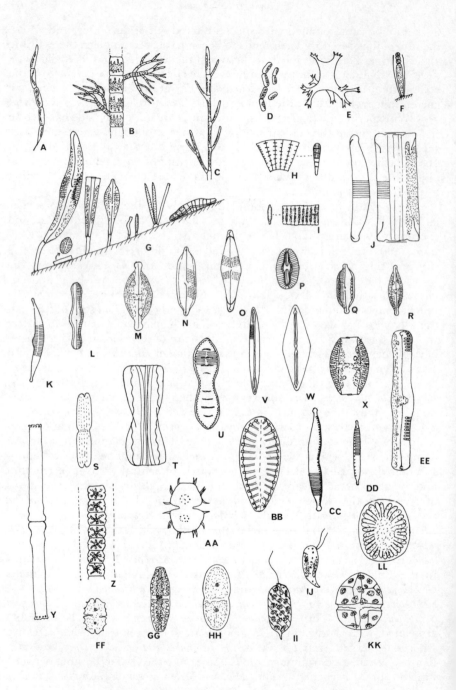

group, are associated with richer waters of higher pH which may also support *Achnanthes minutissima*, *Gomphonema intricatum* v. *pumila* and *Achnanthes lanceolata* and varieties, this latter species being an indicator of alkaline waters, whilst the other two appear to be indifferent. The third important group of associations are those of the macroscopic, filamentous or thalloid forms. The most widely distributed of these is the *Cladophora glomerata* association which occurs attached to stones and rocks in slow flowing rivers and streams with moderately base rich waters. The *Cladophora* is often so dense that the encrusting communities are relatively undeveloped, and the only other algae of this association are those attached to the thick rough walls of the *Cladophora*. Other associations of filamentous types are formed by species of *Vaucheria*, *Ulothrix* and *Draparnaldia*.[386] In some cold fast flowing rivers, e.g. the one from Kilpisjärvi, there is a rich development of filamentous algal associations of species of *Spirogyra*, *Zygnema*, *Mougeotia*, *Oedogonium* and *Bulbochaete*, all with their associated diatom epiphytes;[343] this association is widespread in many Arctic waters but it is also found in small streams draining moorland regions in the British Isles. These algae are all anchored by a holdfast system and tend to be summer forms, particularly *Cladophora glomerata*. Macroscopic thalloid algae are represented by species of the red algal genus *Lemanea* in northern waters and *Sirodotia* and *Caloglossa* in tropical rivers. These are rigidly attached, almost glued to the rock surface, usually in fast flowing regions and have a whip or band-like thallus which streams out into the water. Some of these red algae have branched filamentous juvenile stages (*Chantransia* stage) appearing as black pustules growing on the stone surface. In a mountain stream in Sauerland the *Lemanea* association was developed in the lower reaches and the *Hildenbrandia* association in the upper.[41]

FIG. 17. ATTACHED AND EPIPELIC FRESHWATER ALGAE.

A. *Raphidonema*; B. *Draparnaldia*; C. *Microthamnion*; D. *Stichococcus*; E. *Tetraedron*; F. *Chamaesiphon*; G. Attached diatoms, from the left, *Cymbella*, *Cocconeis* (girdle and valve view), *Gomphonema* (girdle and valve view), *Achnanthes* (girdle and valve view), *Synedra* and *Epithemia*; H. *Meridion*, colony and cell in valve view; I. *Fragilaria*, colony and cell in valve view; J. Girdle and valve view of *Eunotia*; K. *Ceratoneis*; L. *Caloneis*, showing valve workings; M. *Caloneis*, showing chromatophores, etc.; N. *Neidium*; O. *Stauroneis*; P. *Diploneis*; Q. *Mastogloia*; R. *Navicula*; S. *Tetmemorus*; T. *Amphiprora*; U. *Cymatopleura*; V. *Amphipleura*; W. *Frustulia*; X. *Amphora*; Y. *Pleurotaenium*; Z. *Hyalotheca*; AA. *Xanthidium*; BB. *Surirella*; CC. *Hantzschia*; DD. *Nitzschia*; EE. *Pinnularia*; FF. *Euastrum*; GG. *Netrium*; HH. *Penium*; II. *Lepocinclis*; JJ. *Chroomonas*; KK. *Glenodinium*; LL. *Campylodiscus*.

(After Nygaard and original.)

Epiphytic community

An important but little investigated community in running waters is that attached to the larger algae, Bryophytes and Angiosperms, many of which become completely coated with a green or brown mucilaginous mass of algae. The attachment of epiphytic algae is in part related to the structure of the surface layers of the plants, e.g. branching filaments of *Cladophora* have a non-mucilaginous rough wall and are at times so densely coated with epiphytes that the surface is not visible under the microscope and their metabolism must be effected. A great variety of algae may attach themselves to *Cladophora*, amongst which are genera of Cyanophyta, e.g. *Chamaesiphon*, *Oncobyrsa*, *Dermocarpa* and some filamentous species of *Oscillatoria* and *Lyngbya*; the former grow as crusts on the surface of the *Cladophora* cells and the latter stand out at an angle to the filaments. Filamentous species of the Chaetophorales are frequently found creeping over the surface of the cells, e.g. *Aphanochaete repens*, whilst germlings of *Oedogonium*, *Tribonema*, etc. also become attached. Commonly the whole thallus becomes coated with a mass of diatoms some pressed close to the *Cladophora*, e.g., *Cocconeis* spp. and *Epithemia* spp., others on short (*Achnanthes*) or long, often branching stalks (*Cymbella*, *Gomphonema*), and yet others attached by basal mucilage pads and sticking out solitarily or in bunches from the cell surface (e.g. *Eunotia* and *Synedra*, Fig. 17G). Amongst this mass of attached algae grow motile or non-motile unattached species, e.g. flagellates (*Euglena*, *Phacus*, etc.) diatoms of the Biraphidineae (e.g. *Navicula* and *Nitzschia* spp.) and members of the Chlorococcales (e.g. *Scenedesmus*). Filamentous algae producing much mucilage, such as *Chaetophora*, *Mougeotia*, *Zygnema* and to a lesser extent *Oedogonium* and *Bulbochaete*, have a more sparse epiphyte flora, which is usually confined to the smaller needle-like cells of *Synedra*, *Eunotia* and *Achnanthes*. The sparsity of the flora may be related to the difficulty of attachment of the cells to the mucilage wall. A similar sparse epiphytic flora is found on the mucilaginous thalli of *Batrachospermum* and *Lemanea*, e.g. *Lemanea* in a Finnish river system was colonized by *Tabellaria flocculosa*, *Fragilaria*, *Synedra* and *Gomphonema* spp. with some intermingled desmids.[343]

The Angiosperm and Bryophyte flora of rivers always harbours a coating of algae of similar type to that found on *Cladophora*, but containing a larger number of species. The moss *Fontinalis* is often abundantly coated with algae, the latter differing at successive points along a river system, e.g. in a river in Finland the more eutrophic water in the lower reaches resulted in *Epithemia* becoming dominant on *Fontinalis*, whilst upstream *Achnanthes linearis* was dominant, then *Gomphonema acuminatum* v. *brebissonii* and at the uppermost stations in fast flowing clear water, *Tabellaria flocculosa*.[343] Associated with these diatoms are species of desmids, particularly *Cosmarium* and filamentous Cyanophyta, e.g. *Oscillatoria*, *Tolypothrix* and especially *Nostoc*. In calcareous streams, *Meridion circulare*, *Achnanthes minutissima*, *A. lanceolata* and *Cocconeis placentula* are particularly common on *Fontinalis*.

Epipelic communities

Along the length of rivers and streams, sediments are deposited varying from coarse sand to fine silts and rich organic deposits. On these a rich but relatively uninvestigated algal flora grows. This epipelic flora is mainly composed of diatoms, blue green algae, coccoid Chlorophyceae (Chlorococcales and desmids) and Euglenoids. The flora is complicated by the presence of remains from the epilithic and epiphytic floras and great care is necessary to distinguish these, particularly in cleaned material of diatoms. The majority of species are motile, in contrast to those of other river communities, whilst a few are attached by mucilage to sand particles, etc., or lie free on the sediment, e.g. chains of the diatom *Fragilaria* and colonies of *Scenedesmus* and *Pediastrum*. In base rich waters in the streams around Malham Tarn,[344] the sediments are rich in contaminants from the epiphytic community (e.g. *Fragilaria, Synedra, Achnanthes, Cocconeis*), but comparison of counts on sediment and epiphytic material reveals the abundance of the motile species on the sediments; exceptions are *Fragilaria leptostauron, F. construens* and *F. pinnata*, which are non-motile species more frequent on the sediments, a feature also recorded in still water. The main components of the flora, often forming a dark brown coating on the sediment, are species of *Frustulia, Gyrosigma, Caloneis, Neidium, Diploneis, Stauroneis, Navicula, Amphora, Cymbella* (the motile species), *Nitzschia, Cymatopleura, Surirella* and *Campylodiscus*. On sediments of streams in the Midlands (Round, unpublished), species of *Gyrosigma, Navicula, Nitzschia* and *Cymatopleura* were common throughout a year's survey; also frequent in such streams in agricultural country were species of *Euglena* and *Phacus*. In the region around Droitwich the addition of salt from salt springs and as effluent from salt works, results in an even richer production of cells than in the non-saline water; here species such as *Caloneis amphisbaena, Bacillaria paradoxa, Nitzschia closterium, N. obtusa, Amphiprora* spp., *Amphora* spp., etc., were abundant on the sediment. These latter species are common in brackish or marine habitats. The flora of these streams exhibit seasonal cycles with greatest growth in spring and with minor rapid fluctuations due to flooding, etc. (Fig. 18). A similar type of flora is found in the shallow regions of large rivers, e.g. the river between Sweden and Finland; where the sediments were dominated by non-motile *Fragilaria* spp (cf. Malham streams) with motile Biraphidineae, Chroococcales, and the desmids making up the remainder of the flora.[343] The occurrence of desmids in appreciable quantity, particularly in the attached material in this river, was most striking and reflects the moorland type of country through which it flows; much of the bedrock is however calcareous and hence the river flora contained a mixture of species from both base poor and base rich habitats.

The general lack of data on river algae reflects the difficulties of sampling. Reliable evidence of the occurrence and growth of species is only obtained by sampling the actual material; quantitative estimates of the non-diatoms are difficult to obtain since stones and plants have to be scraped or brushed to remove the algae. When the flora is not too rich, direct observation of leaves and stems is possible and estimates can sometimes be made. The diatom data is often confused by the presence of contaminants and of dead cells, but some of the error can be eliminated by combining observations on fresh material with that of cleaned samples. The sediments are simpler to investigate since by the technique given on p. 59 the living motile flora is readily obtained. The motile diatom flora of stream sediments has been shown to undergo very precise vertical migration movements even when transferred to the laboratory and kept under constant conditions. Broadly speaking the maximum number of cells appears on the surface around mid-day.[357a]

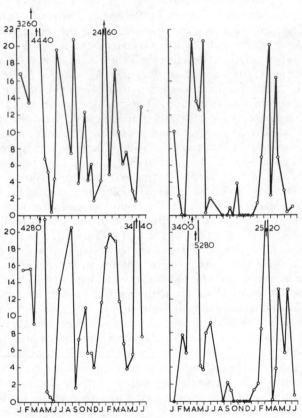

FIG. 18.

The seasonal changes in cell numbers of the diatom population at four stations in the Droitwich area. The left-hand graphs are from stations with rapidly flowing water, hence the greater fluctuations; the right-hand graphs are from very slow flowing canals.

(Round—unpublished.)

Attempts have been made to study river floras using artificial substrata, e.g. the glass slide technique of Butcher and the more complicated 'diatometer' of Patrick *et al.*[316] These are of value in determining the productivity of river water as in the 'diatometer' experiments, but information on the actual flora is biased by the growth of species which tend to grow in dense patches on the slides, e.g. *Achnanthes, Cocconeis,* and *Gomphonema.* It is noteworthy that almost all the data from these methods is on the small attached forms and only rarely are the large filamentous or motile species recorded. The use of such apparatus gives little information on the algal flora of the open water, sediments or plants whilst the flora of the artificial piles, stonework, culverts, etc., is fairly accurately recorded.

Ponds and lakes

The algal flora of small bodies of water is indirectly influenced by size. It is almost impossible to make a distinction between ponds and lakes, yet the flora is frequently quite different; useful criteria in defining ponds (irrespective of local naming) are, the absence of wind induced wave moulding of the shoreline, the relatively shallow depth, the small volume leading to rapid changes in composition of the water and the rapid fluctuations of temperature, CO_2 and pH. The opposite is generally true of lakes, although intermediates can be found. Both the extent and the algal composition of the communities are different in the two habitats; ponds tend to have epipelic, and epiphytic floras developed over the whole area, only occasionally is there an epilithic flora and the phytoplankton tends to be of different composition to that of lakes, often being recruited from the benthic communities and often changing very rapidly. In lakes the epiphytic, epilithic and epipelic communities are developed as a girdle around the periphery, leaving the centre free for plankton, which is itself fairly stable, of specific algal composition and rarely augmented from the other algal communities. Unlike rivers, given the substrata, all four communities are well developed in standing water and so much data is available that only a small selection can be mentioned.

Ecological studies on ponds and lakes fall into the following categories:

1. Single collections, sometimes the only possible type in isolated regions.
2. A study of a single algal group, e.g. the desmids have been extensively worked in many habitats.
3. A study of the complete algal flora of a community, e.g. the phytoplankton, or of a type of habitat, e.g. ponds.
4. A study of a single genus or species over a wide range of habitats.

Very small ponds or even puddles have a well developed epipelic flora and where rock is exposed there is also an epilithic flora, e.g. ponds on rock platforms. Many are dependent on rainwater or seepage water and in barren regions may be almost distilled water pools, e.g. in moorland regions.

The flora is determined by the chemical composition of the water, thus on moorlands it often consists of numerous desmid species (*Cosmarium, Staurastrum, Arthrodesmus, Euastrum*, etc.) with a few diatom genera adapted to extreme acidic, low base status water (*Eunotia, Frustulia, Pinnularia* spp.), together with a few species of Volvocales, Chlorococcales, flagellates and Cyanophyta (e.g. species of *Synura, Uroglena, Dinobryon, Gymnodinium, Peridinium* and *Chroococcus turgidus*). Laub et al.[229] investigated a series of such bog pools in Austria with pH values ranging from $3\cdot7/4\cdot6$–$6\cdot0/6\cdot7$; the most acid were dominated by *Cylindrocystis brebissonii, C. minor, Netrium digitus, Staurastrum scabrum, Cosmarium cucurbita, Tetmemorus laevis* and *Chroococcus turgidus* and less common but nevertheless indicators of the extreme nature of the habitat were *Eucapsis alpina, Stigonema ocellatum, Pinnularia viridis, Frustulia saxonica, Penium* spp., *Euastrum* spp., *Arthrodesmus incus, Staurastrum* spp., *Gymnozygon moniliformis, Tetracoccus botryoides, Glenodinium montanum, Oedogonium itzigsohnii* and *Microthamnion kutzingii*. In less acid waters species of *Closterium, Xanthidium, Micrasterias, Cosmarium, Aphanothece* and diatoms become more common. Similar assemblages occur on the peaty black sediments in many moorland regions. This flora is exposed to extremes of climate, but owing to lack of inflow and outflow, the ponds remain fairly constant in chemical composition and such a flora extends, with some diversification of the components, into the littoral zone of extremely acid lakes. A characteristic of this flora is the copious amount of mucilage formed by many of the species. In general the level of nutrients is extremely low, since the ponds are dependent upon rainfall and leaching from the surrounding peat; these ponds may be classed as oligotrophic, i.e. poor in nutrients or if the water is coloured with humic materials dystrophic. Many are surrounded by *Sphagnum* bog which may extend under the water and some have Angiosperm vegetation growing in the water, e.g. species of *Carex, Rhynchospora, Eleocharis*, etc. This vegetation is usually rich in epiphytic species of desmids and diatoms characteristic of such acid waters, e.g. in two samples of *Eleocharis* from peat pools on a skerry off the S. coast of Finland, the author found *Eunotia lunaris* was the dominant diatom and filaments of *Ulothrix, Cylindrocapsa, Mougeotia, Sphaerozosma* were all common together with species of *Dictyosphaerium, Euastrum, Cosmarium, Staurodesmus, Staurastrum* and *Chroococcus turgidus* dispersed amongst the filaments. Any phytoplankton which appears in such pools is formed by the rapid multiplication of flagellates, e.g. *Synura*, or Chlorococcales, e.g. *Ankistrodesmus* or *Dictyosphaerium*.

Ponds with neutral to alkaline water, generally rich in nutrients, with sediments composed of silt and/or decaying organic matter (leaves, etc.), form a completely different habitat to the above. They often have a rich 'phytoplankton' of flagellates (*Euglena, Phacus, Lepocinclis, Trachelomonas*), particularly where nitrogen, phosphorus and organic content are high; the latter almost certainly supplies growth factors needed by these flagellates. Species of Chlorococcales also tend to form 'phytoplankton,' e.g. *Scenedesmus, Oocystis, Tetraedron, Chlorella* and *Golenkinia*. Both these groups also exist on the sediment and the Chlorococcales can often be regarded as the characteristic species of small bodies of water, where they sometimes form a mass vegetation excluding almost all other species, e.g. in some pools on the skerries off S. Finland (*loc. cit.*) *Scenedesmus* forms over 90 per cent of the vegetation in some pools and it appears that this genus is resistant to grazing by the Crustacea, etc., and passes through the gut in a viable state. It has been proved experimentally that coccoid and some filamentous algae were viable after passing through the gut of a species of Ephemeroptera.[39]

Larger ponds often have a more distinct planktonic community, which is not easily separable from that of eutrophic lakes. Species of diatoms appear, e.g. *Melosira varians, Rhizosolenia eriensis, Fragilaria intermedia, F. crotonensis, Synedra* spp. together with Cyanophyta of the genera *Microcystis, Gomphosphaeria, Aphanizomenon, Anabaena* and *Gleotrichia*. Many of these Cyanophyta form gas vacuoles which render the cells buoyant. When conditions are favourable for growth, usually in late summer, the surface water may be so thick with cells of these algae that it forms a bluish-green film visible to the naked eye and known as a 'water bloom.' Occasionally bluish/black masses float to the surface of eutrophic ponds; these are tangled filaments of species of Cyanophyta (usually of the genera *Oscillatoria, Lyngbya* or *Phormidium*) together with sediment. These have formed from a papery black mat on the sediment and are epipelic species; active photosynthesis results in bubbles of oxygen becoming trapped in the mass, so that pieces are dislodged and rise to the surface where they float as flocs some few centimetres in diameter. There is also a surface film community (neuston) which, when richly developed, forms a 'water bloom.' This only occurs on small bodies of water where the surface is protected from wind. The algae, together with some bacteria and invertebrates, become attached to the boundary layer between the air and water, either on the upper surface of the water (epineuston) or on the under surface (hyponeuston). The earliest organism recorded in this community was *Chromulina rosanoffii*, a unicellular flagellate normally living in the plankton and forming non-motile coccoid cells, which under suitable conditions come to the surface and form a neustonic community. Similarly the cysts of *Ankyra* (*Characium*) *ancora* float on the surface. *Euglena* spp. sometimes form a red surface film, owing to the rich production of carotenoids in the cells—the 'Blutseen' of high mountains. Behre[18] gives details of the phytoplankton of nine small bodies of water near Bremen; one (Zwischenahner Meer) is rich in calcium and eutrophic and has a phytoplankton in which the most abundant species are *Microcystis aeruginosa, M. incerta, M. viridis, M. flos-aquae, Coelosphaerium naegelianum, C. kutzingianum, Chroococcus limneticus, Gomphosphaeria lacustris, Aphanizomenon flos-aquae, Anabaena spiroides* v. *crassa, A. macrospora* v. *robusta, Eudorina elegans, Pediastrum duplex, P. boryanum, Oocystis lacustris, O. crassa* v. *marssonii, Dictyosphaerium pulchellum, Tetraedron limneticum, Scenedesmus quadricauda, S. bibraicanum, Closterium aciculare, Staurastrum paradoxum, Coscinodiscus rothii* v. *subsalsus, C. lacustris, Melosira islandica, M. binderiana,** *Stephanodiscus dubius, S. astraea,*

* Transferred to *Stephanodiscus*, Round (1972).

Asterionella formosa, and *Synedra ulna*. The abundance of Cyanophyta, Chlorococcales and diatoms and the scarcity of flagellates and desmids is noteworthy. Other smaller ponds, poor in calcium and generally oligotrophic had a phytoplankton which was strikingly different, not only in species composition, but in number of species and in quantity of cells produced. Of these other ponds one is neutral/acid and calcium poor and contains a mixed plankton with diatoms dominant (*Asterionella formosa*, *Melosira ambigua*, *Tabellaria fenestrata*, *T. flocculosa* and *Rhizosolenia longiseta*), Cyanophyta reduced to three species (*Anabaena flos-aquae*, *A. scheremetievii* and *Coelosphaerium naegelianum*), with flagellates more abundant than in the Zwischenahner Meer (*Mallomonas caudata*, *M. acaroides*, *Dinobryon divergens*, *Synura uvella*, *Uroglena volvox*, *Gonyostomum semen*, *Peridinium cinctum*, *Gymnodinium uberrimum*, *Ceratium hirundinella*, *Eudorina elegans*, *Gonium pectorale*), Chlorococcales less frequent (*Dictyosphaerium pulchellum*, *Botryococcus braunii*— the two most abundant with *Ankistrodesmus falcatus* v. *mirabilis*, *Pediastrum duplex* and *Quadrigula closterioides*) and only two desmids occurring (*Closterium lineatum* v. *gracile* and *Sphaerozosma granulatum*). Because of the neutral/ acid status of this pond (Sager Meer) few Cyanophyta were present and these did not form 'water blooms,' since conditions were never favourable for the excessive growth required for this. Flagellates were more abundant and the diatom flora was of an oligotrophic rather than a eutrophic type. The other ponds were acidic (pH 6·0/6·5 down to 4·0/4·8). Those with a pH range below 6·0 did not support planktonic Cyanophyta; *Botryococcus braunii* and *Ceratium hirundinella* tended to be the dominants in the least acid and *Dinobryon* in the most acid range. The number of species is reduced from 48 in the eutrophic Zwischenahner Meer, through 26 in the neutral/ acid Sager Meer to 5 and 7 species respectively in the acidic Grosse Bullensee and Kleine Bullensee.

Bethge [22] studied the phytoplankton of a small pond in Berlin from 1929–1944 and presented a most comprehensive study of the phytoplankton in its seasonal and year to year aspects. It is clear from this that although some species are present in all years others are absent in some and present in others (e.g. *Volvox globator*, *Hydrodictyon reticulatum* and *Cosmarium laeve*). Some species tend to grow throughout the year, e.g. *Synura uvella*, *Cryptomonas erosa* and *C. ovata*, whilst others have a growing period in spring, e.g. *Eudorina elegans*, *Stephanodiscus hantzschii*, *Diatoma elongatum*, *Asterionella formosa* and *Ankistrodesmus falcatus* v. *acicularis*; others in summer, e.g. *Microcystis aeruginosa*, *Aphanizomenon flos-aquae*, *Dinobryon divergens*, *Ceratium hirundinella*, *Volvox globator*, and the majority of the Protococcales (Chlorococcales); autumn forms are rare and only *Gymnodinium aeruginosum* is prominent; winter species are *Chroococcus planktonicus* (Fig. 19), *Mallomonas teilingii* and *Gymnodinium tenuissima*. *Chroococcus planktonicus* is interesting in commencing growth after the establishment of the ice cover, continuing for some time afterwards and then decreasing if the ice remains for long periods. During this time the quantity of plankton is much reduced, this is due partly, to sedimentation in the still water under the ice, to decrease in oxygen content and to increase in noxious gases accompanied by an increase in sulphur bacteria. *Asterionella formosa* starts growth soon after the disappearance of ice (usually in April) and rapidly reaches a maximum and then

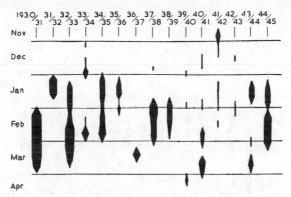

Fig. 19.

The seasonal occurrence of *Chroococcus planktonicus* over a period of years in a pond in Berlin.

(From Bethge, 1953.)

declines; autumn growth is rare. In addition there appears to be a ten-year cycle of growth, for in 1929/30 and in 1939/40 the annual production of *Asterionella* cells was high and between and after it was low (Fig. 20). A similar but shorter cycle seemed to apply to *Scenedesmus quadricauda* and possibly *Synura uvella*; these variations did not correlate with meterological conditions and it is probable that uninvestigated chemical fluctuations were responsible.

Study of a single species, that is an autecological approach, is illustrated in a study of the planktonic diatom *Rhizosolenia longiseta* in five ponds in Denmark.[14] *R. longiseta* was absent from the most eutrophic alkaline pond, where Cyanophyta were abundant, and reached its maximum growth in the oligotrophic humic water of Sorteso. Growth maxima tended to occur in May/June but in one year this was delayed until August/September, in Sorteso only; the number of cells produced was very different in the various ponds, e.g. maxima of less than 100 cells/cm³ in the least productive pond, through 360/400 to 1800 and to 4400 in Sorteso and with annual variation in the cell maxima in this latter pond from 400 cells/cm³ to 4400. *R. longiseta* was rarely the dominant alga in the plankton and when dominant or subdominant it was associated with either *Ankistrodesmus* spp., *Trachelomonas volvocina*, *Melosira granulata*, *Staurastrum uniseriatum*, *Asterionella formosa*, *Scenedesmus setiferus*, *Synura spinosa* or *Dinobryon divergens* v. *schauinnslandii*.

A small number of algae live epiplanktonically either on the phytoplankton or zooplankton, e.g. short threads of *Phormidium mucicola* on colonies of *Microcystis flos-aquae*, whilst cells of *Stylosphaeridium stipitatum* and *Characiopsis curvata* are very common on colonies of *Coelosphaerium naegelianum*. *Chlamydomonas gloeophila* has also been found in the mucilage of *Coelosphaerium* and another species *C. dinobryoni* lives in the thecae of *Dinobryon divergens*.[252] Species of *Characiopsis*, *Chlorangium* and *Chlorangiopsis* occur on planktonic Crustacea. A *Lyngbya* sp. sometimes grows on the antennae of *Daphnia pulex*.

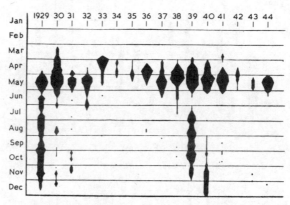

FIG. 20.

The seasonal occurrence of *Asterionella formosa* over a period of years in a pond in Berlin.

(From Bethge, 1953.)

Behre[18] discusses the other algal communities in the eutrophic Zwischenahner Meer; in the epilithic community *Ulothrix* spp., *Stigeoclonium tenue*, *Draparnaldia plumosa*, *Tribonema* spp., *Microspora willeana* and *Cladophora* spp. form macroscopic growths. On these an epiphytic flora grows, in which *Gomphonema olivaceum*, *Cocconeis pediculus*, *C. placentula*, *Rhoicosphenia curvata*, *Gomphonema constrictum* and *Plectonema notatum* are common, whilst less abundant are *Lyngbya* spp., *Chamaesiphon incrustans* v. *angustus*, *Aphanochaete repens* and *Coleochaete scutata*. As epiphytes on higher plants, *Cymbella prostrata*, *Diatoma vulgare*, *Synedra ulna*, *Gomphonema olivaceum* and *Fragilaria intermedia* are listed. Behre recognized the large number of species which live neither floating (i.e. in the plankton) nor attached, but caught up between the macroscopic algae and amongst the leaves of mosses and aquatic Phanerogams. He termed this assemblage the *metaphyton* and lists in this a very large number of species mainly from the flagellate groups, Chlorococcales, desmids and diatoms. This is undoubtedly a common and important, but little studied, community. In small lakes and ponds where the open water is not too extensive this epiphytic/metaphytic population is responsible for an enormous amount of carbon fixation and completely dominates the production aspect.

The epipelic community of eutrophic ponds consists mainly of diatoms, some Cyanophyta, e.g. *Oscillatoria* spp., flagellates, e.g. *Euglena, Trachelomonas, Phacus, Cryptomonas, Chroomonas, Mallomonas, Synura* and Chlorophyta, e.g. *Scenedesmus* and *Closterium* spp.[338] Filamentous diatoms are often common (*Melosira varians* and *Fragilaria* spp.), together with motile species of the Biraphidineae, e.g. *Gyrosigma acuminatum, Caloneis silicula, Diploneis ovalis, Stauroneis phoenicenteron, S. smithii, Navicula pupula, N. pupula* v. *capitata, N. cryptocephala, N. rhynchocephala, N. hungarica* v. *capitata, N. radiosa, N. schonfeldii, N. oblonga, Pinnularia viridis, Amphora ovalis, Cymbella naviculiformis, C. cistula* v. *maculata, Nitzschia palea, N. sigmoidea, N. dissipata, N. acicularis* and *Cymatopleura solea.* Even in small ponds, one less than 1 m in diameter, there was a distinct seasonal growth with either a single peak of diatom cell numbers in April/May or with three peaks in February/March, May/June and August/September. Species which had a single growth peak in spring were *Nacicula pupula, N. pupula* v. *capitata, N. rhynchocephala* and *Amphora ovalis,* those with spring, summer and autumn peaks were *Navicula hungarica* v. *capitata* and *Nitzschia palea* and with summer peaks only *Nitzschia acicularis.*

In some small ponds (and also lakes) some of the species living on the sediments attach themselves to sand grains by means of mucilage pads; this is recorded by Behre for *Tabellaria binalis, Scenedesmus antennatus, S. antennatus* v. *desmiformis* and *Chlorogonium curvicauda.*

Lakes

The large size of lakes results in the development of well defined habitats with mixing of the communities only at their boundaries, thus the plankton is usually more distinct and more clearly separated from the littoral communities. Size also results in greater buffering of the environment and changes tend to occur at a slower rate than in ponds. On the other hand, depth limits light penetration and allows permanent temperature stratification* during some seasons, with all its attendant effects on the algal flora. Wind induced wave action modifies the shore lines and produces currents which keep certain habitats free of silt and render others silted with accompanying change in the flora. The form, depth, position of inflows and outflows, nature of rock basin, nature of surface drift soils, surrounding land flora, aquatic Phanerogamic flora, climatic conditions, etc., all exert an influence on lakes as algal habitats.

The diagram (Fig. 21) is designed to represent some of the features of lakes with which phycologists are directly concerned. The phytoplankton occupies the whole water mass except when the lake becomes stratified and a thermocline develops. Sampling of the phytoplankton in the littoral zone

* The physical and chemical factors are admirably discussed by Ruttner[352], Hutchinson[190] and Gessner[122-123].

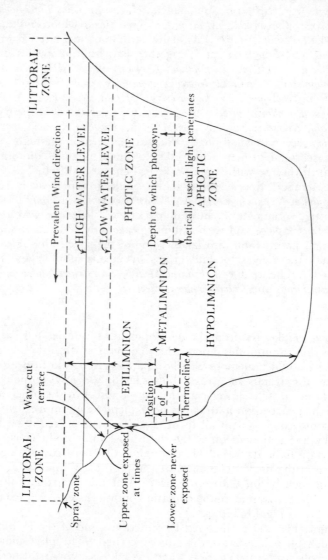

Fig. 21.

Some of the important features of a lake basin.

may yield a sample contaminated by littoral algae but in the centre, contamination will be confined to period of gales or rapid flow of water from
the drainage area.

Nomenclature of the habitats in the littoral zone is complex. Without
recourse to terminology, there is first a spray zone above high-water mark,
where the algal flora is basically that of moist aerial habitats with some
contamination from the adjacent lake flora, then a zone between high- and
low-water mark which supports a typical lake flora on rock, stones, sediment
(silt or sand) and on plants and then below this a permanently submerged
community similar to that between high- and low-water mark. This flora
ceases at a point determined by the depth to which photosynthetically
available light penetrates and this seems to me to be the most useful limit
of the littoral. Exceptions will arise for example in turbid lakes where,
although light may not penetrate and algae may not grow, the littoral fauna
still exists at depths where algal growth is reduced or non-existent. The
lower limit of algal growth in the littoral is often below the limit of Phanerogamic growth. Rarely, algal communities exist on floating plants far from
the littoral zone, but in fact they are similar to those of the littoral in composition. Freshwater algal ecological studies have concentrated on lakes,
and within lakes, on the phytoplankton community; but in fact the littoral
zone usually supports a much greater number of species in many different
associations and can be extremely important in productivity studies and in
the overall limnology of the lake.

Phytoplankton

Phytoplankton is collected from lakes as from ponds by drawing a net
slowly through the water and thus filtering off the organisms of greater size
than the mesh size of the net (pores 50–80 μm diameter) plus some smaller
species as the net becomes clogged. In waters with a sparse flora this method
is often the only one which yields enough cells to enable identification of the
rarer forms. The method unfortunately often yields a biased sample, since
cells may be concentrated in layers either at the surface or at lower depths,
especially during periods of stratification. In winter mixing probably yields
a more representative sample but in summer it may be desirable to lower the
net to a determined depth and then draw it up thus sampling a column of
lake water. Net samples are not quantitative (although methods and equations have been devised to compute fairly accurate quantitative results).
Samples of known volume may be taken using water bottles closing at
definite depths and this is necessary to investigate stratification of the
plankton. Distinct populations of coccoid and flagellate Chlorophyta have
been shown to grow at different depths, during stratified periods, in a small
lake near Bristol. Samples obtained by filling a bottle with surface water
may thus give erroneous results especially in summer. A neat device for
sampling a column of water is given in Lund (1949). A 5 m length of
rubber tubing weighted at one end and with a cord attached near the weight

is lowered until it is hanging vertically in the water with the unweighted end level with the water surface. This end is then closed and using the cord the tube is hauled up and the contents are poured into a bottle. Whatever method is used in the field it is usually necessary to concentrate the samples in the laboratory; filtration, centrifugation or sedimentation may be used. For strict quantitative work sedimenting after killing organisms with a drop of iodine in potassium iodide is convenient and commonly used. Filtration results in losses on the filter paper and centrifugation may break colonies or cells of delicate species. A combination of methods is often desirable, especially since there is no substitute for examination of living material. Filtration through microfilters of known pore size is valuable when investigating the smallest planktonic organisms but preparation of the filter for subsequent microscopic examination damages the cells which cannot be looked at from different angles as when material is mounted in water. When it is necessary to know the composition of the phytoplankton, some form of counting is essential. Sedimentation of known volumes of water in special tubes which can be stood on an inverted microscope is satisfactory; by this method all the species in the volume of water are recorded and identifications can be made. If an inverted microscope is not available, a special sedimentation chamber [256] or a haemocytometer can be used. For some purposes

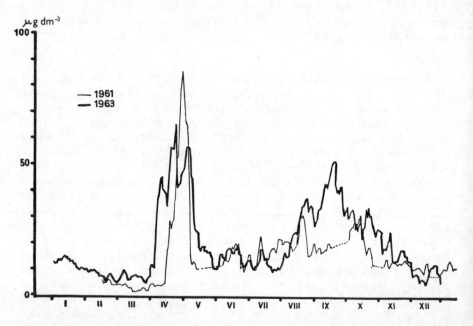

Fig. 21A. Seasonal Changes in Chlorophyll Content of Water Samples from Lake Mikolajskie in 1961 and 1963.
(From Szczepanski, 1966.)

it is necessary to combine counting methods with estimates of cell volume obtained from the means of numerous measurements of the individual species. It is difficult to estimate accurately the number of cells in colonies and sometimes only the number of colonies can be estimated.

Estimation of dry weight (by heating a concentrated volume of plankton at 105°C until the weight becomes constant) or of elements, e.g. carbon, nitrogen or silica, have been used but are rarely adequate for routine ecological studies.

Photometric determinations of light absorbed or scattered in passing through algal suspensions are also used to estimate phytoplankton. The use of this method on natural populations is of doubtful value and it gives no data on composition. Even applied to cultures, there is a danger of error from the variable amounts of wall material, pigment, chromatophores and reserve products present unless the algae compared are in a similar 'physiological state.' The standing crop or growth in culture of phytoplankton has often been related to the pigment content of the cells measured photometrically after extraction using acetone. The method is reliable but open to several objections, e.g. the pigment content varies according to the ecological conditions, pigments and their degradation products are extracted from dead cells in the population and it is not possible to distinguish between species. Nevertheless, as Fig. 21a shows, the pigment extraction method can yield annual estimates which follow the expected spring and autumn maxima.

The phytoplankton of lakes is composed of algae of size ranging from less than 1 μm in diameter to organisms visible to the naked eye, e.g. *Volvox*. An artificial separation is often made into euplankton, which in general is retained by a normal phytoplankton net, the nannoplankton, which passes through the pores of the net and smaller still, the μ-plankton. The euplankton is mainly composed of species of Cyanophyta, Bacillariophyta (mainly of the sections Centrales and Pennales—Araphidineae) Chlorophyta (in particular Chlorococcales and Desmids), flagellate groups (Volvocales, Chrysophyceae and Dinophyceae—mainly of the genera *Peridinium* and *Ceratium*, Cryptophyceae and more rarely Euglenophyceae). The nannoplankton are mainly drawn from the flagellates and coccoid Chlorophyta and to a slight extent from the centric diatoms. The μ-plankton is composed of small flagellates and coccoid Chlorophyta.

Although the morphology of the species in freshwater lake plankton is similar to that of marine plankton (cf. Figs. 22 and 36, p. 110), no species are common to the two habitats, except that in some inland saline lakes oceanic species occur, e.g. the Sea of Aral with species such as *Thalassiosira decipiens*, *Sceletonema costatum*, and *Actinocyclus ehrenbergii*; these are no doubt relict species from the time when the Ponto-Caspian region was a marine basin. Whole groups of algae are confined to one or the other habitat, e.g. the desmids are absent from marine habitats and the Cyanophyta are only represented by a single species. Conversely genera such as *Coscinodiscus*,

Actinocyclus, Chaetoceros, Rhizosolenia are almost confined to the marine plankton, though increasing pollution in some lakes is resulting in growth of some species of these genera. Others such as the Dinoflagellates *Peridinum* and *Ceratium* are present in both, but the number of species in marine plankton is far in excess of that in freshwater.

The chemical nature of the waters exerts a selective effect on lake phytoplankton, similar to that described for pond phytoplankton (see p. 75), so

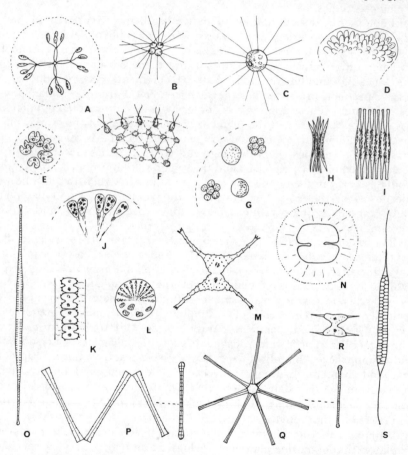

FIG. 22. FRESHWATER PLANKTONIC ALGAE.

A. *Dictyosphaerium*; B. *Micractinium*; C. *Golenkinia*; D. *Botryococcus*; E. *Kirchneriella*; F. *Volvox*; G. *Sphaerocystis*; H. *Ankistrodesmus*; I. *Fragilaria*; J. *Gomphosphaeria*; K. *Sphaerozosma*; L. *Stephanodiscus*; M. *Staurastrum*; N. *Cosmarium*; O. *Synedra*; P. *Diatoma*, colony and single cell in valve view; Q. *Asterionella*, colony and single cell in valve view; R. *Arthrodesmus*; S. *Rhizosolenia*.

(After Nygaard, Skuja and original.)

that the flora of dystrophic, oligotrophic and eutrophic waters tends to be fairly specific.

Planktonic species often have a relatively slow rate of sinking or more rarely some buoyancy mechanism. Since the specific gravity of most freshwaters is only fractionally greater (1·0027) than pure water and the average specific gravity of protoplasm is 1·045–1·050, increased still further by silicified or cellulose walls, there is no possibility of flotation under still conditions. Two factors which increase the bouyancy of algae are the presence of gas vacuoles (e.g. in the Cyanophyta) and oil globules (e.g. in *Botryococcus*, diatoms and dinoflagellates). However excess weight of the silica walls of diatoms and the thick plates of some dinoflagellates probably outweigh the buoyancy effect of the oil. The mechanism of buoyancy is complex for although some Cyanophyta, e.g. *Anabaena circinalis* may form summer blooms in Esthwaite Water, another species also having gas vacuoles, *Oscillatoria agardhii* v. *isothrix*, was collected in the region of the metalimnion (thermocline) at the same time.[255] Increase in surface area to form flat plates may also aid buoyancy provided this is not accompanied by too great an increase in weight. This is achieved in species of *Pediastrum* with cavities in the thallus, e.g. *P. duplex*, but not in the flat plates of *Micrasterias* spp., which would appear to be equally adapted but occur in the plankton only after storms and then rapidly settle.[339] Other species, e.g. many planktonic desmids, have large robust cells, but are embedded in a mass of mucilage which probably has a specific gravity close to that of water. The spines in these species, which are sometimes assumed to be adaptations to flotation increase the weight since they are included within the mucilage and must act adversely. It is doubtful whether form has much influence on flotation since the range is extremely great; it varies from coccoid forms, through plates (*Pediastrum*), spheres (*Sphaerocystis*), needles (*Synedra acus*), radiating needles (*Asterionella*, *Tabellaria*) to filaments (*Melosira*, *Anabaena*). Motility in the plankton is almost entirely by means of flagella, but it is unlikely that this is an asset, except in very still water. Observations on the phytoplankton under ice reveal that species such as *Asterionella formosa* and *Melosira italica* subsp. *subarctica* sink fairly rapidly[255] (see Figs. 23 and 26, p. 90). Cells killed artificially have a greater rate of sinking than live cells of the same species. Whilst recording seasonal cycles of littoral algae on sediments, great increases in planktonic species such as *Asterionella formosa* and *Oscillatoria agardhii* v. *isothrix* were found on the sediments at the end of their growth periods. Thus, although there may be no apparent flotation mechanism, some intrinsic property of the living cell is involved in buoyancy. If this were not so the number of dead cells in the epilimnion would soon outnumber the live. One is forced to the conclusion that turbulence of the water plus some unknown cytoplasmic factor are responsible for maintaining the phytoplankton in the water mass.

The spatial distribution of the phytoplankton is affected by the shape and size of the lake basin, position of inflows, degree of stratification, etc.

In small lakes the horizontal variation in composition is usually slight with the greatest difference in the shallow littoral region, where there is the possibility of contamination from the benthic flora and in the inflow region where the new water may contain species washed in from the inflow. In very large lakes, e.g. the Laurentian lakes of N. America, the phytoplankton community is not at all constant throughout, but communities develop in water masses of different chemical status and these move with the circulation of the water as in the open ocean. It was shown that in the western part of Lake Erie, at least three different communities exist and in such a large lake the mosaic

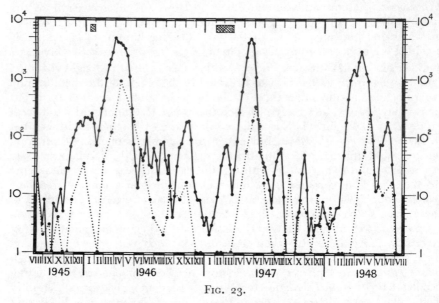

Fig. 23.

Live cells per ml of *Asterionella formosa* in Blelham Tarn plotted on a logarithmic scale, in the 0–5 m water column—continuous line. Cells on the surface of the sediment—broken line. Periods of ice cover indicated by cross hatching.

(From Lund, 1949.)

of communities moving with the water currents, renders the data from a single sampling station unreliable.[403] Variation of the community in the vertical plane is present in all lakes and is particularly striking during thermal stratification. In lakes which stratify, the effective depth to which phytoplankton can grow is reduced to the depth of the epilimnion. Below this the algae are trapped in a zone where water currents are slowing and therefore the rate of algal sedimentation is increasing; in addition this region is usually below that to which photosynthetically active light penetrates. In the epilimnion currents continually circulate the phytoplankton, so that even when light penetration is only slight, each cell is moved into the light zone at some period. Thus cell numbers tend to rise in the epilimnion, so long as other limiting factors do not inhibit this. In these lakes there is thus, not only a temperature stratification (together with the stratification of other physical and chemical variables which become associated with it), but also a biological stratification. There may also be vertical variations within the epilimnion itself, e.g. in Esthwaite Water (see p. 90). Light penetration into the epilimnion may be so reduced by turbidity (which may be caused by the algae themselves) in the upper region, that combined with a slow circulation it becomes a limiting factor. After the breakdown of thermal stratification the phytoplankton community becomes distributed relatively

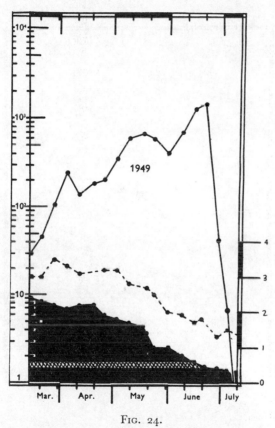

FIG. 24.

Cell numbers of *Asterionella formosa* in Windermere, N. Basin (—.—), together with silicate silica, solid black, and nitrate nitrogen (·-·-·) values during the spring growth in 1949. Cell numbers plotted on a logarithm scale on the left. Nutrients in mg dm^{-3} on the right. Nitrate nitrogen values multiplied by ten for convenience representation.

(From Lund, 1950.)

evenly throughout the water. During this period cells remain in the photic
zone, for a shorter time than under stratified conditions and since this period
corresponds with that of general low light conditions (i.e. during the winter
months), it is highly probable that the lack of growth is associated with the
short periods spent in the photic zone. The deeper the lake the lesser time
spent in the photic zone. Growth of the phytoplankton does however
commence well before the onset of stratification; presumably this is related
to increased day length, which increases the photosynthesis to a point where
photosynthetic production in the photic is greater than the respiratory loss
when the cells are in the aphotic zone.

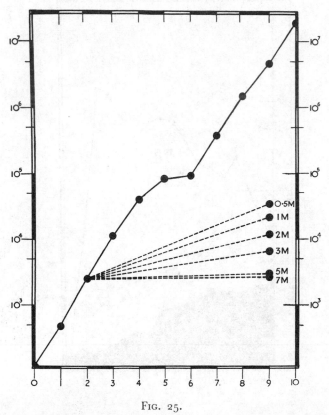

FIG. 25.

The growth of *Asterionella* cells in bottles suspended at various depths (0·5–7 m) in
Windermere (- - -) and in the laboratory (—·—). Cell numbers plotted on a
logarithmic scale (vertical axis) and days along the horizontal axis. Growth rate of
the laboratory culture was reduced between days 5–6 due to utilization of nutrients;
on day 7 subcultured into new media.

(From Lund, 1949.)

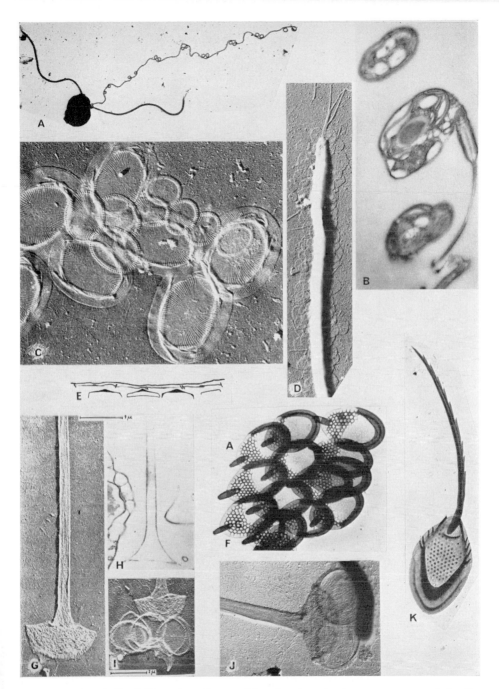

PLATE 3. **A:** Cell of *Chrysochromulina strobilus* showing the haptonema extended. **B:** *Micromonas pusilla* showing the flagellum with a long hair point consisting of the flagellar membrane and two central fibrils. **C:** Body scales of *Chrysochromulina chiton*. **D:** Flagellar tip of *Micromonas squamata* showing the arrangement of imbricated scales along the flagellum. **E:** Diagram of section through scales of *Chrysochromulina strobilus*. **F:** Group of scales of *Synura spinosa*. **G–J:** *Chrysochromulina ericina;* spiny scales and plate scales. **H:** A spiny scale in section. **I:** Plate scales showing inner faces. **J:** Two plate scales lying near the base of a spiny scale and showing outer surface. **K:** Apical scale of *Mallomonas* bearing a long spine. (A, C & E from Parke, Manton and Clarke; B from Manton; D from Manton and Parke; G–J from Manton and Leedale.)

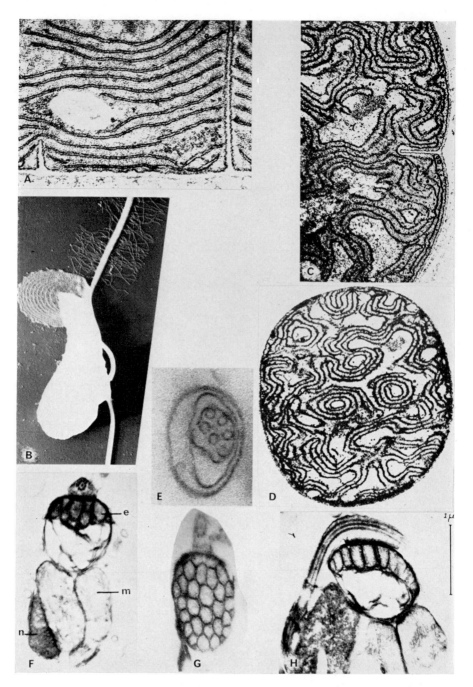

PLATE 4. **A:** Electron-micrograph of a dividing cell of *Oscillatoria*. **B:** Spermatozooid of *Fucus serratus* showing striate proboscis, plain hind flagellum looped back on to body and front flagellum with "flimmer." **C** & **D:** Electron-micrograph of a dividing cell of *Nostoc*, D showing coiled photosynthetic thylahoids. **E:** Section through the haptonema of *Chrysochrumulina strobilus*. **F, G** & **H:** Eyespot of *Fucus serratus*. **F**—section showing the hind flagellum cut transversely and attached to the eyespot (e), two mitochondria (m) and the tip of the nucleus (n); **G**—sectioned parallel to surface showing the pigment chambers; **H**—section through eyespot showing the relationship of the hind flagellum to the eyespot. (A, C & D from Menke; B, F, G & H from Manton and Clarke; E from Parke, Manton and Clarke.)

Intensive studies of individual phytoplanktonic algae have been rarely undertaken. Examples are the studies of *Asterionella formosa* and *Melosira italica*, subsp. *subarctica*.[250, 251, 253] *A. formosa* is a very common planktonic alga, usually producing large spring populations and small autumnal ones. In the lakes investigated in the English Lake District, live cells were always present in the lake water, although at times there were very few. During the build up of the spring population, the number on the sediments always increased but they did not remain alive in any quantity after the fall in numbers in the water (cf. above). There was no evidence to support the theory that populations build up on the sediments and are subsequently distributed into the water, a supposition which has been put forward to explain outbursts of planktonic growth. There are, however, a few exceptions to this general thesis. The graph Fig. 24 shows the spring increase and decrease in cell numbers of *Asterionella* in Windermere, N. Basin, in relation to silicate and nitrate nitrogen concentrations in the water. Growth commences in early spring and ceases when the silicate concentration falls to $0 \cdot 5$ mg dm^{-3}. This data can be compared with experimental data obtained from laboratory cultures and from cultures suspended in bottles at different depths in the lake. A known number of *Asterionella* cells were put into bottles in a culture medium of Chu No. 10, made up in filtered lake water with an addition of an extract of lake mud. These experiments showed that *Asterionella* rapidly changes its growth rate when temperature or light intensity are changed, but that concentration of the nutrient medium does not affect growth rate so long as no chemical is limiting. Data from the cultures suspended in the lake, showed the increase in growth rate when illumination and temperature were high and also the decrease in growth at lower depths (i.e. at lower light intensities) (Fig. 25). In addition to the physical and chemical factors which have been shown to exert a profound influence on the growth of the *Asterionella* populations, there is the secondary effect of parasitism. Many algae are parasitized by fungi and the only detailed study of this effect on seasonal cycles concerns the chytrid, *Rhizophidium planktonicum* growing on *A. formosa* in these lakes.[53] Although the fungus is present in small quantity throughout the year, it rarely assumes epidemic proportions; it may delay the *Asterionella* maximum and also reduce its size. Other slower growing diatoms may increase in numbers due to the absence of normal competition for nutrients from *Asterionella*. At least six chytrideaceous fungi have been recorded on *A. formosa* and the large number now recorded on phytoplanktonic algae suggests that fungal disease plays a not inconsiderable role in the seasonal development and composition of the flora.

Melosira italica subsp. *subarctica*, although often reaching a peak in cell numbers at the same time as *A. formosa*, behaves differently in that it is only present in any quantity between October–April/May, i.e. during isothermal conditions. In some years there is a fairly constant population during this period, sometimes with a peak in early spring; in other years there may be

an autumn population which disappears, to be followed by a spring population.[253] Silica depletion is almost certainly a factor involved in the final
spring decrease, but another important factor is thermal or inverse stratification, the latter occurring when ice covers the lake surface. Being a fairly
robust filamentous diatom, its sinking rate is rapid and decrease in numbers

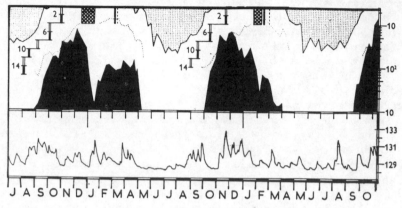

FIG. 26.

The seasonal cycle of *Melosira italica* subsp. *subarctica* in Esthwaite Water from July
1950–November 1952. Solid black, number of cells per cm^{-3} plotted on a log scale.
Dotted area represents periods of thermal stratification. Dotted line, surface
temperature (temp. scale marked 2°C–14°C). Chequered areas represent periods
of inverse stratification under ice and lower graph changes in lake level.

(From Lund, 1954.)

under ice cover is due largely to the decrease in turbulence and subsequent
high rate of sinking onto the sediments. Most algae which reach the sediments are out of the photic zone, unable to photosynthesize and soon
die, but *M. italica* subsp. *subarctica* has been shown to remain viable after long
periods in the dark. These cells are then resuspended in the water when
thermal stratification breaks down in autumn and circulation of water from
top to bottom of the lake recommences (Fig. 26). The blue-green alga
Gleotrichia echinulata is one of the few other algae which has been shown to
accumulate on sediments and then be resuspended in the water; growth of
colonies proceeds during winter months from akinetes which have been
deposited in late summer of the previous year. Resuspension occurs in
May/July.[336a]

Tabellaria has been shown to exist in different morphological strains in
different lakes in the English Lake District and these are illustrated in
Fig. 27.[216] They are not necessarily confined to these lakes and may occur
in the same lake at the same time, at different times or in different lakes.
The short celled 'Coniston form' (*T. flocculosa* v. *pelagica*) has also been recorded from lakes in Ireland,[351] as have some others, and so the suggestion [216]

that these are of recent origin in the English Lake District is not borne out. Some of the forms are known to have been present in Irish Lakes at the turn of this century since photomicrographs of them were published by West and West.[413]

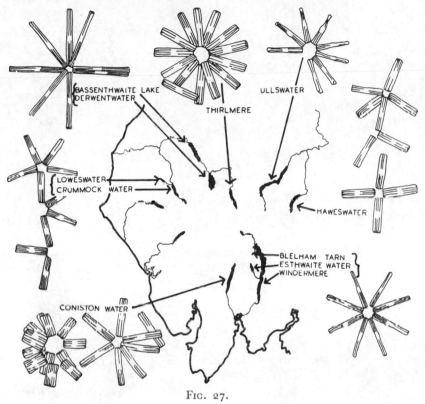

Fig. 27.

The morphological strains of *Tabellaria* found in the plankton of the English Lake District.

(From Knudsen, 1955.)

Production of organic matter by phytoplanktonic species has been measured using ^{14}C incorporation techniques, e.g. in a Danish Lake, Grane Langsø, slightly over 200 g(C)m^{-2} day^{-1} was incorporated in the phytoplankton.[299] Using a similar technique on Swedish lakes it was found that carbon incorporation into the plankton was always at a lower rate just below the surface and reached a maximum somewhere below 0·5 m (Fig. 28).[336] From such data the total primary production in the water column could be computed. Similar 'inhibition' in the surface layers has been detected by other methods, e.g. measurements of photosynthesis by the Winkler method and from calculation of relative growth rates (Fig. 29).[388]

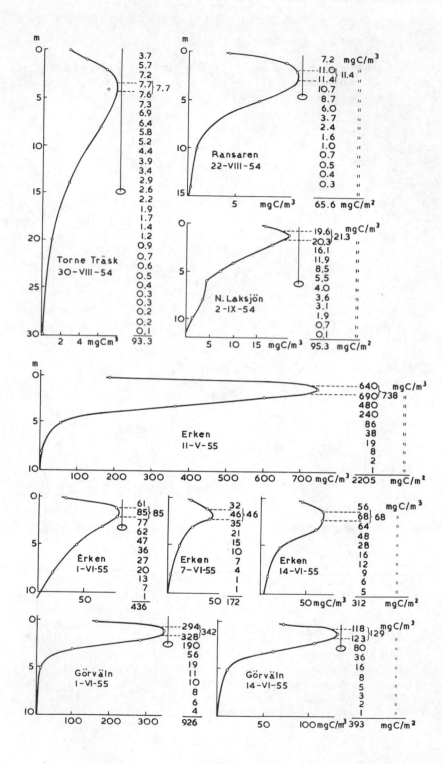

The epilithic flora

This rich flora grows on both the fixed rock faces and on the broken fragments in the littoral zone, and only in large lakes is there sufficient water movement to dislodge the algae. In the littoral zone two factors are continually varying, viz., water depth (and subsequent exposure at the upper levels) and water movement. In the region of exposure and in its spray zone, communities dominated by encrusting Cyanophyta are formed and water movement leads to the appearance of species equally abundant in flowing water. In relatively still water the stone surfaces may become covered with silt and the epilithic flora may give way to an epipelic flora.

The type of flora is determined by the chemistry of the waters (the chemical nature of the rock surfaces are often correlated with this), the position on the shore and the degree of wave action. Since the substrate is relatively permanent, there is usually a perennial flora but there is little data on its seasonal aspects. In lakes with regular ice cover, the flora becomes embedded in ice, in which many algae survive, but where ice movement occurs the flora is removed. In the Traunsee, Austria, a zonation of species has been recorded,[204] viz., the exposed rocks up to 20 cm above mean water level, are often covered with a black algal growth of the Cyanophyta *Gloeocapsa sanguinea* status *alpinus* and *Scytonema myochrous* status *crustaceus.* Nearer the water line and more frequently covered with water *Nostoc sphaeri-cum, Calothrix parietina, C. fusca, Scytonema myochrous* and *Chlorogloea micro-cystoides* occur. Below this is a zone of *Tolypothrix distorta* v. *penicillata* and *S. myochrous* which grow in the 10 cm region on either side of mean water level. At 5–25 cm below mean water level a *Rivularia haematites* community occurs, with intermixed *S. myochrous, Tolypothrix distorta, Mougeotia* sp., *Nostoc coeruleum* and *N. sphaericum.* These latter two zones also support the Rhodophycean alga *Bangia atropurpurea.* Below the *Rivularia* zone and mixing into its lowermost extension, is a *Schizothrix lacustris* community in which *Toly-pothrix tenuis, S. myochrous, Phormidium subfuscum* v. *joannianum, Chamaesiphon polymorphus, Tolypothrix distorta* and *Nostoc coeruleum,* occur. In this zone there is also a considerable growth of filamentous green algae (*Mougeotia, Spirogyra, Oedogonium, Zygnema, Bulbochaete, Stigeoclonium*). Mixed in and below all these zones is a rich flora of diatoms and other microscopic algae. The rocks on which this flora was found were calcareous as is the water of the Traunsee. Although in Windermere the water is of a much lower calcium content and there are not such well developed cliffs sloping down into the water the epilithic flora is similar to that of the Traunsee,[127] e.g. *Pleurocapsa fusca*

FIG. 28.

Examples of daily, primary production in some Swedish lakes. In brackets the production in the optimal light zone and alongside each graph the production in each depth interval and also the total.

(From Rodhe, 1956.)

and *Tolypothrix distorta* v. *penicillata* were recorded as dominant in the spray zone, together with *Phormidium autumnale, Homeothrix fusca, Calothrix parietina, Schizothrix funalis, Pleurocapsa fluviatilis* and *Nostoc (sphaericum?)*. A richer flora

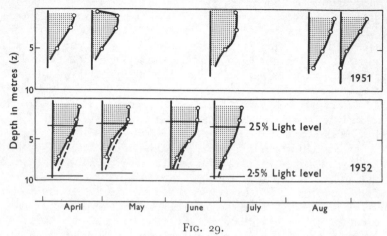

FIG. 29.

Graphs of relative growth rates recorded in cultures of *Asterionella* suspended in bottles in Windermere, North Basin. Broken lines show calculated values.
(From Talling, 1955.)

occurs in the zone 0–0·5 m below water level, with *Ulothrix zonata*, the diatoms *Synedra radians, Achnanthes minutissima, A. microcephala, Cymbella ventricosa*, and the Cyanophyta, *Pleurocapsa fusca, Phormidium fovaeolorum, P. autumnale, Calothrix parietina, S. funalis, S. fusca* and *Dichothrix orsiniana*. In winter and spring *Draparnaldia plumosa, Stigeoclonium amoenum* and *Chaetophora* appear and *Coleochaete* spp. are also found on the stones. At intermediate depths the flora is a mixed collection of diatoms and filamentous green algae and below 2 m Cyanophyta again become more important in the community, e.g., *Nostoc verrucosum, Dichothrix baueriana* v. *crassa, Plectonema tomasinianum* v. *concinnatum*.

In some lakes, the rocks and stones become encrusted with calcium carbonate (e.g. in Malham Tarn, Yorkshire) and on these, diatoms, *Achnanthes* spp., *Synedra* spp., *Tabellaria flocculosa, Cymbella prostrata* are abundant, whilst in summer and autumn *Spirogyra* is frequent. Cyanophyta are less abundant, species of *Oscillatoria, Tolypothrix* and particularly *Rivularia* do occur (Round, unpublished data). An interesting association occurs on cliffs rising out of Lake Van in Turkey.[124] Brown stripes extending up and down the cliff 20 cm above and below the water line proved to be a mixture of Cyanophyta, mainly *Entophysalis granulosa* and *Anabaena variabilis* and diatoms *Rhopalodia musculus* and *Nitzschia* spp. The absence of other encrusting Cyanophyta may be due to the high soda content of this lake.

Quennerstedt [330a] gives more details of the epilithic flora of some base poor Swedish lakes. Above low-water line Cyanophyta are abundant, e.g. species of *Calothrix*, *Dichothrix*, *Schizothrix*, *Stigonema* and *Gloeocapsa*. When covered by water, these were rapidly colonized by diatoms, e.g. *Tabellaria flocculosa* v. *flocculosa* and then filaments of *Binuclearia*, *Oedogonium* and *Zygnema*, together with intermixed diatoms, *Anomoeoneis*, *Eunotia*, *Frustulia* and *Peronia*. Below low-water level, Cyanophyta were richly developed, e.g. *Tolypothrix saviczii* and *Scytonema figuratum* on which there was a rich diatom flora of *T. flocculosa* v. *flocculosa*, *Anomoeoneis exilis*, *Eunotia lunaris* and *Peronia heribaudii*. Also large mucilaginous masses of *Frustulia rhomboides* v. *saxonica* and *Lyngbya* spp. covered parts of the rock. On smaller stones the Cyanophyta tend to be replaced by filamentous Chlorophyta and diatoms.

In some of the Laurentian lakes in N. America there is a prolific growth of *Cladophora* on the rocks; the thalli grow to lengths of 30 cm and more and when washed up on shore they decay and the whole shore line becomes 'polluted'.[17a]

Although it is reported that the type of rock does not affect the flora it is obvious that there is a difference between the Austrian calcareous and the Swedish non-calcareous epilithic flora. The flora in relation to chemical factors and depth zonation, obviously require much more detailed consideration. It is also clear that some seasonal fluctuations of numbers and species takes place, whilst colonization sequences of exposed rock and the non-Cyanophycean flora of both the rocks and the macroscopic epilithic algae, need to be thoroughly investigated before the epilithic communities can be reliably characterized. The effect of grazing and other factors is relatively unknown.

The epiphytic flora

This flora is found growing on macroscopic plants in the littoral zone where it is exposed to factors similar to those operating on the epilithic flora; these are a variation in water level accompanied by exposure of some plants, varying light intensity, and water movement. Chemical composition of the water and seasonal variations will influence the flora as will the length of life of the macroscopic host plant, its surface and leaf arrangement. The plants at or above high-water level have a sparse flora, which varies with the degree of wetting by spray; this flora is developed on Angiosperms and particularly on Lichens and Bryophytes. In the zone of fluctuating water level the latter two plant groups are often abundant (especially on rocky shores) and rich in epiphytes. On silted shores, small Angiosperms are the main hosts. Below water level the macroscopic Charales, numerous mosses and liverworts and the fern *Pilularia*, the horse-tail *Equisetum*, the Lycophyte *Isoetes* and Angiosperms such as *Potamogeton*, *Littorella*, *Lobelia*, *Myriophyllum*, etc., form the host material. Floating plants such as *Lemna*, Water Lilies, *Azolla*, etc., all possess a rich epiphytic flora.

Two main types of algae are found; the first are the species appressed to the cuticle of the plants, such as *Coleochaete scutata*, and *Protoderma* of the Chaetophorales, *Xenococcus* (Cyanophyta) and numerous diatoms, in particular *Cocconeis*, *Eunotia*, *Rhopalodia* and *Epithemia*. These encrusting forms sometimes coat the entire surface of the host. Between these and on them, the second growth form appears, producing small attachment discs from which either a single cell or a filamentous growth projects. The attaching pad may support the cell(s) of *Synedra* spp. or the zig-zag filaments of *Tabellaria*. The disc may extend into a short or long branched or unbranched mucilage stalk, e.g. *Achnanthes* spp., *Cymbella* spp. and *Gomphonema* spp. The stalks of the two latter species may themselves be host to small *Achnanthes* and *Synedra* spp. Unicells such as *Characium*, *Characiopsis* and *Ophiocytium* are attached by small stalks to the cuticle. Larger filamentous genera attached by a basal disc or by a basal system of creeping filaments are *Oedogonium*, *Bulbochaete*, *Tribonema* and *Stigeoclonium*. On these, numerous epiphytic diatoms may occur, e.g. *Achnanthes*, *Cymbella* and *Gomphonema* species. Another growth form in the epiphytic community is the branching filament system enclosed within thick mucilage and often occurring as macroscopic colonies, *Nostoc* (particularly common on submerged Bryophyta), *Chaetophora*, *Gleotrichia*, and *Tetraspora* (not strictly filamentous). Amongst the weft of epiphytic algae, numerous motile species are found, e.g. flagellates, *Navicula* spp. and also non-motile coccoid species, e.g. *Scenedesmus*, *Pediastrum*, *Cosmarium*, *Euastrum* and other desmids, filaments of *Spirogyra*, *Zygnema* and *Mougeotia*, etc. These are not morphologically adapted to the habitat but are nevertheless often a constant feature of the flora and can be considered a sub-community. This sub-community is also found amongst the leaves of Bryophyta and is also similar to that found amongst epilithic algae; the term metaphyton has been used by Behre for this community (see p. 78).

Very few sociological studies of the epiphytic communities have been made, but there is no doubt that associations can be distinguished, e.g. *Achnanthes/Cocconeis/Epithemia* associations are found on the underside of *Lemna* leaves. *Achnanthes hungarica* is often the dominant on the underside of *Lemna* leaves whilst the roots tend to be colonized by *Eunotia* species. This is a striking example of a host/epiphyte relationship though nothing is known of the factors responsible for such a segregation. In Malham Tarn the *Potamogeton* leaves have an epiphytic association of *Gomphonema* and *Achnanthes*; *Chara aspera* and *C. delicatula* have an association of *Achnanthes/Comphonema* and *Tabellaria flocculosa* with many motile *Navicula cryptocephala* amongst them; *Carex* has a sparse flora of *Achnanthes/Gomphonema/Spirogyra* and on *Fontinalis* there is an *Achnanthes/Cymbella prostrata/Tabellaria flocculosa* population. New plants are rapidly colonized and also there is a great difference in the density of the population on different species; *Carex* and to lesser extent *Chara* have few cells, whilst *Fontinalis* and *Myriophyllum* have a dense flora.

Jørgensen [201] records the most frequent diatoms on *Phragmites* stems and also their seasonal occurrence (Fig. 30).

Autecological studies of *Tabellaria flocculosa* have been made in lakes of the English Lake District, where the distribution of 4 species has been shown to be correlated with alkalinity of the waters.[215, 217] In lakes with alkalinity of 0–1·0, expressed as mg dm^{-3} CaCO$_3$, *T. binalis* occurs; in lakes not exceeding 2·8 *T. quadriseptata* occurs, in waters in which the alkalinity exceeds 2·1 *T. fenestrata* occurs, whilst *T. flocculosa* has the widest range from 0–112. By far the most widespread sp. is *T. flocculosa* as the following Table 2 shows.

Table 2. The number of lakes or tarns (small lakes or ponds) in the English Lake District in which *Tabellaria* species have been found.

(Knudsen, 1954.)

Species	*No. of bodies of water where present*
T. quadriseptata	24
T. fenestrata	58
T. flocculosa	113
T. binalis	2
All spp. absent	7

The only combinations of these species found are

T. fenestrata + *T. flocculosa*

T. quadriseptata + *T. flocculosa*

T. binalis + *T. quadriseptata* + *T. flocculosa*

Thus *T. fenestrata* has never been found with either *T. binalis* or *T. quadriseptata*, suggesting that these may have different ecological requirements and although *T. fenestrata* and *T. quadriseptata* may be found in waters with mean alkalinity in the range of 2·1–2·8, it may be that further chemical analysis of the water (e.g. of the Mg, Na and K contents), may reveal quite different nutrient requirements for the two species. These species are all attached and only rarely is *T. fenestrata* found in the plankton (the main planktonic forms being varieties of *T. flocculosa*). It was found that *T. flocculosa* v. *flocculosa* grew on the submerged shoots of *Phragmites communis* and *Schoenoplectus lacustris* at densities from 1–4500 cells mm^{-2}. A distinct seasonal growth cycle has been recorded for several lakes of which one is illustrated in Fig. 31. This shows the similar cycle on the two different plants and in contrast to some phytoplankton diatoms, high cell densities are recorded in winter, whilst low numbers in June/July correspond with the

depletion of silica below values of 0·5 mg dm⁻³. Other lakes do not show quite
the same sequence and in general there is greater variation in the epiphytic
habitat than in the open water. Experiments on a strain of *T. flocculosa* v.

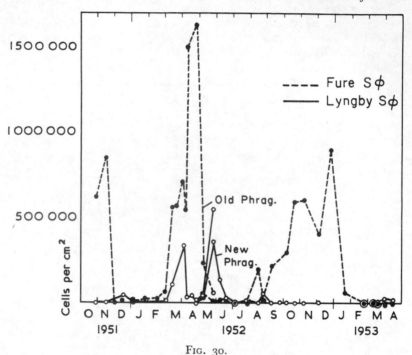

FIG. 30.

The seasonal cycle of epiphytic diatoms on old and new *Phragmites* stems in two
Danish lakes.

(From Jørgensen, 1957.)

flocculosa, grown in bottles suspended in Windermere, resulted in a cell
division rate of less than 2 divisions per week from December to April when
temperature varied between approx. 3°C and 5·5°C, daylength 8–13·5 h,
and radiation 1·25–7·5 kJ cm⁻² week⁻¹.⁵² Thus although a considerable
increase in radiation occurred over the experimental period, there is little
increase in growth at these low temperatures. From mid-April until early
June growth increased from 1·5 to 5·75 divisions, temperature rose from 5° to
13°C, daylength from 13·5 to 17 h and radiation from 11·3 to 5·5 kJ cm⁻²
week⁻¹. Then until September divisions were somewhat higher 5·3–7·1,
temperature was high 17–19°C but daylight decreased (17–13 h) and radiation decreased from 11·3 to 5·5 kJ cm⁻² week⁻¹. From mid-September all
factors and growth rate decreased to the January level. In early summer
there is obvious light saturation, for in autumn when temperature is higher
and light less there is greatest growth, cf. the graph Fig. 31 of the natural

population. The experimental data also suggest that growth is possible in summer when, in nature, a minimum occurs and this confirms Knudsen's view that at that time in nature, the effects of nutrient depletion and to a lesser extent grazing, keep the population low.

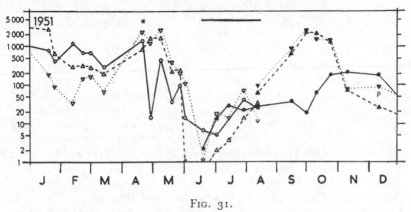

FIG. 31.

Seasonal fluctuation in the density of *Tabellaria flocculosa* on *Phragmites communis* (—○—) and *Schoenoplectus lacustris* (—△—) in Blelham Tarn. Change from open to closed symbols indicates change from old to new plants. Black line above graphs indicates period when silicate concentration was below 0·5 mg dm^{-3}.

(From Knudsen, 1957.)

Growth was at a maximum at 0·5 m except during winter and spring when there was inhibition at this depth and the maximum was at 1 or 2 m. By February growth of *T. flocculosa* v. *flocculosa* is possible to depths below 6 m. Only one week in the year (July 1–8) was suitable for growth at 8 m.

In a study of both phytoplankton and epiphytes, in Danish lakes, it was found that the growth maxima of the two did not coincide and it was assumed that the growth of the plankton had a depressing effect on the epiphytes. The maximum of epiphytes on *Phragmites* stems occurred when the silica content of the lake water was very low and the assumption was made that the diatoms could utilize silica from the stems; from spring to summer there was indeed a decrease in silica content of the stems.[201]

The epipelic flora

There are three distinct components within the algal flora of the sediments. 1. The macroscopic algae rooted in the sediment (e.g. *Chara* and *Nitella*). 2. The non-motile often mucilaginous colonial or filamentous masses which rest on the surface of the sediment and are often visible to the naked eye (e.g. *Aphanothece, Spirogyra, Mougeotia*, etc.). 3. The motile microscopic flora forming a film on and in the surface layer of sediment (e.g. innumerable diatoms, desmids, flagellates, filamentous and thalloid Cyanophyta). This epipelic flora is present on all types of sediment (peat, silt, sand, decaying vegetation, calcium carbonate grains, iron deposits, etc), and is found in the littoral zone of lakes extending down to the lower limit of penetration of photosynthetically available light; this is usually to a greater depth than the lowest depth to which the macrophytic Angiosperms grow. Some of the factors affecting this flora are sediment structure and chemistry, nutrient status of the water, depth and shading, wave action and grazing.

Genera of the Charophyceae grow anchored, by means of branching underground rhizoids in sand and silt of the littoral zone. They form a macroscopic association comparable to that of the Angiosperms, and are frequently included in the descriptions of macroscopic aquatic vegetation. Many reports describe them as forming unstable associations, lasting only a year or so, but in large lakes they are frequently constant over many years and form thick underwater swards. Calcareous waters are more frequently populated by this group, which also extends into brackish and even saline water in the tropics. They are often coated with calcium carbonate and this may be a factor in reducing the epiphytic flora which they support. There is evidence of a vertical zonation of species and they may occur in both shallow and deep water.[426] Observations in Malham Tarn, where dense beds of *Chara* occur some distance from the shore, showed them to have a pronounced effect on the underlying sediment which was a black, reducing, organic mud containing *Chara* fragments and on which the motile epipelic flora is greatly reduced.

The association of algae lying loose on the sediments is somewhat arbitrarily distinguished from the actual sediment community merely by its size and lack of motility. In many lakes, particularly eutrophic waters, it is composed mainly of species of Cyanophyta (*Aphanothece stagnina*, *Nostoc pruniformae*) and some Chlorophyta, e.g. *Cladophora*, which often occurs here as matted balls of filaments. In oligotrophic waters it is more frequent to find loose mucilaginous masses of *Spirogyra*, *Mougeotia*, *Zygnema*, *Ulothrix*, *Microspora*, *Oedogonium*, etc., and intermingled with these are epiphytes and motile species derived from the sediments. The lack of attachment means that these are often transitory associations and they are frequently very contaminated by casual species.

The flora living on the surface of the sediment is composed of species, 90 per cent of which are actively motile, the remainder are probably attached to sand grains by mucilage or are light mucilaginous species which settle slowly after disturbance and so avoid burial. In still water this association can often be seen by the naked eye owing to the colouring of the dense film of swarming species—brown when diatoms, green when Euglenoids or Chlorophyceae (e.g. desmids) and bluish black when Cyanophyta are dominant. Sampling can be achieved by sucking the surface sediment up with a tube or by sinking glass or metal corers into the sediment and then removing the surface layer. The technique described on p. 59 for obtaining soil algae is an extremely efficient means of concentrating the flora which can then be identified and cell counts made;[337] this does however underestimate the non-motile species and only direct observation of the sediment on a slide can be used to record these.

A number of species are present on the sediments of lakes of varying nutrient status (the so-called 'indifferent' species), but this indifference is only a matter of degree and investigation of a very wide series of sediments will reveal a definite tolerance level. Also the range of a species is not synonymous with favourable growth of that same species. Table 3 shows the presence or absence of a few species growing on the sediments of lakes of the English Lake District during eighteen months sampling. Even from the presence or absence data it is obvious that *Caloneis silicula* and *Neidium iridis* are by no means equally abundant over the whole series. More clearly defined are species confined or almost confined to the sediments of low nutrient status, e.g. *Frustulia rhomboides* and *Eucocconeis flexella*. The number of these could be greatly multiplied and there are undoubtedly species which only occur on even more oligotrophic sediments, e.g. *Actinella punctata, Amphicampa hemicyclus, Eunotia bactriana, E. polyglyphus, E. septentrionalis, Fragilaria constricta, F. hungarica, F. polygonata, Tabellaria binalis* and *Tetracyclus*

Table 3. The distribution of some common epipelic species on sediments of the English Lake District. (From Round, 1958.)

| | Increasing nutrient status | | | | | | | | | | | | | | | | | | | | | | |
| | Low | | | | | | | | | | High | | | | | | | | | | | | |
Species	Crum.	Wast.	Enn.	Der.	Brot. (S)	Brot. (N)	Bass.	Lowes.	Ulls. (S)	Butt.	Wind. III	Ryd.	Con.	Wind. II	Elt.	Wind. I	Ulls. (N)	Blel. I	Lough.	Blel. III	Est.	Blel. II	Gras.
Caloneis silicula	13*	7	27	58	61	21	61	80	59	12	60	28	78	55	23	55	43	79	82	69	75	66	5
Neidium iridis	7	7	—	37	31	57	6	13	12	29	37	28	39	7	29	35	—	38	35	13	50	41	22
Frustulia rhomboides	33	40	53	5	—	14	—	—	—	53	—	5	—	—	—	2	—	—	—	—	—	—	—
Eucocconeis flexella	7	—	13	—	—	7	—	—	—	18	—	—	—	—	—	—	—	—	—	—	—	—	—
Neidium hitchcockii	—	—	—	10	—	—	—	—	—	—	20	—	—	2	—	35	—	15	94	—	—	5	—
Stauroneis smithii	—	—	—	—	—	—	11	—	—	—	2	—	—	—	—	22	—	59	—	10	36	23	—
Diploneis ovalis	—	—	—	—	—	—	—	13	6	—	2	—	—	—	—	5	14	20	76	5	86	—	—
Gymnodinium aeruginosum	—	—	—	10	—	—	—	—	7	—	10	24	39	17	24	10	—	26	6	20	29	23	23
Cryptomonas ovata	—	—	—	—	—	—	—	20	12	—	38	12	17	5	—	40	2	20	29	41	71	33	23
Synura uvella	15	—	—	10	—	—	—	—	6	11	13	18	6	13	18	5	—	10	18	13	21	13	18
Holopedium geminata	—	—	—	—	—	—	—	13	—	—	25	6	—	10	—	32	6	15	70	7	36	5	—
Aphanothece stagnina	—	—	—	—	—	—	—	—	—	11	28	—	—	15	—	2	—	14	24	59	7	38	—

* Numbers refer to the number of times a species was encountered in counts over a period of 18 months expressed as % of the possible total.

---

emarginatus which were recorded from some Finnish Lakes;[344] one, *T. binalis*, is recorded from the Lake District but from a tarn. When the ranges of such species are adequately worked out they will be of great value as indicator species and can be used to typify conditions under which sediments were deposited—see Chapter 11, p. 213. Apart from the diatoms, the other most frequent group on oligotrophic sediments are the desmids, many of which

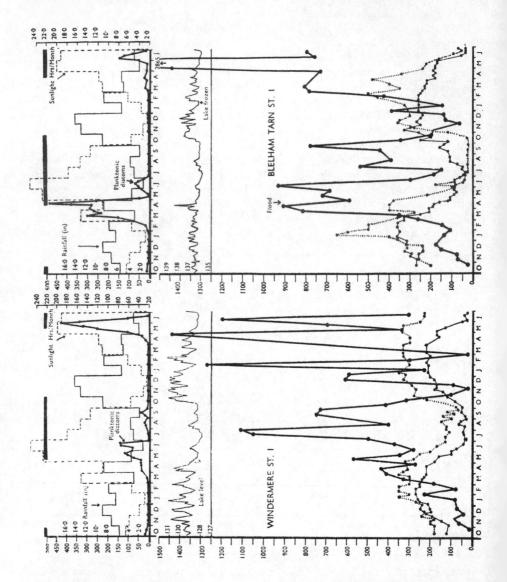

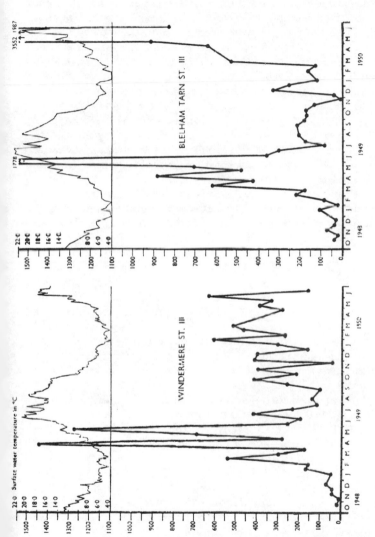

FIG. 32.

The seasonal counts of diatom cells on samples from the littoral sediments of two stations in Winder-mere and one in Blelham Tarn. On the graphs for Windermere Station I and Blelham Tarn Station I the values for nitrate nitrogen (-·-·-) and silicate silica concentrations (——) in the water are also plotted. The scales are the same as those for cell numbers but divided by 100 to give silica in mg dm⁻³ and divided by 1000 to give nitrate in mg dm⁻³. Also plotted as the top of these graphs are the water-level changes for the two lakes. Above this is a combined graph of planktonic diatom cell numbers (——) and histograms for monthly rainfall ☐ and sunlight hours ⋮⋮. The period during which the lakes were stratified is shown thus ■. On the graphs for Windermere Station III and Blelham Station III are plotted the surface water temperatures in °C.

(From Round, 1957.)

are confined to oligotrophic waters. The eutrophic end of the Lake District series also has its 'indicator' species (see Table 3), and it is noteworthy that the flagellate groups and the Cyanophyta play a conspicuous part on these sediments. On even more eutrophic, base rich sediments, e.g. in some loughs in Ireland, species are found which are rare or absent from the English Lake District lakes, e.g. *Mastogloia* spp., *Navicula costulata, N. oblonga, N. tuscula, Cymbella leptoceros, C. ehrenbergii, C. helvetica, C. thumensis, Denticula tenuis, Epithemia intermedia, E. sorex, Nitzschia denticula* and *N. sinuata.*[343a] These are a group of 'indicator' species of base rich conditions. Numerous other examples could be quoted, but these are sufficient to point out the selective effect of the environment on the species of this community.

The physical and chemical nature of the sediments affects the flora, thus the peat sediments in alkaline waters of Malham Tarn are sufficient to influence the epipelic flora, and species such as *Amphora ovalis, Neidium dubium, Navicula pupula. N. placentula, Cyamatopleura solea, C. elliptica, Nitzschia angustata* and *Cymbella ehrenbergii* are common on the calcareous sediment, but not on the peat sediment. The converse is true of *Amphipleura pellucida, Cymbella prostrata* and *C. lanceolata.*[337] In lakes where the difference in sediment structure is not as striking as this, there are still differences although they are minor, so that a single sample usually gives a reasonable picture of the epipelic flora. Differences due to sand: silt ratios can be detected; two bays in Windermere, one silted (Pull Wyke) and one sandy (Sandy Wyke) are colonized by different species of diatoms, whilst Cyanophyta and Euglenophyceae are markedly more abundant in Pull Wyke. These and many other minor variations occur and reflect the physiological tolerances of species in nature and the sensitive reaction of many species to fine changes in the environment. Since sediments are rarely homogeneous over large areas, there is almost certainly a mosaic of associations but as yet no attempts have been made to unravel these. No autecological studies have yet been made on species of the epipelic flora.

As in the plankton and attached communities there is a distinct seasonal pattern of growth. Fig. 32 shows the seasonal growth of the diatom population in two lakes in the English Lake District, together with some of the habitat factors.[341] The peak-growing period is the spring or at some stations early summer. After the spring peak(s) there is often a smaller July/October growth followed by low numbers prior to the build up of the population during late winter and early spring. The variation from station to station is related to the particular position, depth, sediment type, etc. The low populations during October–December coincide with the lowest values of incident light, which is almost certainly a limiting factor at this time. The fall in population numbers in spring occurs whilst nitrate nitrogen and silicate silica concentrations are falling, but is not always as rapid as is the decrease in the phytoplankton. In some habitats it is probable that silica is more readily obtained from the sediments than from others.

The other algal groups also have a seasonal growth pattern but only the

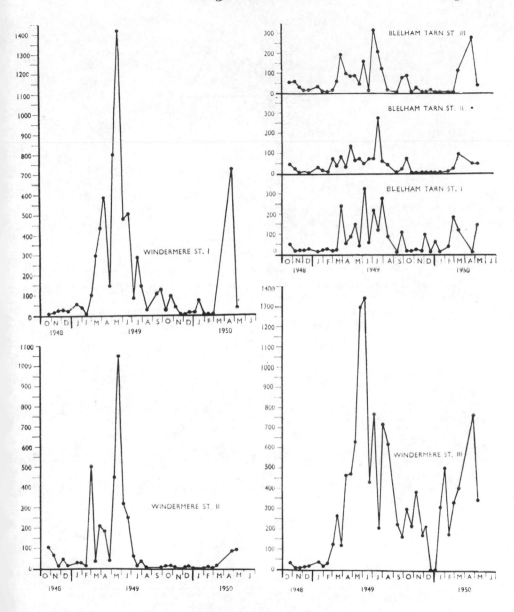

Fig. 33.

The seasonal growth of colonies and filaments (combined) of epipelic Cyanophyta at three stations in Windermere and Blelham Tarn.

(From Round, 1961.)

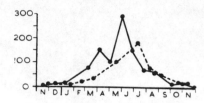

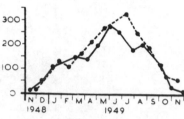

Fig. 34.

The seasonal growth of the epipelic Cyanophyta (upper graphs) and Bacillariophyceae (lower graphs) in Windermere (—•—) and Blelham Tarn (---•---). Data calculated from counts at depths from 0·5 to 6 m at each sampling date thus giving a measure of the total seasonal productivity.

(From Round, 1961.)

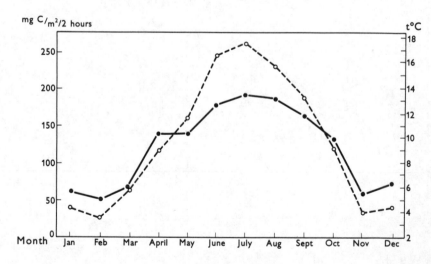

Fig. 35.

The average rate of potential gross production of the microbenthos in a Danish fjord. Continuous line is the rate of production. Broken line is temperature.

(From Grøntved, 1960.)

Cyanophyta were abundant enough to show this clearly (Fig. 33). The difference in productivity between Windermere and Blelham Tarn is clearly shown. In general the major growth peak occurs in spring coincident with that of the diatoms.

The seasonal growth cycles vary somewhat with depth, the tendency being for the peak to occur later in the season at the lower depths. This is to be expected from a consideration of light penetration. Below 6 m growth is greatly reduced and below 8 m it is practically nil in these lakes. The growth of algae on the sediments was greatest around 3 m depth, above this wave action tends to remove cells and below this, lack of light probably reduces the population. However there are other factors also involved, such as redistribution of sediments by water currents, e.g. there is evidence that current scour reduces the flora at a depth of 4 m in these lakes. Fig. 34 shows the total cell counts for the six stations at 1–5 m in the two lakes during the year's cycle, illustrating that the total growth on the littoral sediments follows the general seasonal pattern of incident light and temperature. Growth of this community has also been measured in some Danish fjords using a radioactive carbon incorporation technique and the overall seasonal pattern obtained in this way (Fig. 35) agrees well with the data from cell counts.[138]

Epipsammic algae

A host of small diatom species belonging to the genera *Opephora, Fragilaria, Achnanthes*, etc., attach to sand grains and in many lakes, especially in N. America, form a very important element of the total benthic flora.

Endophytic algae

A few species of Cyanophyta (*Nostoc, Anabaena*) occur in spaces within Bryophyta, e.g. *Anthoceros* and in roots of Angiosperms, e.g. *Gunnera* and *Cycas*. Little is known of their distribution or function.

Epizooic algae

Attached algae, e.g. *Stigeoclonium* grow on the shells of molluscs, whilst on turtles (*Emys, Chelydra, Chrysemys*, etc.) the genera *Basicadia, Dermatophyton* and various *Oscillatoria* species are found. A few algae are reported to grow on fish possibly after injury although the hold fast of the algae is reported to penetrate the bone.

Endozooic algae

The occurrence of *Chlorella* cells in *Hydra viridis* and *Paramoecium bursaria* is well known. The symbiotic algae secrete maltose which is utilized by the animal cells. Green algae also occur in the freshwater sponges (*Spongilla, Meyenia* and *Tubella*) but little is known of their biology.

5   Ecology: marine

In the marine environment the range of habitats is more restricted than in freshwater; the algae occupy two main regions, the surface mass of water and the narrow littoral zone adjacent to the land. The oceans cover approximately 70 per cent of the earth's surface and throughout this area, the algae are distributed and are the primary producers. Thus they are a vital link in the productivity of the oceans, where their distribution, the composition of the communities, their seasonal growth, etc., are of great importance. In addition they play a major role in the chemical exchanges between the atmosphere, the water and the sediments. Biogeochemical transformations of major elements, such as calcium and silica, are associated with algae of both open waters and of the littoral zone, particularly in tropical and semi-tropical regions where reef formation is an important feature. The algae of the open ocean (pelagic algae) are microscopic floating species (with the exception of restricted collections of macrophytic species maintaining themselves in open waters, e.g. the *Sargassum* species of the Sargasso Sea), whereas, in the littoral zone, the dominant algae are the macroscopic Rhodophyta, Phaeophyta and Chlorophyta, almost all of which are attached to rocks, whilst on and amongst these and on the rocks and sediments, non-motile and motile microscopic species abound and undoubtedly contribute greatly to the productivity of this region.

1. THE OPEN WATER

Phytoplankton

As in freshwaters the phytoplankton of the oceans is composed of large celled species which are taxonomically fairly well known and the smaller nannoplankton which is very incompletely studied, although in cell volume they may be equal to or in excess of the larger forms. The oceans are traversed by large and small currents; each water mass has its own chemical and physical characteristics, and as a consequence its phytoplankton varies in species composition and productivity. There are distinct Arctic and Antarctic groups of species, although very many of the common phytoplankton species are recorded from almost all oceans of the world. A distinction is frequently drawn between the plankton in the waters adjacent to coasts (neritic) and that of the open water (oceanic). The neritic phytoplankton tends to be contaminated by species derived from the non-planktonic littoral communities, e.g. species of *Grammatophora*, *Licmophora*, *Actinoptychus*, etc., but also supports species whose growth is favoured by the higher nutrient and particularly higher organic content of the inshore waters. Some species of the neritic plankton may pass through stages during which resting spores are formed; these sediment out and only in shallow water will their products be capable of resuspension. The neritic plankton certainly appears to contain a higher proportion of strongly silicified, i.e. heavy, species (e.g. *Coscinodiscus*) compared with the oceanic. Some of the oceanic species do not develop to the same extent in shallow water and it may be that here the increased nutrient status and increased turbidity affects them adversely.

The major groups of the marine phytoplankton are the Desmophyceae, Dinophyceae, Bacillariophyta and Haptophyta. Obviously there are genera which are more important than others in some oceanic regions or in certain seasons. In general the important constituent genera of the Desmophyceae are *Exuviaella, Prorocentrum, Phalacroma, Dinophysis, Ornithocercus* and *Histioneis*, and of the Dinophyceae *Gymnodinium, Peridinium, Gonyaulax* and *Ceratium*. Conspicuous planktonic genera of the Bacillariophyta—Centrales are *Thalassiosira, Sceletonema, Stephanopyxis, Coscinodiscus, Planktoniella, Corethron, Eucampia, Hemidiscus, Guinardia, Rhizosolenia, Chaetoceros, Bacteriastrum, Ditylum* and *Biddulphia*, and of the Pennales *Fragilaria, Fragilariopsis, Thalassiothrix, Thalassionema, Asterionella, Pseudoeunotia, Tropidonesis* and *Nitzschia* (see Fig. 36). These constitute the bulk of the large phytoplanktonic species which are obvious in ordinary net or centrifuged samples. The Haptophyta are important constituents of the net-passing nannoplankton. Two other conspicuous groups are the Prymnesiales (Coccolithineae or Coccolithophoridaceae), *Discosphaera, Syracosphaera, Coccolithus, Pontosphaera* and the Dictyochineae (Silicoflagellineae), *Dictyocha*. In addition to these genera with skeletal material of calcium carbonate and silica respectively, there are a number of other genera of the Haptophyta in the plankton, e.g. the colonial *Phaeocystis* and numerous, as yet incompletely known, flagellates. Genera of other groups are extremely rare, only *Halosphaera* and *Pterosperma* (Prasinophyta) and *Trichodesmium* (Cyanophyta) are regularly recorded. The spheres of the non-motile *Halosphaera* tend to float to the surface and may be missed if only the sedimented plankton is examined.

Owing to the enormous areas involved, the geographical distribution of most species is undetermined, an aspect complicated by varying seasonal and depth distribution of species. A quantitative study adds yet another variable since so-called cosmopolitan species may be abundant in some areas but scarce and near their limit of tolerance in others. It is also suggested that geographically separated races may occur, so that species apparently common to different regions may yet represent discrete physiological units.[30] Current transport may also carry species out of the range in which they are actively growing. Some examples of distribution studies will emphasize some of the factors involved. For instance *Thalassiosira antarctica* appears to be circumpolar in the Antarctic, indeed most Antarctic species probably are due to the circulatory current system and absence of land barriers in this region.[371] 228 records of this species showed that it is stenothermal ($-1 \cdot 77°C$ to $3 \cdot 49°C$ mean at $-0 \cdot 05°C$) and stenohaline ($32 \cdot 61$ to $34 \cdot 54\text{‰}$).

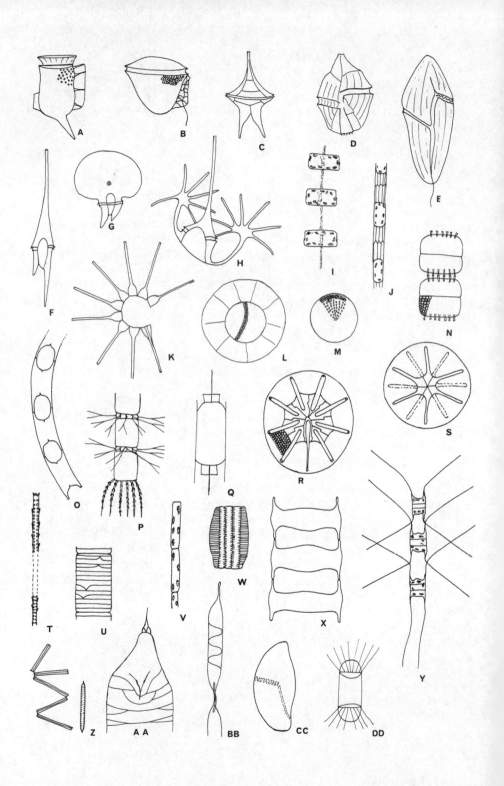

This range of temperature and salinity, possibly controls the Antarctic flora south of the Antarctic convergence; few dinoflagellates and perhaps no Coccolithineae can withstand these conditions. Similarly in the Arctic seas *Thalassiosira hyalina* is confined to the cold water and cold currents and is absent from the region south of Iceland and in the eastern half of the Norwegian Sea where the warmer Gulf Stream currents enter. It is also recorded from the Arctic Pacific region, but further data is required on this. Like its Antarctic counterpart it is stenothermal ($-1\cdot35°$C to $9\cdot03°$C mean $2\cdot3°$C) and stenohaline ($33\cdot88‰$ mean). The Arctic flora, unlike the Antarctic, has few species which are dominant in the region owing to the splitting up of the Arctic waters by land barriers and to the northward flow of warm currents carrying species from temperate and tropical regions which tend to swamp the Arctic elements of the flora. A circumtropical distribution is exemplified by *Planktoniella sol*, which also extends up to 60°N. in the Gulf Stream and is a good indicator of Gulf water. It is a eurythermal species (mean $19\cdot2°$C) and stenohaline (mean $35\cdot71‰$, a high salinity associated with tropical waters). *P. sol.* may have a greater temperature tolerance than most tropical species; it tends also to be oceanic rather than neritic. As a cosmopolitan species *Thalassionema nitzschioides* is quoted.[371] Records have appeared in the literature of bipolar species, i.e. occurring in polar waters but not in the tropics, e.g. *Thalassiothrix longissima* and *Rhizosolenia hebetata* f. *semispina*, but it is now known that these are also present in tropical zones, the former having been found abundant in the warm waters of the Gulf of California where it forms large blooms. Unlike the zooplankton, it is unlikely that the phytoplankton migrates through the tropics in the cold water currents below the sub-surface layers since these are below the limit of light penetration and hence of photosynthesis. Nevertheless it is surprising that no species have been accidentally transported, since it would seem that conditions are similar in regard to temperature, salinity, etc., in both Arctic and Antarctic waters.

The distribution of *Ceratium* species in the Atlantic from approximately 65°N. to 10°S. and in the Pacific from approximately 55°N. to 40°S. has been plotted from samples taken during the 1928-9 cruise of the *Carnegie* and illustrates the relationship between species composition, water masses and

---

FIG. 36. EXAMPLES OF MARINE PLANKTONIC ALGAE.

A. *Dinophysis*; B. *Phalacroma*; C. *Peridinium*; D. *Gonyaulax*; E. *Gyrodinium*; F. *Ceratium furca*; G. *Ceratium cephalotum*; H. *Ceratium ranipes*; I. *Thalassiosira*; J. *Sceletonema*; K. *Asterionella*; L. *Planktoniella*; M. *Actinocyclus*; N. *Stephonopyxis*; O. *Eucampia*; P. *Bacteriastrum*; Q. *Ditylum*; R. *Asteromphalus*; S. *Asterolampra*; T. *Thalassiothrix*; U. *Guinardia*; V. *Leptocylindrus*; W. *Pseudoeunotia*; X. *Climacodium*; Y. *Chaetoceros*; Z. *Thalassionema*, colony and single cell in valve view; AA, BB. End of a *Rhizosolenia* cell and two cells of a colony; CC. *Hemidiscus*; DD. *Corethron*.

(After Schiller and original.)

water chemistry.[136] On the basis of the distribution of the *Ceratium* spp. several regions were distinguished, e.g. Cold North Atlantic and Warm North Atlantic. In the former there are few species (14) but high cell numbers in water which is below 16°C and with phosphate content above 20 mg/PO_4/m^3. Of the species in this group, *C. lineatum*, *C. macroceros* and *C. arcticum* were designated as subpolar; also present at more than five out of eleven stations were the cosmopolitan *C. furca*, *C. fusus*, *C. horridum* and *C. tripos* v. *atlanticum*. Subdominant to these were species which are tolerant tropical forms carried in by the Gulf Stream (cf. the diatom flora). Similar data[151] shows a very sparse and species poor *Ceratium* (indeed Dinoflagellate) flora for the cold waters of the Antarctic. In warm Atlantic water south of 40°N. (temperature about 20°C and phosphate concentration generally below 10 mg) 46 species were found with average number of species per station 10–33; the lower averages being recorded in the Caribbean Sea. The species were all tolerant, intolerant tropical, or cosmopolitan. A similar subdivision of the Pacific species of *Ceratium* was possible. The number of species in the regions tended to confirm earlier data with small numbers (0–10) in the subpolar regions, succeeded by a transitional zone (11–20) around 40°N., whilst south of this a rich flora is developed (21–30 species); smaller regions of very high numbers of species per station (31–40) north of the Sargasso Sea and on either side of the equator in the Pacific were also recorded. No correlation was found between distribution and salinity, but the number of species is lowest in regions of high phosphate concentration and vice versa; this may not be a direct effect of phosphate but of some associated factor. The species were grouped according to mean surface temperature giving three groups, subpolar, cosmopolitan and tropical; the latter was subdivided into intolerant tropical, i.e. species restricted to temperatures above 19°C, slightly tolerant, i.e. species extending into the transition zone and tolerant tropical, i.e. forms carried by current far from the tropical zone yet still capable of growth. The most striking displacement of species was noticed in the great current systems which were crossed by the ship, i.e. the Gulf Stream, Kuroshio, California and Humboldt currents. All these carry water of a given physico-chemical nature and a characteristic *Ceratium* flora into regions of different water with a different flora. On the other hand, the equatorial currents had little effect on species composition and cell numbers probably because they carry water to regions of similar climatic conditions.

Eight species of *Ceratium* were found to be confined to the Pacific where all the Atlantic species were also present. These eight species were found to be tropical forms or species absent from stations with temperatures less than 20°C. They may be species which have evolved in the warm Pacific and cannot reach the Atlantic via the Bering Strait or around Cape Horn since in both regions water temperature is too low. The Atlantic forms could all reach the Pacific via the warm water around the Cape of Good Hope and across the Indian Ocean, the currents being predominantly west to east. Isolation of the subspecies in the cold waters of the two oceans has also

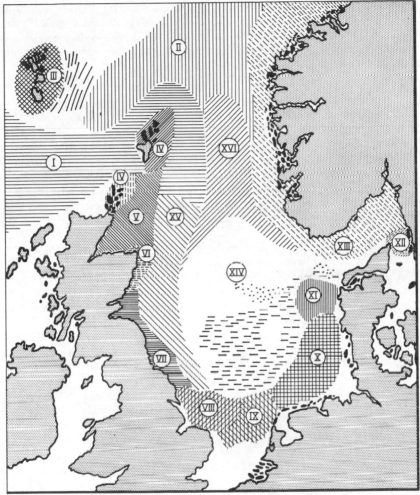

FIG. 37. PHYTOPLANKTON ZONES OF THE NORTH SEA.

For description see text.

(From Braarud *et al.*, 1953.)

occurred since the only connection is via the Arctic Sea (under ice for most of the year); a journey which does not seem to be feasible.

Transport beneath the permanent ice may be possible for short periods since on melting of the surface snow, increased light penetration results and a phytoplankton has been found to bloom under the Arctic ice[367] but the distances are probably too great for active transport of species unadapted to periods of low light intensity.

The North Sea has been intensively worked and the phytoplankton shown to be a good indicator of the various water masses. Braarud *et al*.[30a] described the communities of the various currents and eddies of this complicated area (see Fig. 37). The water masses are characterized by the following species and conditions.

I. Inflowing Atlantic water. *Coccolithus huxleyi* and *Exuviaella baltica*. A sparse flora.

II. Local Atlantic water. *Sceletonema costatum, Thalassiosira gravida*.

III. Faero Isles. Rich diatom population. *T. gravida, S. costatum, Chaetoceros debilis* and other spp., *Nitzschia delicatissima* and *Coccolithus huxleyi*.

IV. Shetland and Orkney Islands. Many diatom species, *Asterionella japonica, C. debilis, C. decipiens, T. gravida* and *S. costatum*.

V. *T. gravida* was the major species.

VI. Coastal water, off Rattray Head. *Rhizosolenia fragilissima*.

VII. Rich diatom flora in the coastal current. *A. japonica, Chaetoceros* spp. and *N. delicatissima*.

VIII. Coastal water off the R. Humber and the Wash. *Cylindrotheca (Nitzschia) clostrium* mixed with *A. japonica* and *Chaetoceros danicus*.

IX. Turbulent waters of the Southern Bight. Poor vegetation. *C. closterium* in small numbers and rich in other benthic species, e.g. *Bellerochea malleus, Biddulphia* spp., *Campylosira cymbelliformis, Cymatosira belgica, Navicula membranacea*.

X, XI. Coastal waters off German and Danish coasts. Numerous diatoms in particular *A. japonica* and *C. debilis* and further off shore *Cerataulina bergoni, Eucampia zoodicus* and *Phaeocystis*. XI was distinguished from X by an occurrence of *Guinardia flaccida*.

XII. Kattegat. The dominant alga was *Chaetoceros tortissimum*.

XIII. Skagerak and Norwegian coastal current. Extremely low numbers of diatoms (*Chaetoceros compressus, N. delicatissima, Leptocylindrus danicus* and *R. fragilissima*). Richer in Dinoflagellates, *Ceratium* spp., *Exuviaella baltica* and *Peridinium trochoideum*.

XIV. Central North Sea and Dogger Bank. A poor flora of *Rhizosolenia imbricata* v. *shrubsolei*. There may have been a lack of nutrients in the thermally stratified water of this region.

XV. South flowing Atlantic water. Poor production, increasing slightly to the south as mixing with water on either side occurs *C. debilis, C. decipiens, C. borealis, Thalassiosira bioculata, N. delicatissima, Exuviaella baltica* and *Coccolithus huxleyi*.

XVI. Mixed water of the N. North Sea. A large number of mixed species; *A. japonica* prominent in the north and *C. furcellatus* and *C. tortissimum* in the south.

The close relationship between the flora and the currents is clearly demonstrated, as is also the characteristic vegetation of the neritic regions in particular off the Wash (VIII) where a common diatom of the littoral sediment, *Cylindrotheca closterium*, occurs. It is interesting that this widespread species is also recorded as a neritic, ice-edge species in a classification of Antarctic phytoplankton.

Long term records of the phytoplankton of the North Sea have also been made using a continuous plankton sampler towed behind ships on regular routes.[261] Examples of the data obtained are given in Figs. 38 and 39 which show that distinct patches of plankton occur, although the production of such regions varies considerably from year to year (cf. the data on freshwater plankton, Fig. 19, p. 77).

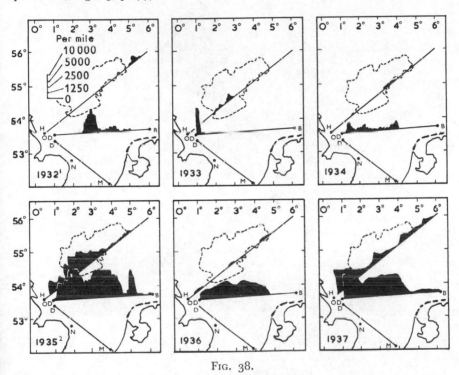

FIG. 38.

The maximal quantities of *Rhizosolenia styliformis* in numbers per mile recorded in different years along three lines across the North Sea. Note the preponderance of cells in the central zone where the graphs are blacked in.

(From Lucas, 1944.)

The phytoplankton flora of water masses also varies with depth. The above results of Braarud *et al.* are only comparable because they were taken at known depths and within a short space of time. The occurrence of *Ceratium* species at particular depths has been known for some time and is well authenticated. Nielsen[295] found that about one-third of the *Ceratium* species occurring in the Southern Pacific were deep water 'shade forms.' In plankton rich waters, where light penetration is reduced, the 'shade forms' were found nearer the surface. These forms tend to have thinner cell walls and are packed with chromatophores which often fill the horns, especially of the expanded type, e.g. *C. platycorne*. None of the species with expanded horns occurs in the surface water, so that the theory suggesting that these are flotation devices is erroneous. Graham and Bronikovsky [136] consider that rather than a phototactic migration, a movement to deeper nutrient rich zones may be involved, since in the summer the nutrients are often depleted in

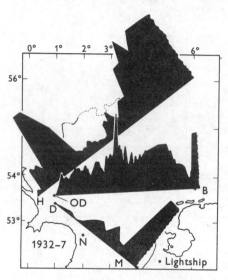

FIG. 39.

The maximal quantities of Dinoflagellates in numbers per mile recorded by continuous plankton recorder along three lines across the North Sea.

(From Lucas, 1944.)

the upper zone of the ocean, indeed Nielsen observed that the 'shade species' are all warm oceanic forms and therefore distributed in the regions where thermal and chemical stratification is often acute and continuous. Owing to the difficulty of occupying ocean stations for any length of time, data on the seasonal stratification of phytoplankton is sparse. Two examples may be quoted, one in cold water at a weather ship station in the Norwegian Sea at 66°N. and 2°E.[139] and the other in warm semi-tropical waters of the North Central Sargasso Sea 35°N. and 48°W.[335] Fig. 40 shows the vertical distribution in the Norwegian Sea during a year's observations, from which it is seen that the algae are fairly uniformly dispersed down to 75 m during winter, spring and autumn, when mixing of the water mass prevented any surface increase. During summer the temperature of the upper water increased and a thermocline developed in May/June at 25–50 m depth allowing increase in cell numbers. Cooling commenced in August and the thermocline was depressed and finally broke down in October. This sequence is very similar to that in many temperate lakes. The dinoflagellates do not appear to have shown any characteristic vertical zonation, confirming the view that only warm oceanic dinoflagellate species exhibit this. During summer, numbers were slightly lower in the 0–10 m region than below 10 m;

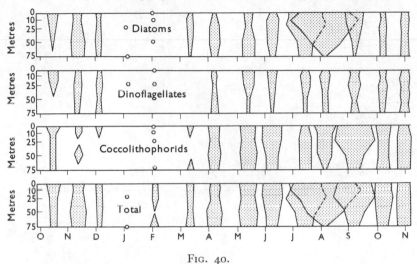

FIG. 40.

The vertical distribution of the phytoplankton in the North Sea during one year's sampling.

(From Halldal, 1953.)

this feature has been frequently observed (cf. Fig. 28). In the N. Central Sargasso Sea, the vertical distribution showed an increase in diatom cell numbers in passing from the surface downwards to maxima at 50 or 100 m.[335] The reduction of the surface population was most marked in summer and autumn suggesting a rapid sinking rate at this time. Algae other than diatoms had a surface maximum in autumn and winter (Fig. 41).

Important data relating to the productivity of oceanic waters, in different regions and at different depths has been obtained from measurements of photosynthesis in closed bottles suspended in the sea; the oxygen production of mixed or unialgal cultures in the bottles is determined by the Winkler method. Results from pure cultures of *Coscinodiscus excentricus* grown in bottles suspended in the English Channel, compared with similar cultures in blackened bottles, showed that the oxygen production was greatest at a depth of 5–10 m, followed by a steady fall down to a depth of 40 m. Above 5 m the oxygen production was approximately half that in the 5–10 m zone.[197] Similar results have been obtained for *Chaetoceros affinis*.[390] Graph Fig. 42 shows the light saturation effect at depths between 5–10 m and the high light inhibition effect from 0–5 m which was not reproducible under fluorescent light in the laboratory. The light inhibition effect may depend on the spectral composition of the light in shallow water. The higher rates of photosynthesis in the sea at light saturation compared with those in the laboratory, probably result from the higher temperature during the sea

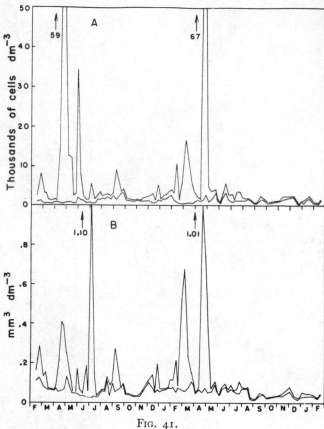

FIG. 41.

The seasonal cycle of phytoplankton in the north central Sargasso Sea. A. Mean number of cells in upper 150 m exclusive of small nannoplankton. Upper curve, total cell count; lower curve, non-diatom fraction. B. Upper curve, total estimated phytoplankton; lower curve, nannoplankton and other non-diatom volumes.

(From Riley, 1957.)

experiments. Using radioactive tracers it is possible to measure the incorporation of carbon into the organic matter of the cells during photosynthesis. Assuming that isotopic $C^{14}O_2$ is incorporated at the same rate as $C^{12}O_2$ it is possible by adding known amounts of the former to a solution containing known amounts of the latter to follow the incorporation of carbon into the

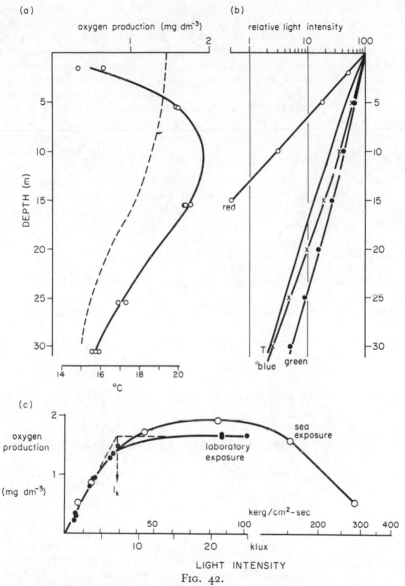

FIG. 42.

The variation of phytosynthetic rate of *Chaetoceros affinis* (solid line) and temperature (broken line) with depth (a). Light penetration in the red, blue, green spectral region and total energy (T) (b). The variation of phosynthetic rate with light intensity obtained from the sea and laboratory experiments (c).

(From Talling, 1960.)

cells. A solution of $Na_2C^{14}O_3$ is usually used. The phytoplankton is allowed to photosynthesize in a mixture of the two, then filtered out and the amount of ^{14}C assimilated, determined by measuring the β-radiation of the plankton. This technique has been used with mixed plankton samples and photosynthesis depth curves obtained, similar to those determined by measurement of oxygen production;[197] the compensation point was at the depth to which approximately 1 per cent of surface illumination penetrated. A daily periodicity in the rate of carbon fixation by oceanic phytoplankton has been noted with a maximum before midday and a minimum around 1900 hours, so that the time at which the experimental data is obtained may affect the results.[81]

The ^{14}C technique has also been used to determine the primary production in different oceanic regions, since it may be a more meaningful measure than cell counts. Figures for the Eastern Pacific show very variable surface production in mg (C) m^{-3} day^{-1} with high values off the coast of Central America, low values further out to sea and extremely high values off the Aleution Islands. Comparisons with chlorophyll a extraction values, show fair agreement and high cell counts are recorded for the region off Central America but not off Alaska;[183] other workers have however reported very large growths in sub-Arctic waters.

Very variable algal productivities were found in oceanic regions during the cruise of the *Galathea*.[378] Again using ^{14}C techniques, four classes of oceanic production were distinguished in tropical and subtropical zones. (1) Daily productivity 0·5–3 g (C) m^{-2} day^{-1}. High productivity associated with considerable admixture of nutrient rich deep water into the surface waters, e.g. Benguela Current. (2) 0·2–0·5 g (C) m^{-2} day^{-1}. Moderate productivity in regions with a fairly steady admixture of nutrient rich water, e.g. in the regions of divergence caused by Equatorial Counter Currents. (3) 0·1 g (C) m^{-2} day^{-1}. Low productivity in regions where inflow of nutrient rich water is slow owing to turbulent mixing only, e.g. much of the tropical and subtropical ocean. (4) 0·05 g (C) m^{-2} day^{-1}. Very low productivity in regions of old, nutrient poor waters, e.g. Central Sargasso Sea. This latter figure is lower than that given by Riley[335] for the North Central Sargasso Sea (0·15 g (C) m^{-2} day^{-1}) but it is clear from Riley's data that there is admixture of new water into the northern area which would put the region into Steeman-Nielsen's group 3. The *Galathea* data on daily and annual carbon production showed a positive correlation with the phytoplankton as measured by cell counts and also with zooplankton, colour of the sea and phosphate concentration. Data for northern and Arctic waters give relatively high productivity figures, e.g. 0·4–1·4 g (C) m^{-2} day^{-1} in the region between Norway and Greenland.[21a] Attempts have been made to construct maps of oceanic productivity (Plate 8, p. 89 of Gessner[123]), from which it is clear that the annual production of carbon per m^2 is low ($<$50 g (C) m^{-2} day^{-1}) in the central subtropical and tropical oceans. A tongue of higher productivity reaches almost across the Central Pacific along the Equator from Central America. Coastal waters are all more productive and between these and the central oceans pro-

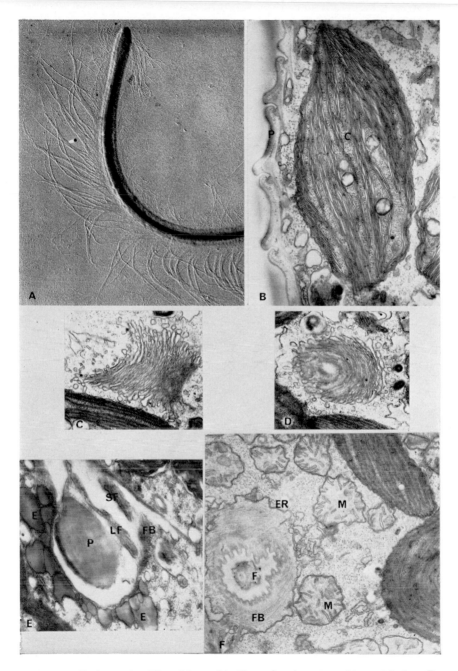

PLATE 5. *Euglena*. **A:** Tip of long flagellum showing row of lateral hairs. **B:** Section through the pellicale (P) and a chloroplast (C). **C & D:** Two Golgi bodies (Dictyosomes) sectioned in different planes. **E:** Transverse section of the canal showing the short flagellum (SF) and the long flagellum (LF) with its photorecepter (P), fibrils (FB) surrounding the canal and vesicles of the eyespot (E). **F:** Transverse section of the canal containing a flagellum (F). Note the convoluted wall of the canal and the fibrils (FB) surrounding it and delimited from the general cytoplasm by endoplasmic reticulum (ER). Several mitochondria (M) are present showing the cristae in section and in surface view. (Electron-micrographs kindly supplied by Dr. G. F. Leedale.)

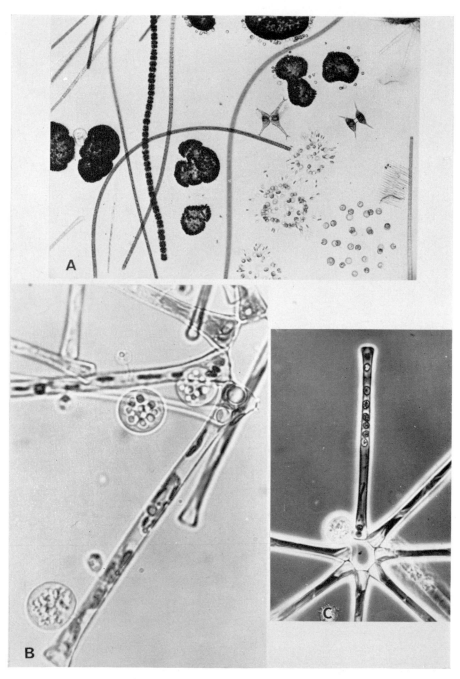

PLATE 6. **A:** Freshwater phytoplankton containing colonial and filamentous Cyanophyta, desmids, diatoms, colonial and epiphytic green algae. **B:** Colonies of *Asterionella* infected by chytrids. **C:** Phase contrast photomicrograph of *Asterionella* infected by a chytrid. (Photographs kindly supplied by Dr. H. Canter-Lund.)

ductivity decreases. Around the Arctic and Antarctic, there are bands of high productivity (50–100 g (C) m^{-2} year^{-1}) increasing to a maximum (200–400 g (C) m^{-2} year^{-1}) in temperate waters and then decreasing again into the subtropics. These figures, although only approximations, are in agreement with much of the early data on phosphate and nitrate distribution, phytoplankton cell numbers and zooplankton volumes. Comparison of these values with those for the land is difficult and early workers suggested that productivities were of a similar order. Gessner[123] suggests that per area oceanic production is about one-third of that on the land; however the ocean surface is about 2·5 times that of the land, which brings the total productions to approximately similar figures.

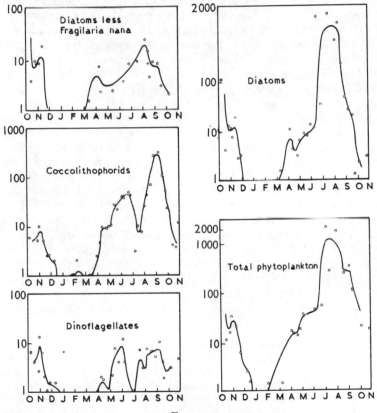

FIG. 43.

The seasonal growth cycles of the phytoplankton in the North Sea.

(From Halldal, 1953.)

Seasonal fluctuations in cell numbers and species composition occur in the phytoplankton of the seas, even in the tropics where climatic changes are less pronounced. Data for the N. Sargasso Sea, indicates that there is only a single spring (April) burst of growth (see Fig. 41). It is suggested that the spring increase occurs when mixing is reduced by temperature stratification and that earlier in the year cells do not remain in the photic zone long enough to build up a large population. The observed increases in population were sufficient to utilize the available phosphate and nitrate in the water (which was at a very low concentration) and subsequent to the spring growth, nutrient replenishment was at a minimum, hence the lack of large growths. Seasonal growth in the Norwegian Sea has also been recorded;[139] between December and March growth was insignificant due to low light intensity and the onset of the spring growth was later and less abrupt than in the semi-tropical zone of the Sargasso Sea. The growth peaks (Fig. 43) occurred late in the year, diatoms in July/August, Coccolithophorids and dinoflagellates in June/July and again in September/October. The occurrence of autumn growth peaks is reminiscent of temperate freshwater plankton. The extended growing period coincided with the presence of a thermocline and although only isolated chemical analyses were made, there must have been a fair supply of nutrient rich water. The decrease in midsummer and subsequent recovery in the autumn may have been due to partial depletion of nutrients followed by replenishment as autumnal mixing occurred, coincident with the depression of the thermocline. The seasonal cycles of individual species were also recorded (Fig. 43) and show a series of diatom and dinoflagellate maxima at later and later dates during summer and autumn, but with maxima of all but one coccolithophorid species (*C. pelagicus*) during late August/early September. *C. pelagicus* in fact also had a second maximum at the same time as the other species. Another interesting feature of Halldal's survey is the difference in species composition during each autumn sampling period. This is an effect of mass movement of water and its associated flora, thus in November, 1948, the diatom species are those of the Atlantic water around the Faroe/Shetland channel and in October, 1949, *Ceratium* spp., from the Norwegian coastal water spread into the sampling region; in 1948 these complications were absent.

The factors affecting the distribution and growth of the marine phyto-

---

FIG. 44a. SOME MARINE LITTORAL SPECIES.

A. *Rhabdonema*; B. *Achnanthes*; C. *Striatella*; D. *Licmophora*; E. *Biddulphia*; F. *Navicula* in mucilage tube; G. *Triceratium*; H. *Bacillaria*; I. *Porolithon*; J. Cells of fragment of *Porphyra* thallus; K. *Amphidinium*; L. *Plumaria*; M. Three stages in the development of a thallus of *Bangia*; N. Part of a branch of *Plumaria*;* O. *Chylocladia*; P, Q. *Griffithsia*, Q being a much enlarged tip of a branch; R. Three parts of a *Polysiphonia* thallus. Uppermost being the bifurcating apex; S. *Plocamium*; T. *Centroceras*; U. *Gelidium*; V. *Lomentaria*; W. *Champia*; X. *Odonthalia*; Y. *Caloglossa*; Z. *Gastroclonium*; AA. *Liagora*; BB. *Hypnea*; CC. *Spyridia*.

(After Børgesen, Taylor, and original.)

* Most of the succeeding figure are of fragments of these larger algae.

plankton are a complex of physical (light, temperature, viscosity, current velocity, and turbidity), chemical (nitrate, phosphate, silicate, organic factors) and biological features (growth rate, interaction, grazing, etc.). The gross correlation between nutrient status and organic production suggests that nutrients are a limiting factor particularly in tropical and semi-tropical regions.

2. THE LITTORAL REGION

The junction between land and sea, where many large algal groups are confined, is a complex region of great algal productivity, where the habitats are numerous, the effects of man and animals on algae are often pronounced and where there is considerable confusion in nomenclature both of habitats and algae. On the last point a stand, albeit rashly, must be taken, in the hope that some order can be brought into the subsequent discussion.

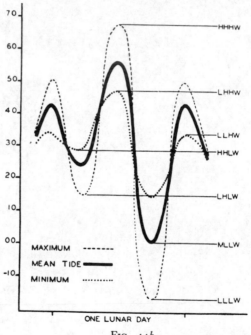

Fig. 44*b*.

Tide levels in feet above or below mean lower low-water level at San Francisco, showing the complexity of tidal heights and hence tidal cover of the shore when there are two high and two low tides of differing height. HHHW = Highest of higher high tide; LHHW = Lowest of higher high tide; LLHW = Lowest of lower high tide; HHLW = Highest high of lowest tide; LHLW = Lowest of higher low tide; MLLW = Mean of lower low tide; LLLW = Lowest of lower low tide.

(From Doty, 1946.)

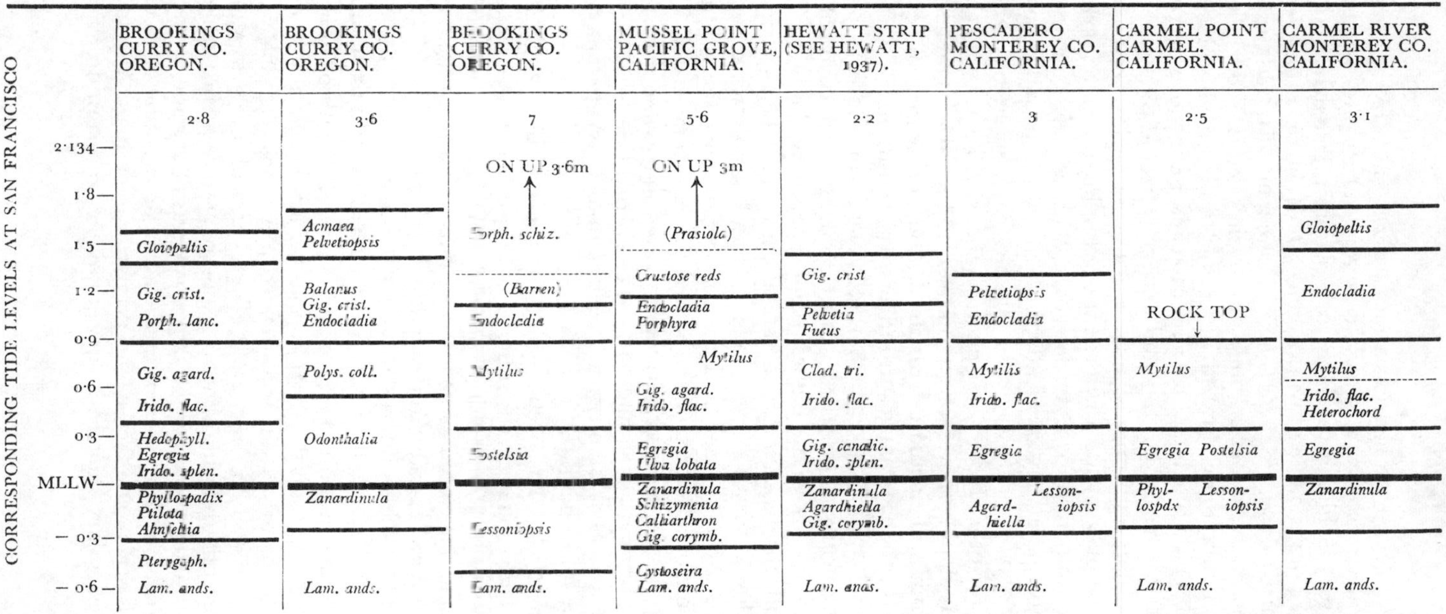

Fig. 44c — The algal zonation on some Pacific coast shores in relation to tide levels at San Francisco.

CORRESPONDING TIDE LEVELS AT SAN FRANCISCO	BROOKINGS CURRY CO. OREGON. 2·8	BROOKINGS CURRY CO. OREGON. 3·6	BEDDINGS CURRY CO. OREGON. 7	MUSSEL POINT PACIFIC GROVE, CALIFORNIA. 5·6	HEWATT STRIP (SEE HEWATT, 1937). 2·2	PESCADERO MONTEREY CO. CALIFORNIA. 3	CARMEL POINT CARMEL. CALIFORNIA. 2·5	CARMEL RIVER MONTEREY CO. CALIFORNIA. 3·1
2·134			ON UP 3·6m → Porph. schiz.	ON UP 3m → (Prasiola)				
1·8	Gloiopeltis	Acmaea / Pelvetiopsis	(Barren)	Crustose reds	Gig. crist	Pelvetiopsis / Endocladia	ROCK TOP →	Gloiopeltis
1·5			Endocladia	Endocladia / Porphyra	Pelvetia / Fucus			Endocladia
1·2	Gig. crist. / Porph. lanc.	Balanus / Gig. crist. / Endocladia		Mytilus				
0·9			Mytilus			Mytilus	Mytilus	
0·6	Gig. agard. / Irido. flac.	Polys. coll.		Gig. agard. / Irido. flac.	Clad. tri. / Irido. flac.	Irido. flac.		Mytilus / Irido. flac. / Heterochord
0·3	Hedophyll. / Egregia / Irido. splen.	Odonthalia	Eystelsia	Egregia / Ulva lobata	Gig. canalic. / Irido. splen.	Egregia	Egregia / Postelsia	Egregia
MLLW	Phyllospadix / Prilota / Alariitia	Zanardinula		Zanardinula / Schizymenia / Calliarthron / Gig. corymb.	Zanardinula / Agardhiella / Gig. corymb.	Agard- hiella / Lesson- iopsis	Phyl- lospdx / Lesson- iopsis	Zanardinula
− 0·3			Lessoniopsis					
− 0·6	Pterygoph.			Cystoseira				
	Lam. ands.	Lam. ands.	Lam. ands.	Lam. ands.	Lam. anas.	Lam. ands.	Lam. ands.	Lam. ands.

Clad. tri. = Cladophora trichotoma, Gig. agard. = Gigartina agardhii, Gig. canalic. = Gigartina canaliculata, Gig. corymb. = Gigartina corymbifera, Gig. crist. = Gigartina cristata, Hedophyll. = Hedophyllum sessile, Irido. flac. = Iridophycus flaccidum, Irido. splen. = Iridophycus splendens, Lam. anders. = Laminaria andersonii, Polys. coll. = Polysiphonia collinsii, Porph. lanc. = Porphyra lanceolata, Porph. schiz. = Porphyra schizophylla, Pterygoph. = Pterygophora californica.

FIG. 44c.

The algal zonation on some Pacific coast shores in relation to tide levels at San Francisco. (From Doty, 1946.)

The term 'littoral' has been applied in various ways to parts of the coastal regions; here it will be used as a broad term referring to the boundary between land and sea, including the landward regions affected by the sea and the seaward regions modified by the land. This is the broad sense which Odum uses in *Fundamentals of Ecology*.[301] The extent of the littoral in either direction depends somewhat on one's approach, chemical, biological, geological, etc. Excluding the coastal plankton and taking a phycological view, the *littoral* is a region in which algae are attached to or move over the coastal deposits, and it extends onto the land until the effect of the sea water is negligible and the flora indistinguishable from that of typical freshwater habitats; this may be only a short distance above the highest tide mark or it may be a considerable distance as on low lying skerries, reefs, and coral atolls. The lowermost point phycologically must surely be the point below which growth of the algal flora ceases on the deposits (rock, stone, silt, sand), due to lack of light (or other factors) for photosynthesis. This may be close to the land on steeply sloping shores, or out on the continental shelf on gentle slopes. Its lower limit will fluctuate with the season and with changes in turbidity, etc., which produce changes in radiation penetration.

Within the littoral region as defined, three major zones are at once apparent—(1) Permanently submerged. (2) Covered and uncovered by tidal movement, and (3) Above the highest point reached by the tide. The first zone is probably the most constant habitat, any point being defined relative to depth below sea level at mean tide level and being always at this depth plus or minus the tidal range. This has been termed the subtidal zone. The middle region has been aptly named the intertidal zone. The uppermost zone, supratidal, is least clearly demarcated, but is only feasibly marked by the point beyond which highest tides or normal tide spray do not reach; a point which is at least physically determinable. Water may be carried above this in storm periods.

Until recently most work has been confined to the intertidal zone, but now that methods of investigating the subtidal zone are being increasingly used, it would appear to be wise to adopt a broad view of the littoral zone. Algal and animal names have been given to zones, but these are not universal and a combination of floral and faunal designations seems undesirable. The most fundamental feature of the intertidal zone is the movement of the tide over it and particularly the rate of tidal cover which is usually most rapid over the middle range and less rapid above and below. If length of time of exposure for numerous points on the short are plotted against elevation, it is found that 'breaks' occur at certain well defined elevations, e.g. Fig. 44b and c for the Pacific coast of N. America.[80] These 'critical levels' separate zones[5] of shore with greatly differing times of exposure and frequently correspond with breaks in the flora and fauna. The consensus of opinion seems to be that this 'exposure factor' is the important factor in distribution of species on the shore. It is a secondary factor, the primary factor being the tidal movement. The secondary factor is quantitatively measurable, since it is directly related to a measurable primary factor. Much more work is needed, but should these critical levels prove to be a constant feature of shores (and they will be more obvious on irregular shores where changes in slope will exaggerate the effects of changes in rate of tidal flow), then they may be used to define zones. On some shores with diurnal or semidiurnal tide patterns, it is possible to subdivide the intertidal zone into upper, middle and lower zones corresponding to the intervals between highest high water and lowest high water, between lowest high water and highest low water and between highest low water and lowest low water. Fig. 44*b* illustrates the changes in such tidal levels, Fig. 44*c* shows how very complicated these zones can get in regions of mixed tides, where there are two different levels reached by high and low water in one lunar day. The number of subdivisions will depend upon the worker, shore type, tidal type, etc., and so long as the appropriate quantitative data are given, the actual number and naming of the subdivisions can be according to dominant algae (or animals) or by numbers, preferably starting with zone 1 at the top so that each succeeding zone will indicate a decrease in exposure time.

Subtidal zone

This zone has received comparatively little attention except from examination of dredged material. In the subtidal flora on the rock faces of a gully at Wembury, the uppermost species (*Himanthalia elongata, Chondrus crispus, Laurencia pinnatifidia, Gastroclonium ovatus* and *Gigartina stellata*), all occur in the lower intertidal zone and in fact die out before the lowest level of extreme spring tides and must therefore also be included in the intertidal flora.[212] The remaining large species (*Saccorhiza polyschides, Corallina* spp. and *Laminaria* spp. mainly *L. hyperborea*) and some *Desmarestia* extend from the lower intertidal down to approximately 1·5 m, 2 m, and 2·5 m below low water of ordinary spring tides. The *Laminaria* formed a submarine forest with *Rhodymenia palmata* and other species epiphytic on it, whilst *Corallina, Rhodymenia palmata* and *Cladostephus verticillatus*, formed a subflora on the rocks. The overhanging wall of the gully was devoid of the large Laminarians but on slight overhangs *Rhodymenia pseudopalmata, Cryptopleura ramosum* and *Nitophyllum bonnemaisoni* were widespread, with rarer occurrences of smaller species of *Ceramium, Plocamium, Dictyota*, etc. Subtidal forests of *Laminaria hyperborea* occur down to depths of 12–13 m below extreme low-water spring tides off the S.W. coast of the Isle of Man.[202] *Saccorhiza polyschides* occurred in the lower zone of the *Laminaria* forest and extends below this (e.g. down to 19 m). It appears that at each station some factor reduces the *Laminaria* at a certain depth and below this it is replaced by *Saccorhiza*. In the subflora of the *Laminaria* forest the following were common: *Cutleria multifida* sporophytes, *Dictyota dichotoma* (disappearing in winter), *Desmarestia aculeata, Cryptopleura ramosa, Delesseria sanguinea, Phycodrys rubens* (mostly on *Laminaria* stipes—see below), *Odonthalia dentata, Pterosiphonia parasitica, Plocamium coccineum, Nitophyllum* agg. and *Callophyllis lacinata*. It is noteworthy that few of the lower intertidal species penetrate into the subtidal, but a few species found in intertidal rock pools and crevices are more abundant in the subtidal zone. Also species such as *Alaria esculenta* and *Himanthalia elongata* occurring around low water, do not in fact penetrate very far down into the subtidal. On loose gravel in the subtidal, off the Isle of Man, a flora was found in which brown algae were predominant, e.g. *Chorda filum*, *Myriocladia* sp., *Stictyosiphon tortilis*, *Cutleria multifida* (gameto-phytes), *Sporochnus pedunculatus*, *Cladostephus spongiosus* and *Acrothrix gracilis* together with some red algae, e.g. *Brongniartella byssoides*, *Antithamnion plumula*, *Bonnemaisonia asparagoides* and *Polysiphonia* spp. whilst only a few of the large subtidal species were still present. Burrows[47] found a similar flora on rock surfaces and also a loose lying population on the floor of Port Erin Bay in which *Laminaria saccharina*, *Saccorhiza polyschides*, *Chorda filum* and *Desmarestia aculeata* were the dominants. Some of these were apparently originally attached to small pieces of gravel, etc., and some had formed adhesions, e.g. thalli of *Dictyota* and *Plocamium* were adhering to other algae and stones. Attached in this way the fronds of *Dictyota* grew to form expanded sheets.

There is a rich epiphyte flora on *Laminaria hyperborea*, four major species are found, viz. *Rhodymenia pseudopalmetta*, *Phycodrys rubens*, *Membranoptera alata* and *Ptilota plumosa*.[279] Plants growing in shallow water were found to have *R. palmata* along the length of the stipe, whereas in deeper water it occupied the distal portion and *Phycodrys* the proximal. At intermediate depths these two species were at a minimum and *Membranoptera* and *Ptilota* were at a maximum. Sections of stipes showed that the cells of *Ptilota* actually penetrated into the host tissue.

In sandy and silted subtidal regions the bottom may be coated with diatoms and some Cyanophyta, forming an epipelic flora very similar to that in lakes. The diatom flora of the sediments of a sea loch in Scotland was investigated by the glass slide method (see p. 73) and by observations on sediment from cores.[373] Major species on the slides were *Amphora coffeaeformis*, *A. laevis*, *A. macilenta*, *A. marina*, *Cocconeis scutellum*, *Navicula bahusiensis*, *N. pygmaea* and *Cylindrotheca* (*Nitzschia*) *closterium*. A motile flora and a flora attached to sand grains was recognized and it was clearly the latter which colonized the glass slides; the former only appeared when the slides were covered with sediment. Isolated species were recorded to a considerable depth and evidence for a seasonal cycle with high spring/summer and low winter numbers was found. The cores proved difficult to handle by direct observation. A similar flora has been investigated down to a depth of 35 m

---

Fig. 45.

A. *Dumontia*; B. *Gracilaria*; C. *Ahnfeltia*; D. *Calliblepharis*; E. *Membranoptera*; F. *Gloiosiphonia*; G. *Gigartina*; H. *Laurencia*; I. *Callophyllis*; J. *Phyllophora*; K. *Dilsea*; L. *Rhodymenia*.

(Original.)

off the California coast, at La Jolla (Round—unpublished). The samples
were short cores taken by divers, and proved to be so rich in diatoms that a
visible brown film formed on the surface of the sediment after it had stood for
a few hours. The material was examined by the method on p. 59 and an
attempt was made to separate out the attached from the motile flora. The
former consisted mainly of species of *Achnanthes, Cocconeis* and *Fragilaria,*
which were sparse in the surf-beaten shallow region and reached a peak at
about 15 m and then decreased as silting increased. Direct observation
showed them to be attached quite firmly to the sand grains. The motile
flora was very sparse at 5 m but increased greatly to 25 m where there was
a peak in cell numbers which was reduced slightly at 35 m. This pattern
was constant during six months observations (Fig. 46).

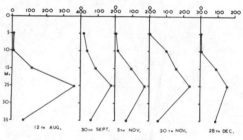

FIG. 46.

The variation in the number of diatom cells on the sediment at depths from 5–35 m
off the coast at La Jolla on different dates.

(Round—unpublished.)

The number of species showed a similar sequence, e.g. in one series there
were 3 species at 5 m, 18 at 10 m, 26 at 15 m, 32 at 25 m and 21 at 35 m.
These were common species recognizable during counting of live material;
if recognition of all species had been possible at the time, the numbers
would have increased slightly for the shallow samples and enormously for
the deeper, where in cleaned material nearer 200 species are recognizable.
In addition to diatoms, but by comparison extremely scarce, are species of
Cyanophyta (*Holopedia, Anabaena*) and flagellates (Cryptomonads, *Eutreptia,*
and Dinoflagellates). The main diatom genera were *Amphora, Navicula,*
Nitzschia and very much subordinate were *Pleurosigma, Diploneis, Surirella* and
Caloneis.

Intertidal

On sandy beaches in this zone only microscopic algae are common.
Patches of Dinoflagellates occur on the sand in Port Erin Bay.[170, 171] Species
of *Amphidinium* were frequent, but *Gymnodinium, Prorocentrum, Euglena* and
colourless flagellates were also present; intermingled with these were *Navicula,*
Pleurosigma and an *Oscillatoria* species. The patches discolour the beach and
each patch seems to be dominated by a certain species. Some of the Dino-

flagellates were reported to disappear when covered by the tide, whereas the diatoms did not. The Dinoflagellates tended to decrease in number during summer, whilst the diatoms flourished. Rhythmic movements related to light and tide were reported (see also p. 72). On the same shore and on the shores of the R. Mersey, sand grains can be seen to be coated with numerous attached diatoms whilst others move freely.[126] Attached species are indeed common, e.g. species of *Synedra, Rhabdonema, Grammatophora, Licmophora, Achnanthes*, together with the motile genera *Amphora, Caloneis, Diploneis, Navicula, Gyrosigma, Pleurosigma, Amphiprora, Nitzschia, Hantzschia* and *Surirella*. The physical nature of the beach has a profound influence on the flora; on coarse sandy beaches motile species seem to be absent and only attached species occur on the sand grains e.g. *Achnanthes, Cocconeis* and *Coscinodiscus nitidus* were found on very large sand grains in La Jolla Cove (Round—unpublished), whereas on fine sand, the attached species are less obvious but motile species of the genera *Hantzschia* and *Nitzschia* often form a brown coloration on the sand surface, e.g. during stable periods on La Jolla beach. On the very fine silty muds on coasts and particularly along estuaries, a rich motile flora is present, e.g. the following are dominant at Whitstable,[3] *Pleurosigma balticum, P. aestuarii, Stauroneis salina, Scoliopleura latestriata, Navicula cancellata, N. digito-radiata, N. ammophila, Tropidoneis vitrae, Nitzschia sigma, N. closterium* and *Biddulphia aurita*. Earlier work on the diurnal movement of this community was confirmed for it disappears from the surface when covered to a certain depth by the tide, and reappears about two hours after low tide, providing light intensity is sufficient. On the intertidal salt flats of the R. Dee estuary the diatom flora of the pans is distinct from that of the flat sand. The pans in the upper intertidal region are populated by *Diploneis didyma, N. gregaria, N. pygmaea, Amphora ovalis, Nitzschia apiculata, N. closterium* and *Cylindrotheca gracilis*, together with many less common species; in the middle intertidal *Navicula gregaria, N. digito-radiata, Pleurosigma angulatum* v. *quadratum* and *Cylindrotheca gracilis* were the dominants. The more silted stations of the upper marsh were dominated by *Gyrosigma spenceri, Diploneis didyma, Navicula gregaria, N. cincta* v. *heufleri, Nitzschia naviculiformis, N. apiculata* and *N. obtusa* v. *scalpeliformis*; only the smaller species seem to be able to live amongst the fine silt. On the coarser sand in the lower intertidal, a characteristic flora, composed of *Pleurosigma aestuarii, Caloneis amphisbaena* v. *subsalina, Navicula gregaria, N. viridula, N. pygmaea, Scoliopleura tumida* and *Amphora coffeaeformis* v. *acutiuscula* was developed. Seasonal variation in the flora has been recorded at all these stations with peaks of cell numbers in spring and summer.[346] The rich flora at Whitstable and in the Dee estuary is present because of relatively calm tidal flow over the sediment; where surf beats on the shore the flora is either absent or a single species is dominant, e.g. a *Pleurosigma* species is the only common diatom in the surf region on La Jolla beach (Round—unpublished). Silty shores on salt marshes often have a rich growth of filamentous species which bind the sand together, e.g. Chapman[55] distinguishes communities dominated by

Ulothrix, Rivularia/Phaeococcus and *Lyngbya,* but also containing numerous other species of Cyanophyceae. In some regions the sand is bound by *Vaucheria.* Sandy shores rarely have any macroscopic algae growing on them but silted regions and particularly the salt marshes, where Angiosperm vegetation grows, often have a flora of macroscopic algae, e.g. *Enteromorpha* spp., *Bostrychia scorpioides* and the unattached forms of *Fucus spiralis, F. vesiculosus* and sometimes *Ascophyllum mackaii;* sand over rock surfaces is often bound firmly by *Rhodochorton* species. In some tropical regions sand becomes consolidated by binding with calcium carbonate to form beach rock.[222] It is most frequent in the intertidal zone but can occur above and below. The algae growing on the surface appear to assist the consolidation and probably also contribute a considerable amount of biogenic calcium carbonate. On some Caribbean beaches, fragments of *Halimeda* form almost the entire beach. The beach rock itself is the substratum for numerous coccoid and filamentous Cyanophyta. A zonation occurs on some of these beaches in which the upper intertidal zones are dominated by the red alga *Herposiphonia tenella,* the Cyanophycean *Hydrocoleum comoides,* together with *Spirulina, Lyngbya* and *Symploca* species. Lower zones are dominated by *Cladophoropsis, Herposiphonia, Champia, Eucheuma, Centroceras,* and *Caulerpa* with fewer Cyanophyta.[56] Krauss and Galloway [222] also record the species on a transect and show similar distribution, i.e. Cyanophyta in the upper intertidal, *Calothrix, Chroococcus, Gloeocapsa* together with diatoms and lower down larger thalli of *Halimeda, Galaxura, Lithothamnion, Chaetomorpha, Sargassum, Dictyota, Goniolithon, Jania* and *Penicillus.* In some regions a definite 'algal rock' was formed derived from calcareous Rhodophyta (*Goniolithon* and *Peysoniella*). 'Worm rock' formed from the calcareous deposits of Serpulidae also had an associated algal flora, e.g. the Siphonaceous *Dictyosphaeria* and *Halimeda, Chaetomorpha* and the Rhodophyta, *Laurencia* and *Griffithsia.*

Rocky intertidal shores can often be subdivided into three zones, (1) the upper, where exposure is greatest and where in the uppermost region the shore may be uncovered more than covered, (2) the mid zone, where there is always tidal cover with each tide, and (3) the lower zone, where exposure is for relatively short periods. These zones are frequently characterized by algal communities and on many shores can be split into subzones. The extent of each zone will depend on the tidal pattern of the particular region, degree of exposure, slope of shore, e.g. on vertical faces the zones are narrow where tidal range is small, and wider where the range is greater; on almost flat rock the middle zone may extend for many metres. The delimitation of these three zones is an extremely thorny problem and both the upper and lower intertidal zones extend into the supratidal and subtidal zone as defined by the level of extreme high and extreme low tide. Likewise there is variation in the boundaries between these and the middle intertidal. Nevertheless as Stephenson and Stephenson[381a] say, 'there *are* three chief zones to be seen, over a very large part of the world.' The upper intertidal species around the British Isles are *Pelvetia canaliculata,* often the most conspicuous species and sometimes forming a dense sward, *Fucus spiralis* often somewhat lower on the shore than *Pelvetia* and *Porphyra umbilicalis*, all of which are attached to the rocks and hang down from them. Small tufted species occurring particularly in cracks in the rock, are *Catenella repens* and *Bostrychia scorpioides* and these may form a dense subflora. On the rock, patches of Cyanophyta occur, e.g. *Calothrix scopulorum* (and also the lichens *Verrucaria maura* and *Lichina pygmaea*), whilst a coating of diatoms, and creeping green and red algae may be present. In this upper intertidal, *Enteromorpha* is often abundant particularly where freshwater flows onto the shore. The upper margin of the upper intertidal communities varies according to the amount of wave splash, e.g. wetting of plants 2·4 m (8 ft.) above high-water level on Fair Isle has been observed,[48] whilst Børgesen records intertidal algae as high as 15 m (50 ft.) above high water in the Faroes, where the moist air conditions assist in keeping the algae wet. Thus it is clear that the important factor at this uppermost point on many shores is not tide level, but the level to which regular wetting by splash or spray occurs and associated with this the resistance of species to drying and in some climates freezing. Some of the upper (*Bangia, Porphyra*) and middle intertidal algae (e.g. *Fucus vesiculosus, F. serratus, Ascophyllum nodosum*) can withstand temperatures as low as −18°C for up to ten hours whilst some of the lower growing species (e.g. *Delesseria, Laurentia,* and *Laminaria*) cannot tolerate temperatures much below − 5°C. On some shores certain species may be absent, e.g. the *Pelvetia* zone is absent on chalk cliffs[10] and the upper region is dominated by *Fucus spiralis* (uppermost) and *F. vesiculosus* (lowermost).

The larger algae of the intertidal zone are often densely covered with epiphytes, e.g. Anand records *Elachista fucicola, Blidingia minima, Ulothrix pseudoflacca, Rhizoclonium riparium, Polysiphonia spiralis, Spongonema tomentosum, Cladophora rupestris, Ceramium* spp. and *Ulva lactuca* on *Fucus* spp. The plants also often have a rich epiphytic growth of coccoid and filamentous Cyanophyta and diatoms, the latter also grow abundantly on the filamentous epiphytes (e.g. on *Spongonema* and *Polysiphonia*). In this zone on chalk cliffs several other communities occur, one of which, the chalk boring community, is of interest.[10] It is first obvious as small circular patches of *Gomontia polyrhiza*, sometimes together with species of *Phormidium, Hyella* and *Plectonema*, which penetrate the chalk to a depth of about 2 mm and are later all covered by a thick growth of *Dermocarpa violacea*. Rock pools in this upper region are often coated with a layer of *Lithophyllum* spp. and bush-like growths of *Ceramium, Polysiphonia* and *Cladophora*. From the bottom, grow tubular thalli of *Scytosiphon lomentarius, Dumontia incrassata* and *Enteromorpha*; all the plants are often brown with diatom epiphytes (e.g. species of *Grammatophora, Licmophora, Synedra, Achnanthes, Cocconeis* and tube forming *Navicula* and *Pleurosigma* spp.).

The mid-intertidal zone around the British coasts is commonly a zone with abundant *Fucus vesiculosus* (often towards the upper margin), *Fucus serratus, Ascophyllum nodosum, Chondrus crispus* and *Gigartina stellata*. The two latter species are often found as a subflora underneath the fronds of the Fucoids, and *Ascophyllum* is frequently the substrate for bushy growths of *Polysiphonia, Ceramium* and *Ectocarpus*, together with their flora of epiphytic diatoms. The rock beneath this flora may be covered with *Lithophyllum* spp. and sometimes *Corallina*. Invading from the lower intertidal, one often finds a subflora of *Rhodymenia palmata* (often attached to the stripes of the Fucoids), *Laurencia pinnatifida* and *Lomentaria articulata*. The rock pools are rich in encrusting *Lithophyllum* spp., *Ceramium, Callithamnion, Polysiphonia, Corallina, Scytosiphon, Punctaria*, etc. In places the pools are filled with growths of the Fucoids *Bifurcaria bifurcata* and *Halidrys siliquosa* and the dichotomously branching Rhodophyta *Polyides* and *Furcellaria*. Deeper pools particularly in the lower part may contain the leafy *Membranoptera alata*, the *Sedum*-like *Gastroclonium ovatus* and the fern-like *Bryopsis plumosa*. On limestone shores the rock is sometimes too friable to support the large Fucoids and the flora is of smaller species, e.g. *Rhodochorton, Gelidium, Cladophora* and *Corallina*.[246] On very exposed shores and headlands this mid-intertidal zone may be absent, or present only as fragments in crevices, rock pools, etc.

The lower intertidal is a zone just above lowest water mark, where algae may be only rarely exposed to the air or exposed only for short periods insufficient for any degree of desiccation. The species of the mid-intertidal zone extend down into it and form a conspicuous part of the flora, e.g. *Ascophyllum nodosum, Fucus serratus, Laurencia pinnatifida, Lomentaria articulata*. Around much of the British Isles it is the zone into which the subtidal Laminarians penetrate and may be delimited at its upper margin by the disappearance of these. The major species are *Laminaria digitata, L. hyperborea, L. saccharina, Alaria esculenta* and *Saccorhiza polyschides*. *Alaria* is only common on very exposed coasts and rarely extends much above the low-water mark. Other species which are met at this level are *Codium* spp., *Himanthalia elongata, Cystoseira tamariscifolia* (and also in rock pools at higher levels) and *Desmarestia* spp. Attached algae such as *Rhodymenia pseudopalmetta* are common in the subflora on rock and algal stipes, e.g. the stipes of the Laminarians are often rich in encrusting red algae, e.g. *Melobesia* spp., *Lithothamnion* and *Lithophyllum* spp., amongst which filamentous Phaeophyta, *Ptilota plumosa* and diatoms, are common. In pools and crevices of this region many of the rock pool algae of the mid-intertidal are still present and in addition, leafy Rhodophyta are found (e.g. *Delesseria sanguinea, Apoglossum ruscifolium, Hypoglossum woodwardii* and *Nitophyllum* spp.). *Dictyota dichotoma* is often frequent in the pools and on the steep sides of rocks. Brownish streamers of *Plumaria elegans* are common

---

FIG. 47a.

A. *Chondrus*; B. *Furcellaria*; C. *Apoglossum*; D. *Avrainvillea*; E. *Nitophyllum*; F. *Udotea*; G. *Cladophoropsis*; H. *Caulerpa*; I. *Chaetomorpha*; J. *Endoderma*; K. *Struvea*; L. *Penicillus*; M. *Acetabularia*; N. *Codium*.

(After Børgesen, Kylin and original.)

hanging down the rock sides, brown due to the usual dense covering of epiphytic diatoms. On rough surf-beaten shores the larger Laminarians may be completely absent and the rocks coated with encrusting *Lithothamnion* spp. together with *Corallina* spp. in the crevices.[97]

In the upper intertidal of shingle beaches the flora tends to be sparse presumably owing to the movement of the stones but, *Pelvetia, Fucus spiralis* and to a lesser extent *Catenella, Bostrychia* and Cyanophyta may all be present. In the muddy areas *Enteromorpha* and *Rhizoclonium* become more important. In the mid-intertidal only Rhodophyta (*Chondrus crispus, Laurencia pinnatifida, Dumontia incrassata*) and Chlorophyta (*Ulva* and *Enteromorpha*) occur, but not abundantly. In the lower intertidal *Chorda filum* is found and some of the species of the Laminarian zone of rocky coasts are also present.[245]

Supratidal

Sand beaches above high tide mark are usually so desiccated that algal species are rare. Where more organic soils, which hold water, come down into the zone of sea spray, the soil flora is modified and the normal soil diatoms are often replaced by species such as *Caloneis amphisbaena, Achnanthes brevipes, Nitzschia obtusa*, etc. Rock substrata have a flora composed of thalloid encrusting species, e.g. *Prasiola stipitata*, and *Hildenbrandia* and species of diatoms often coat the rock surface and are especially abundant in the damper fissures. Thalli of *Blidingia minima* and *Porphyra umbilicalis* often hang from the rocks and gelatinous Cyanophycean pustules are common in this zone, e.g. *Calothrix scopulorum* together with species of *Plectonema, Rivularia, Lyngbya, Phormidium* and *Oscillatoria*. The growth of Cyanophyta often gives a black appearance to the substratum; it has been recognized in many parts of the world. On calcareous rock in the Adriatic there is a very distinct zonation of Cyanophyta, with *Pleurocapsa* and *Scytonema* at the top, below which is a zone of *Mastigocoleus* and nearest the water line species of *Hyella* occur and some of these actually penetrate into pores in the rock. It is interesting that similar morphological types occur in this supratidal zone wherever it has been investigated. A specialized group of communities on chalk cliffs has been admirably described by Anand [10] and some of these species also occur in the Baltic.[407] On the English coast three communities were distinguished above the high water, spring tide mark:[10] *a*. At the upper limit of the spray zone is a community dominated by the green alga *Entocladia perforans*; *b*. Below this is a zone of globular light brown Chrysophyta—*Apistonema carteri, Chrysotila stipitata, Thallochrysis litoralis* and *Gloeochrysis maritima*; these genera should almost certainly be transferred to the Haptophyta. Associated with these are *Endoderma perfornans, Lyngbya*

FIG. 47*b*.

A. *Nereocystis*; B. *Agarum*; C. *Saccorhiza*; D. *Ecklonia*; E. *Macrocystis*; F. *Laminaria*; G. *Alaria*; H. *Bifurcaria*; I. *Desmarestia*; J. *Lessonia*; K. *Dictyopteris*.

(After Fritsch, Oltmanns, Taylor and original.)

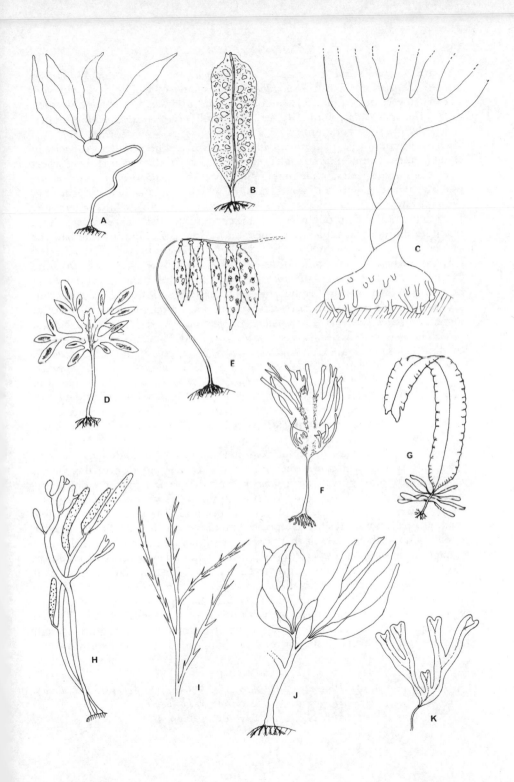

rivulariarum, *Plectonema nostocorum*, *Calothrix pulvinata* v. *prostrata*, *Schizothrix fritschii*, *Rivularia atra* and *Phormidium* species, any of which may achieve a greater degree of dominance, which led Anand to describe five communities: (1) *Chrysotila stipitata* community, (2) Chrysophyceae (*Apistonema* dominant)/ *Entocladia/Lyngbya* community, (3) *Schizothrix fritschii* community, (4) *Calothrix* community, (5) *Rivularia atra* community. The number of species in some of these communities is fairly large, e.g. 33 in the second; here apart from the name species, other genera such as *Ulothrix*, *Phormidium*, etc., occur, together with a group of diatoms, most of which grow on such surfaces (e.g. *Navicula*, *Nitzschia*, *Pleurosigma*, *Surirella*, *Cocconeis*, *Synedra*), whilst others may be incidental and brought in by spray (e.g. *Sceletonema costatum*). This example shows the complexity of these supratidal communities when all the component algae are examined; *c*. The lowermost community is dominated by *Enteromorpha* spp. Some of the species from the Chrysophyta zone extend down into it (e.g. *Gloeochrysis*) and others from the intertidal *Fucus* belt, extend up into it. Epiphytes such as *Pringsheimia*, *Mikrosyphar* and *Xenococcus* occur and diatoms move over, or are attached to the surfaces of algae and rock, e.g. *Navicula scopularum* v. *perlonga*, *N. cryptocephala* v. *pumila*, *Nitzschia apiculata*, *N. obtusa* v. *scalpelliformis* and *Synedra* spp. Species extending from below are *Callithamnion roseum*, *Polysiphonia spiralis*, *P. urceolata*, *Cladophora arctiuscula* and *Spirulina subsalsa*. Here also the chalk may be penetrated by the chalk boring algae *Gomontia polyrhiza* and *Phormidium* spp. Many of the species of these southern English chalk cliffs are widely dispersed and the same or closely related forms occur in the Öregrund archipelago in the Baltic where the salinity is below 6 per cent and the rock not chalk but granite, gneiss, etc.

Rock pools in the supratidal region tend to be populated by mats of Cyanophyceae and diatoms and often have a rich plankton of flagellates, e.g. Droop [85] found *Brachiomonas submarina* and *Oxyrrhis marina*, the dominant flagellates in pools off the south coast of Finland. Also present were *Cryptomonas* spp., *Glenodinium armatum*, *Massartia* spp. and *Gyrodinium fissum* and less common were some freshwater species extending down from the freshwater pools. The author working in the same region found *Scenedesmus* spp. and some marine diatoms, *Synedra pulchella*, *Fragilaria* and *Nitzschia* spp. common in these pools. They were characterized by a large population of a small number of species. Pools fertilized by gull excrement were rich in *Chlamydomonas pulsatilla*. In other regions *Dunaliella* is frequent, whilst almost pure growths of *Amphipleura rutilans* were found in pools at Peveril Point.[3] It is noteworthy that no macroscopic algae occur in these pools and only a small number of species can withstand the rapid changes of salinity, temperature, etc.

FIG. 47*c*.

A. *Himanthalia*; B. *Ascophyllum*; C. *Durvillea*; D. *Halidrys*; E. *Sargassum*; F. *Fucus*: G. *Turbinaria*; H. *Hormosira*; I. *Phyllospora*.

(After Kjellman, Taylor and original.)

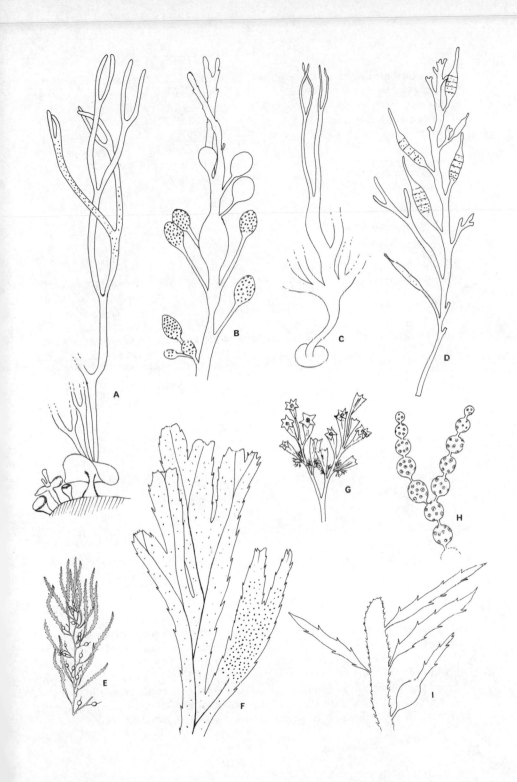

Zonations similar to those round the British Isles are recorded for much of the N. European coasts, e.g. in the fjords near Stavanger (Norway) the following profiles for the supratidal and intertidal zones are recorded [35] (only the common algae are listed).

I

Calothrix scopulorum
↓
Lichens
↓
Porphyra umbilicalis f. *umbilicalis*
↓
Ceramium Shuttleworthianum
↓
Fucus distichus f. *distichus*
↓
Callithamniom arbuscula
Corallina officinalis
Gigartina stellata
Leathesia difformis
↓
Alaria esculenta

II

Lichens
↓
Algae absent
↓
Ceramium Shuttleworthianum
↓
Nemalion multifidum
↓
Polysiphonia brodiaei
↓
Chondrus crispus
↓
Corallina officinalis
↓
Fucus serratus
Cladophora
Lithothamnion } subflora }
↓
Laminaria digitata
Corallina officinalis
Hildenbrandia prototypus
Lithothamniom
↓
Corallina officinalis
Codium tomentosum

III

Lichens
↓
Pelvetia canaliculata
↓
Fucus spiralis
↓
Fucus vesiculosus
↓
Ascophyllum nodosum
↓
Fucus serratus
↓
Laminaria digitata
↓
L. saccharina
Chorda filum }
↓
Corallina officinalis

IV

Lichens
↓
Hildenbrandia prototypus
↓
Fucus vesiculosus
Hildenbrandia prototypus
↓
Fucus serratus
Gigartina stellata
Hildenbrandia prototypus
↓
Gigartina stellata
Hildenbrandia prototypus
Cladophora rupestris

The four profiles are taken from stations starting on the outer islands (I) exposed to full wave action, where the common fucoids are absent or rare and passing to extreme protection in the innermost fjord. In the sheltered locality of (III) there is an almost perfect North European zonation. In this region the longitudinal zonation of the algae repeats to a certain degree that of the vertical on the shore, e.g. the lower intertidal and subtidal species (*Alaria, Himanthalia, Laminaria hyperborea, Saccorhiza polyschides*) are confined to the outer islands and do not penetrate up the fjords. On the other hand *Pelvetia* and *Fucus spiralis* are rare on the open islands, penetrate into the fjords but not into the innermost, where only the intertidal *Fucus vesiculosus*, *F. serratus*, *Chondrus crispus* and *Gigartina stellata* are common.

Similar zonations are present in the Arctic Seas, e.g. in Iceland there is a *Calothrix/Prasiola/Ulothrix/Urospora/Monostroma/Bangia/Porphyra* association in the supratidal; a *Pelvetia/F. spiralis*, *F. vesiculosus/Ascophyllum/F. inflatus/F. serratus* upper and mid-intertidal association together with subflora and rock pool flora similar to N. European coasts: a lower intertidal of *Monostroma/Chorda/Polysiphonia/Corallina/Lithothamnion* association; and a subtidal group of associations, viz. *Laminaria/Sacchorhiza/Alaria/Desmarestia/Lithothamnion*.[200] Around the coasts of Arctic Seas, the lower subtidal is often a rich zone of reef-like *Lithothamnion/Lithophyllum* species. In regions w'ere ice forms in quantity along rocky coasts the intertidal is usually poor in species, e.g. in this region around Novaya Zemlya, Fucoids are absent and only a small number of filamentous algae are present; in the subtidal zone the uppermost region was also fairly barren probably due to ice action. Below this at 3–10 fathoms *Laminaria*, *Alaria* and *Saccorhiza* were common with the usual subflora (*Odonthalia*, *Rhodomela*, *Polysiphonia*, *Ptilota*, *Desmarestia*, etc.). From 10–20 fathoms a Lithothamnion association was present whilst in other places a rich *Rhodymenia palmata* association was formed.[213]

Around the mouth of the St. Lawrence and into the Bay of Fundy, the majority of species are common to the British Isles, only *Agarum*, *Ilea*, and *Sargassum* being new, whilst *Pelvetia* and *Himanthalia* are absent.[17] Stephenson and Stephenson [381] also describe the zonation in this region and recognize their universal zones at many places; the absence of *Pelvetia* is noteworthy, whilst *F. spiralis* is still present, and there is a zone of *Chondrus crispus*, replaced in some regions by *Alaria* in the lower intertidal below the Fucoids; in some places the *Laminaria* zone is replaced by one of *Chordaria*. In regions of friable sandstone, the fucoid zone was absent or occurred in crevices (cf. its absence on chalk around the British Isles) and in the subtidal zone, *Chordaria* replaced *Laminaria*. Further south in the Beaufort region [380] the zonation is Lichens/*Porphyra leucostricta*/(*Gelidium pusillum* locally)/*Ulva/Enteromorpha/Fucus vesiculosus* (the most southern extension of this species)/*Sargassum filipendula/Dasya pedicellata/Ulva lactuca*— the latter group replacing the Laminarians of more northern waters. Still further south on the Florida Keys,[379] the upper black zone is present, consisting of Cyanophyta (*Entophysalis deusta*) together with a moss-like growth of *Bostrychia* spp., but is as yet incompletely described. In the intertidal zone there is a short moss-like turf of algae (*Bostrychia*, *Valonia*, *Anadyomene*, *Cladophoropsis*, *Catenella*, *Centroceras*, *Ceramium*, *Polysiphonia*), reminiscent of species on beach rock. This community occupies the flattish upper platform of rock (the coasts are not rocky in the northern sense but shelving platforms), and below this there is a lower platform, almost entirely subtidal, and beyond that the reef flat. On the lower platform *Laurencia papillosa* is dominant, with *Valonia ocellata* and *Halimeda opuntia* present, amongst which small carpeting forms such as *Cladophoropsis*, *Centroceras*, *Ceramium*, *Herposiphonia*, *Jania*, *Polysiphonia* and *Spyridia* occur. This flora, partly conditioned by the flat topography and limestone rock, is composed of tropical species with siphonaceous Chlorophyta assuming greater importance, and calcareous algae such as *Halimeda* and *Jania* replacing *Corallina* whilst the larger Fucoids and the *Chondrus/Gigartina* type of Rhodophyta are absent. This tropical zonation is also present in a somewhat similar form on rocky tropical coasts, e.g. where there is an upper zone of *Bostrychia tenella* and *B. binderi* in fissures, and *Entophysalis crustacea* on open rock on the coast of Ghana. In the intertidal zone 'turf'-forming species grow on

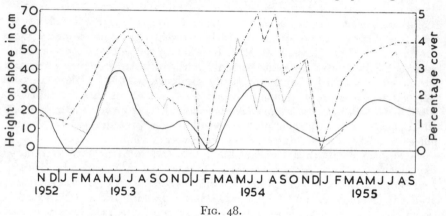

FIG. 48.

Relationship between seasonal tidal changes and the zonation and quantity of *Hypnea musciformis* at a station on the coast of Ghana. Continuous line is the tidal curve of the heights of the lowest of the daytime low waters in each month. The broken line represents the seasonally fluctuating upper limit of *Hypnea* and the dotted line the percentage cover of *Hypnea*.

(After Lawson, 1957.)

the encrusting *Lithothamnia*, e.g. *Hypnea musciformis*, *Centroceras clavatum*, *Chaetomorpha antennina* and *Ulva fasciata* at various levels. Just above the subtidal zone, the 'red algal turf' consists of *Laurencia* spp. with *Hypnea*, *Gigartina* and *Centroceras* in varying amount and sometimes as pure stands. Below this and corresponding to the Laminaria zone of northern shores, is a zone of *Dictyopteris delicatula*, growing as a turf on these exposed coasts. In more sheltered localities *Sargassum* occurs in or above the *Dictyopteris* and the intertidal zones are compressed. On this shore the seasonal raising of algal levels during March–September has been admirably described and related to the semidiurnal tides of this coast.[231] These tides never expose the lowermost parts of the shore at daytime during this period, since the higher low waters are then occurring during the day. If the heights of the daytime lower low waters are plotted, a variation in height given in Fig. 48 is seen.

Taking *Hypnea musciformis* as an example and plotting the variation of this on the shore, the relationship between the seasonal tidal change and the zonation and quantity of *Hypnea* is obtained. The difference in height between the tide levels and the algae is due to the effect of splash.

On the Pacific coast of N. America, a striking relationship between tide levels and algal zonation was demonstrated, which is illustrated in Fig. 44c.[80] The tidal pattern is again semidiurnal (Fig. 44b). Very definite breaks in the flora occur at mean lower low water, 30 cm (1 ft.) and 1 m (3 ft.) above this (Fig. 44b) and these correspond to sudden increases in exposure time. Compared with the Atlantic coast of America the species are quite different, but there is clearly a similar zonation from supratidal *Prasiola* (*Gloiopeltis*) → Upper intertidal *Endocladia*/*Pelvetiopsis*→Midtidal *Iridophycus flaccidus*/ *Egregia* → Lower intertidal *Zanardinula*→Subtidal *Laminaria andersonii*/ *Pterygophora californica*/*Cystoseira osmundacea*/*Desmarestia herbacea*. The four groups of communities in the intertidal zone are reflected by the time of submergence (or emergence), there is 10 hours maximum submergence at about 3 ft. above mean lower low-water level, 10–20 hours between 1 m and 45 cm, 20–40 hours between 45–30 cm and 40–80 hours below this height. One of the most striking features of the subtidal vegetation off this coast are the beds of *Macrocystis pyrifera*. This species also occurs down the Pacific coast of S. America and around Antarctica just reaching S. Africa, Tasmania and New Zealand. Off S. Africa it forms subtidal beds with *Laminaria pallida* and *Ecklonia buccinalis*, whilst above this zone Rhodophyta are the abundant littoral species with *Porphyra capensis* uppermost on the shore, followed by *Chaetangium* spp., *Iridaea capensis*/*Caulacanthus pustulatus*/*Splachnidium rugosum* in the mid-intertidal and *Bifurcaria brassicaeformis* and *Champia lumbricalis* in the lower intertidal.[192]

A peculiarity of Australian and New Zealand coasts is the dominance of animals above the lower intertidal zone. Cyanophyta, *Bostrychia* and Lichens are found, but subordinate to the limpets, etc. On more tropical coasts, e.g. Arnhem Land, there is little growth above low tide level and below this grows the usual tropical 'turf' of *Spyridia*, *Hypnea*, *Dictyota*, *Padina*, etc., followed by the large Phaeophyta of the subtidal (*Sargassum*, *Turbinaria*, etc.). Whereas in northern latitudes the Fucales are mainly intertidal, in Australasia only *Hormosira banksii* occurs in the lower intertidal, the other fucoids (e.g. *Cystophora*, *Durvillea*, *Xiphophora*, *Sargassum*, *Phyllospora*) replacing the Laminarians (except *Macrocystis* and *Ecklonia*) in the subtidal. In the lower intertidal and extending into the mid-intertidal in some localities, *Hormosira* and/or *Gelidium* form a distinct belt, above a subflora of coralline algae (*Corallina*, *Jania* and *Lithothamnia*). The large Phaeophyta so characteristic of the coasts of the southern hemisphere are present in regions of extreme wave action, but where this is reduced they tend to be replaced by Rhodophyta (e.g. *Hypnea*, *Spyridia*).[425] In New Zealand the subtidal Fucales, *Durvillea*, *Carpophyllum*, *Xiphophora* and *Cystophora*, all extend up above low-water level in the same manner as the *Laminaria* species of the British coasts.

The southern Laminarians, *Ecklonia, Macrocystis* and *Lessonia*, on the other hand occur below the Fucales and are only very rarely exposed.

Two further important algal habitats are the mangrove swamps and the coral reefs of the tropics. In the former the algae are partly epiphytic on the stems and roots of the mangroves and partly bottom living on the sediment of the sheltered waters (lagoons) around the mangrove swamp. *Bostrychia tenella* and *Catenella repens* are epiphytic on the upper parts of pneumatophores of mangroves in the West Indies; both species may be exposed by low tide.[27] Below these are found *Caloglossa leprieurii, Murrayella periclados, Caulerpa verticillata, Polysiphonia* spp., *Bryopsis* spp., *Ceramium nitens, Centroceras clavatum* and *Acanthophora spicifera*. Twined in amongst these and epiphytic on them are species of *Falkenbergia, Enteromorpha, Rhizoclonium, Lyngbya, Callithamnion, Chantransia* and diatoms. The sedimented lagoons are the habitat of the larger siphonaceous Chlorophyta, e.g. species of *Halimeda, Caulerpa, Udotea, Avrainvillea, Dictyosphaeria, Penicillus* and *Acetabularia*. In New Zealand, the same or similar algae have been recorded on pneumatophores; on the sediment *Gracilaria secundata* f. *flagellifera* grows, together with a free living form of *Hormosira banksii* and *Enteromorpha, Monostroma*, etc.[58]

Coral reefs are physiographic features of tropical seas which are never formed at temperatures below 18°C and best developed when the mean annual temperature is 23–25°C. They are continually growing and are broken down to form calcareous deposits from the skeletons of the corals (Coelenterates) and calcareous Rhodophyta (see p. 209). The reef forming algae are almost as important as corals in the growth of the reef, whilst the corals themselves contain algal zooxanthellae (see below) and filamentous species creeping on and in the skeleton. Thus the reef is dependent on photosynthesis for its formation and hence only forms in shallow waters. On the seaward side of reefs an algal ridge grows (*Lithothamnion* ridge, *Corallina* ridge), which extends above and below tide level; it is often exposed to massive wave action and only the calcareous crustose *Archaeolithothamnion, Lithophyllum, Lithothamnion, Goniolithon* and *Porolithon* flourish. It is usually broken by surge channels, down which the water pours as it drains off the reef flat. Sometimes these channels are bridged over by calcareous algae and the channels themselves lined with a smooth veneer of such algae. Sloping inwards towards the shore or lagoon is the reef flat which also supports a considerable growth of coralline algae and an increasing number of corals, sponges, etc. Chlorophyta such as *Caulerpa* and *Halimeda* grow in protected places and articular genera such as *Jania* may form a subzone. Algal ridges are less well developed on leeward reefs, but sand flats in the lagoons may be covered with a 'turf' of Siphonaceous algae (e.g. *Caulerpa, Boodlea, Dictyosphaeria, Avrainvillea*) and genera such as *Laurencia, Sargassum, Turbinaria*, together with marine angiosperms. On the lagoon slope, *Halimeda* is often the predominant alga.

The importance of algae in the economy of coral reefs is much greater than appears from a study of the free living algae. Algal cells (zooxanthellae) were found in all reef building corals on the Great Barrier Reef and also in planulae.[428] They were also common in many of the other animals on the reefs, e.g. gorgonids, the zooanelid *Palythoa*, actinarians, foraminiferans (*Polytrema*), in the mantle edges of clams (*Tridacna* and *Hippopus*) and in colonial tunicates (*Tridemnum*, *Didemnum* and *Diplosoma*). Sections of corals showed a great concentration of algal cells in the endoderm. Odum and Odum[302] found that the algal zooxanthellae, made up only a small part (6 per cent) of the plant material of corals, the remainder being formed by the filamentous green algae embedded in the skeleton and thought by previous workers to be 'parasitic,' or 'boring' algae; a large amount of this latter material is also symbiotic, since on dead corals different species of 'boring' Chlorophyta, Rhodophyta and Cyanophyta were found, whereas only Chlorophyta were found in live corals. Estimates of plant and animal tissue in corals suggested a preponderance of plant material (0.063 g cm^{-2} compared with 0.021 g), whilst the algal mats, shingle, etc., contained a still greater amount of plant material. Zooxanthellae have now been extracted from host tissue and cultured; many of them are not green algae as was assumed by many workers but non-motile cells of Dinoflagellates since in culture they produce typical *Gymnodium* like cells.[264] The green symbiont of the platyhelminth *Convoluta* has recently been shown to be a species of *Platymonas* (Prasinophyta). This identification was confirmed by electron microscope study of the symbiont and comparison with free living species of *Platymonas*.[312b]

Some marine mollusca feed on sephonaccous algae, e.g. *Caulerpa* and injest the chloroplasts which then enter the cells around the gut and remain in a viable state and continue to photosynthesize. This is a rather special case of symbiosis since normally the symbiont is a complete algal cell.

Free living macroscopic marine algae occur in two main habitats, salt marshes (see above) and in the region of the North Atlantic known as the Sargasso Sea. The latter consists of a vast mass of floating *Sargassum* species, north-east of the Caribbean. The seaweed is trapped in a region of calm water and persists as a constant feature known to navigators at least since the ancient Greeks (Theophrastus refers to it in his *Historia Plantarum*) and it is vividly described in the diary of Columbus who recognized the weed as of a type growing on rocky shores. The main mass of weed belongs to the taxa *Sargassum natans* and *S. fluitans*, but many forms have been described and the taxonomy of *Sargassum* is extremely complex. Unlike the attached littoral species of *Sargassum*, those of the Sargasso Sea reproduce only vegetatively.[313] There is great variation in the amount of weed from region to region and it is mainly concentrated in the surface layer of the ocean. Much speculation has been indulged in over the origin of the weed in the Sargasso Sea; there seems to be little evidence for a continued littoral origin of the weed and although it may have originated in this way at a date in the past it now appears to be a self maintaining population unconnected with the littoral region. Floating masses of *Phyllophora* (Rhodophyta) occur in the Black Sea and there is a region off the coast of Japan in which macroscopic weeds are abundant.

The detailed geographical range of marine littoral species is likely to be dependent upon a large number of variables, many of which are not yet analysed, whilst the range of many species is still incompletely known. However, one of the most important factors is likely to be temperature. Only a small number of species are ubiquitous, the remainder being confined to greater or smaller geographical regions, e.g. along European coasts three main regions can be distinguished, Arctic (North Norway) with temperatures below 5°C, cold temperate (Norway, British Isles, Baltic, French coast) and warm temperate (Spain, Mediterranean). Characteristic of the two extremes here are the *Lithothamnion* species of the subtidal Arctic and the *Caulerpa, Acetabularia, Sargassum* species of the Mediterranean. The Arctic and north temperate group of species extend to the Atlantic coast of North America, but are prevented by land barriers from reaching the North Pacific. The subtropical and tropical regions are distinguished by the presence of numerous species of siphonaceous Chlorophyta, *Sargassum, Turbinaria*, coral reef algae, etc., and the absence of elements of the north and south temperate flora. Since there are no land barriers to prevent the spread of this flora northwards and southwards, it is probably temperature alone which confines the species. In the southern hemisphere there is likewise an Antarctic element, a cold temperate element extending to the south shores of New Zealand, Australia, South Africa and South America. A further division, sub-Antarctic, between Antarctic and cold temperate is sometimes made; the sub-Antarctic and southern cold temperate floras are characterized by large species of Phaeophyta, almost all of which are confined to the southern hemisphere (*Macrocystis pyrifera* being an exception). The southern Australian flora is characterized by a 'degree of endemism probably higher than in any other part of the world,'[425] and it is highly probable that the spread of species is prevented by temperature conditions.

6   Physiology: culture and nutrition

Although in many aspects the physiology of the algae is similar to that of higher plants, the diversity of form, pigmentation, life cycle, motility, wall structure, reserve products, etc., yield a range of physiological problems unparalleled in any other plant group.

The lack of differentiation into absorbing and photosynthesizing organs and the slight differentiation into attachment and photosynthetic parts, make the algae favourable material for physiological studies uncomplicated by the transport problems of higher plants. Since almost all may be cultured completely submerged, the problems of measuring and controlling environmental factors are confined to those of the liquid media; the complications of soil, soil water and air phases are eliminated. Some of the earliest plant physiological observations were made on algae, but progress was hampered until the principles and methods of pure cultures were established. It is rare for experiments to be done on material collected direct from nature; such work being mainly concerned with analysis of algal thalli, e.g. for chemical constituents, pigments, light absorption, chemical constituents of vacuolar sap, cytoplasm, gas analysis of bladders in Phaeophyta, etc. The great bulk of algal physiology is undertaken with unialgal, bacteria-free cultures and study of these also yields valuable data on cytology, morphology, reproduction etc. in addition to that from the planned experiments.

CULTURE

The first stage in obtaining cultures is a knowledge of the distribution of the required species in nature. This is necessary not only so that the species may be found initially, but because the more thorough the knowledge of its ecology, the simpler will be the choice of media, pH, temperature of culture, etc. Unfortunately, many organisms, which are required in culture, occur only in small numbers in their natural habitats and direct isolation is thus difficult since individual cells have to be picked out. With practice it is possible to pick up single cells in small pipettes and transfer these to culture media. However in many instances the sample from the natural habitat, e.g. soil, aquatic plant or plankton, can be stimulated into growth by the addition of nutrient media. Large growths may then result and the required organisms can be more easily removed into purer cultures. In order to reduce the number of contaminant bacteria and other algae, the technique of washing by transference through a number of watchglasses containing sterilized culture media, is commonly used. The cells of the algae (either one or more) are picked up in small pipettes drawn out to a fine point and closed by a piece of plugged pressure tubing. Most microscopic algae can be picked up and transferred in this way under a binocular microscope. Surface sterilization of the algae can be carried out in the same way by passing the alga through solutions containing hypochlorite or by exposure to ultraviolet light. Passage through solutions containing antibodiotics (e.g. penicillin, streptomycin, choramphericol, etc.) is a useful technique for removing bacterial contaminants. Algae which form zoospores are obtained bacteria-free by subculturing the zoospores immediately after release. Cultures are generally made initially in liquid media, which may be relatively simple inorganic media or may contain organic compounds known to be or thought to be necessary for growth of the organism, e.g. many flagellates have been shown to require vitamin B_{12}. Many organisms require either a soil, peat or lake mud extract or a solution made up in sterilized lake- or sea-water. Pringsheim[325] made use of a biphasic culture method, employing garden loam at the bottom of the test tube, covered with sand and above this water or a culture solution; organic materials, e.g. cereals, may be added to the soil. Other additions such as dextrose, peptones, acetates, beef extract, yeast extract, vitamins, etc., are sometimes made to an inorganic medium. Algae may be grown successfully on gelatine, silica gel or agar media, the latter being the only one in common use. The agar gel of 1–2 per cent concentration is used in flasks, petri dishes or as 'slopes' in test tubes; nutrients are often incorporated into the agar. It is usually best to sterilize the liquefied agar and the nutrient solution separately and mix just before pouring. Details of the techniques are to be found in many textbooks.[325, 326] The agar can be made up with the addition of dextrose, yeast extract, etc., when testing for bacterial contaminants. One of the most important uses of agar slopes is in maintaining pure stock cultures growing slowly and needing only occasional subculturing. Petri dish cultures are used to investigate algal floras (but see p. 59 for objections to this method), to obtain mixed cultures by spreading enriched inoculum containing a range of algae from which individual colonies can be picked out, to obtain unialgal colonies free from bacteria and to test for the presence of bacteria in cultures. The agar in the dish may be inoculated by spraying a suspension of the algae on the surface of the agar or by streaking suspensions by means of wire loops; this latter being more valuable when trying to separate algae and bacteria. Motile algae can sometimes be separated by allowing them to grow across the agar surface away from the bacteria; unfortunately, many species also carry the bacteria with them but the method is useful for fast-moving diatoms and flagellates. Algal growth is usually much slower than that of either bacteria or fungi, which are the two main contaminants, and hence it is necessary to take all the normal precautions of sterilization of tubes, dishes, pipettes, wire loops, etc., for whereas an airborne fungus spore although it is undesirable may not seriously harm a fungal culture, in an algal culture it may completely overgrow the alga before this has grown to be of any use. Some algal species will not grow permanently on agar, but the technique can still be used to separate the alga from others and from bacteria by plating out a suspension and immediately picking individual cells off the surface and transferring them to liquid culture.

In the pursuit of actively growing pure cultures, much has been learnt of the nutrition of algae. Nowhere is this better illustrated than in the attempts to devise an artificial seawater. The early workers all attempted to culture marine organisms in natural seawater to which certain minerals had been added (e.g. KNO_3, $MgSO_4$, $Na_2HPO_4.12H_2O$, $CaCl_2.6H_2O$, HCl, $FeCl_3$ and distilled water were the main additions),[330] and although much valuable work resulted, the repetition of experiments proved difficult since precipitates formed on autoclaving. The recognition that soil extracts stimulated growth led to the addition of 5 cm³ of a soil extract to Schreiber's medium ($NaNO_3$, 10 mg; $Na_2HPO_4.12H_2O$, 2 mg; seawater 100 ml) and with this medium, known as Erd-Schreiber, many more algae were cultured successfully. Precipitates still led to some difficulties and methods using 'aged' seawater (i.e. seawater stored in bottles in the dark for some months) were developed. All these attempts pointed to the importance of organic factors which was substantiated by the enhanced growth obtained when extracts of marine algae (but not their ash) were added to cultures and the discovery that inshore water and water circulating through aquaria tanks was more effective than seawater taken off shore or at 30 m or deeper. In addition trace elements were shown to be more abundant in inshore waters. Thus the recognition of the need for trace elements and organic factors was made. The action of precipitates and soil extract as chelating agents and buffers was realized and in the last decade this has enabled various workers to develop artificial seawater media giving consistent results. The tedious and detailed experiments leading to the design of artificial seawater media are described by Provasoli *et al.*[330] Of great nutritional interest was the confirmation that the salinity could be lower than that of seawater, that Mg/Ca ratios could be varied greatly, that a small variation in Ca content had to be counteracted by a larger variation in Mg, that the heavy metals had to be chelated with ethylenediamine tetra-acetic acid (EDTA) if they were not to be toxic, that the pH could be lowered below that of seawater (from around 8·0 down to 7·0–8·0) and for this tris-hydroxymethyl aminomethane (TRIS) was used, that vitamins of the B group and particularly B_{12} were necessary for many marine algae and finally that amino acids (particularly glycine and glutamic), purines and Krebs cycle intermediates were sometimes needed. Thus a much more complex medium is necessary for marine than for freshwater algae, and still the media are not suitable for many oceanic planktonic species.

Another important aspect of culture work is the genetical study of algal biochemical mutants, e.g. those of *Chlamydomonas reinhardtii* requiring, for example, either ornithine, citrulline or arginine, p-aminobenzoic acid or thiamin. The growth of strains not requiring these factors is achieved on a minimal medium composed of Beyerincks soln., phosphate buffer, trace element soln., and 1·5 per cent agar; for the mutant strains this is supplemented with the above factors or combinations of these. Briefly the technique is to mate haploid cells from palmelloid colonies of different mating type, by suspending them first in sterile distilled water, illuminating for 2–4 hours and then mixing the suspensions. Diploid zygotes are formed in 20 minutes and **these are poured onto plates containing minimal media, illuminated for** 18 hours and placed in darkness for 5 days during which time the zygotes mature. These are then transferred to media containing p-aminobenzoic acid, thiamin and arginine and are manipulated with needles into lanes cut in the agar. Vegetative cells carried over from the mating are killed by inverting the petri dish over chloroform for 35 seconds. The zygotes are illuminated for 18 hours during which time meiosis occurs, each zygote producing 4 or 8 haploid cells, which are separated under a dissecting microscope to form a row of cells 3 mm apart in the lanes. The plates are then incubated in the light for 6 days and colonies appear from each of the haploid cells. These are replica-plated by picking them up on filter paper and transferring to the various test media and the growth or absence of growth after five days' incubation is used as a criterion for determining the genotype of the cells in each colony.[234]

Synchronous culture of many unicellular algae e.g. *Euglena*, *Coccolithus*, diatoms, etc., has been achieved, usually by subjecting the cultures to alternate light and dark periods combined with dilution with fresh medium after each cycle. Large numbers of cells can be harvested from such cultures all in approximately the same developmental stage. Since most biochemical processes undergo changes during the growth cycle it is possible using synchronous cultures to study these processes from cell division to senescence. The shortest possible generation time in culture is however a genetically controlled feature of each alga.

Mass culture techniques have been designed to test the uses of algae for food production, for inoculating soils and sewage disposal beds, for industrial extraction of chemicals, antibiotics, etc. The algae used are generally species of *Chlorella* or *Scenedesmus*, but in some wartime experiments, species of diatoms were used because of their high fat content. The main aim of these cultures is to achieve a high cell density, and hence a high rate of carbon dioxide supply is maintained either by bubbling CO_2-enriched air through the medium, or by stirring, shaking or circulating the media; the nutrients must also be replaced as quickly as they are absorbed and complicated systems have been designed to measure the rate of uptake, and changes in balance in the media, and to correct these. The cell density is often measured photoelectrically and the nutrient supply automatically controlled, so that the culture maintains a high rate of division. Algae are also cultured in mass in outdoor tanks; here trouble from bacteria, other algae and micro-animals is a problem. The animals eat the algal crops but can be controlled by adding 1–3 p.p.m. of 2,4-dinitro-6-cyclohexyl phenylacetate or pentachlorophenyl acetate.[391]

Nitrogen-fixing Cyanophyta supply nitrogen to rice fields and the natural populations can be supplemented by the addition of cultured material. Watanabe[410] tested many algae for this purpose and found *Tolypothrix tenuis* most suitable; under laboratory conditions it grew at the rate of 4 g (dry wt.)/m²/12 hour and fixed nitrogen at a rate of 0·24 g m⁻²/12 hour. This he calculated to give 1315 kg of nitrogen/acre/year. The alga was grown on the moist surface of fine porous gravel soaked in culture solution held in a tube of vinyl sheeting and aerated with CO_2-enriched air. The culture could be transported to the experimental rice farms in vinyl bags and there used to seed the fields after spreading powdered lime on the water so altering the pH and reducing the existing algal flora. Seeding over a period of years increased the rice crops by as much as 20 per cent.

Nutrition

A study of the chemistry and bio-chemistry of algal habitats yields information on the nutritional requirements of algae. Thus the minimum level of silicate concentration for the growth of two freshwater diatoms was determined by an analysis of the silica in the lake waters, combined with cell counts; e.g. 0·5 mg dm⁻³ silica was the lowest level for *Asterionella formosa*[250, 251] and 0·8 mg dm⁻³ for *Melosira italica* subsp. *subarctica*,[253] values later confirmed by culture experiments. Examination of floras growing in mineral waters often reveals unexpected tolerances of elements or replacements, e.g. species which are normally found in Ca-poor waters grow in Ca-rich waters, if additional Na is present. Few oceanic species have been obtained in bacteria-free culture and detailed examination of the range of nutrients in ocean waters may reveal requirements or low levels of tolerance as yet unsuspected. Information may be obtained from chemical analysis of the algae themselves but care is necessary owing to the absorption of certain elements in excess of requirements and of others which may be absorbed but not utilized, e.g. iodine in many Phaeophyta and phosphorus in freshwater algae. A distinction must be made between absolute requirements, i.e. essentiality of a nutrient for growth, reproduction or photosynthesis [207] and normal requirements, i.e. the quantity of each nutrient in the cells during active growth with no nutrient limiting. Thus for *Chlorella* for every 100 parts by weight of carbon the following are normally required: N—15; P—5; Mg—2·5; K—1·8; S—1·6. The minimum and optimum requirements may also be distinguished. Early workers concluded that the elements required by algae were the same as for higher plants; to a certain extent this is true but some features are peculiar to the algae. The basic minerals required are similar, with the addition of silica for some groups. Sodium is not generally regarded as an absolute requirement for the majority of algae, but *Anabaena cylindrica* was found to require Na and this could not be substituted for by K, Li, Rb or Cs; 5 p.p.m. of Na allowed optimal growth.[4] This is the first record of the essentiality of Na for an autotrophic plant, but subsequent work suggested that other Cyanophyta require Na and it was found that the maintenance of logarithmic growth of *Anabaena variabilis*, *Anacystis* (*Microcystis*) *nidulans* and *Nostoc muscorum* required Na.[223] In addition to the major elements carbon, nitrogen, phosphorus, sulphur, potassium, magnesium, and calcium, trace elements such as iron, manganese, silicon, zinc, copper, cobalt, molybdenum, boron and vanadium are required at least by some algae. Chemical analyses of algae have shown even more trace metals to be present in (or on the surface of) algal cells and at least some of these may be essential requirements. In addition certain algae require either traces or larger amounts of organic compounds.

The uptake of some ions (e.g. Cl^-) may be twenty times greater in the light than in the dark. The action spectrum for this is similar to that for photosynthesis with which it is therefore assumed to be linked. The amounts of ions contained within the various organelles and the vacuole can vary greatly and differ considerably from that of the external medium.

Carbon

Carbon is derived from carbon dioxide, carbonates, bicarbonates or organic compounds. The former is the common source for the bulk of the algae which are photolithotrophic, and the latter is the source for the chemo-organotrophic algae. Since carbonates are generally present in excess in natural waters, carbon dioxide is usually available as the normal carbon source for photosynthesis. Algae in aquatic habitats live in a solution in which the carbon dioxide is present in various forms, the equilibrium depending on the hydrogen ion concentration, amount of excess base, the partial pressure of carbon dioxide in the atmosphere and the temperature:

$$CO_2 + H_2O \rightleftharpoons H_2CO_3 \rightleftharpoons HCO_3^- + H^+ \rightleftharpoons CO_3^{2-} + 2H^+$$

Below pH 5 only free CO_2 is of any importance, between pH 7–9 bicarbonate is most significant and above pH 9·5, carbonate begins to be important. Thus in very acid waters, only CO_2 is likely to be utilized, whereas at higher pH, bicarbonate may enter the cells and above pH 9·0 calcium will be precipitated resulting in calcium-deficient water and the major cations will be Mg, Na and K. In some hard-water lakes, calcium bicarbonate has been recorded in large quantities and it is now known that colloidal calcium carbonate is present in some waters.

It is generally considered that algae use free CO_2 in photosynthesis but at very high pH, i.e. from 9·0 upwards the absence of free CO_2 may be an important ecological factor; the number of species is reduced at this level although many other factors could also be involved. *Scenedesmus quadricauda* has been shown to utilize both undissociated CO_2 and bicarbonate ions whereas *Chlorella pyrenoidosa* does not.[307] On the other hand carbonate ions cannot be directly utilized and may even have an inhibitory effect. Although carbon dioxide is the normal source in experimental studies, it has been shown that excess (above 10 per cent) inhibits growth.

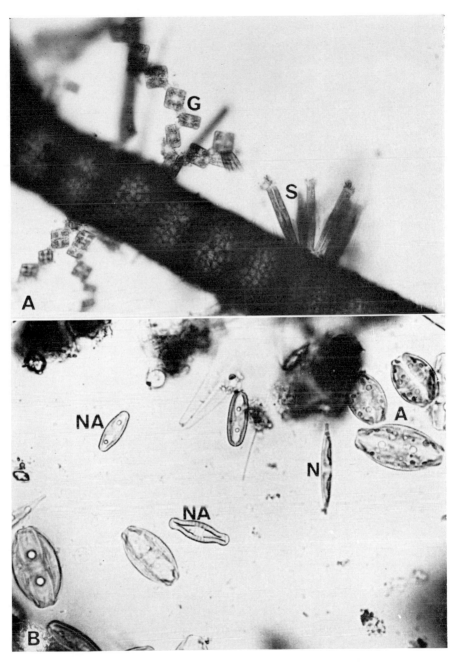

PLATE 7. **A:** Diatoms (*Synedra* S, and *Grammatophora* G) epiphytic on a red alga (*Ceramium*). **B:** Epipelic diatoms from a lake sediment (*Amphora* A, *Nitzschia* N, *Navicula* NA).

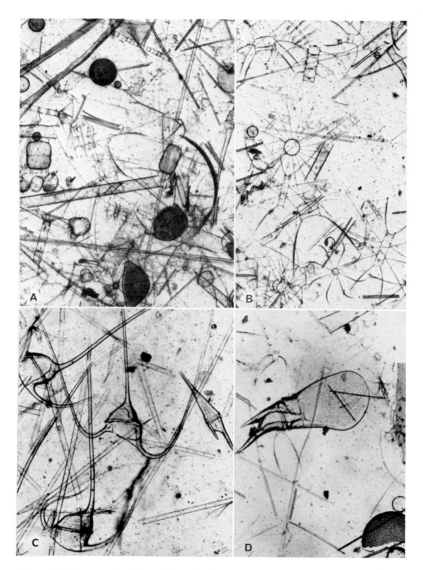

PLATE 8. Four collections of marine phytoplankton, cleared by boiling in hydrogen peroxide to reveal the details of wall structure. **A:** *Bacteriastrum*, *Stephanopyxis* and *Hemidiscus* are clearly visible. **B:** Filaments of *Chaetoceros* species and end views of *Bacteriastrum* are common. **C:** Four cells of *Ceratium* species and several long needle-like cells of *Rhizosolenia*. **D:** An inflated species of *Ceratium* and in the bottom right-hand corner a fragment of a *Coscinodiscus* cell.

Algae growing under continuous illumination and adequate nutrient supply have a carbon content of between 51–56 per cent of the ash-free dry weight,[208] whilst 49·5–70·17 per cent has been recorded for *Chlorella* grown under varying environmental conditions.[376]

Some algae possessing photosynthetic pigments can also absorb and utilize high-energy organic compounds. These are termed facultative chemo-organotrophic species and grow with or without the absorption of light energy. There are others which having no photosynthetic pigments are obligate chemo-organotrophic species. Most experimental work, on chemo-organotrophy has been done with the common cultivated algae such as *Scenedesmus*, *Chlorella* and *Euglena* using hexose sugars and acetic acid as substrates, although other substances, e.g. alcohols, organic acids, amino acids, peptones and proteins have also been used.[105] In addition *Nostoc punctiforme* can assimilate polysaccharides (starch and inulin). The so-called 'acetate-organisms' are those which grow best in acetate solutions and not at all on sugars; they are mainly flagellates of the Euglenophyceae, Crypto-phyceae and Volvocales. Large molecules do not seem to be able to pene-trate into the majority of algal cells and thus to utilize these, the production of extracellular enzymes is necessary and it is suggested that algae such as *Scenedesmus costulatus* v. *chlorelloides* and *Nitzschia putrida* which can liquefy gelatine, produce extracellular proteinase.

Nitrogen

Elemental nitrogen can be utilized by some species of the Cyanophyta. Other Cyanophyta and members of other algal groups utilize inorganic nitrogen compounds, in particular nitrate, ammonium salts, and, to a much lesser extent, nitrites. Organic nitrogen compounds can also be utilized. In natural habitats the main nitrogen sources are nitrates and ammonium salts, but in highly polluted waters the organic nitrogen compounds may become important and there may be a relationship between some of the products of animal excretions (ammonia, urea, uric acid and amino acids) and the growth of certain flagellates.

In artificial culture, nitrogen is usually supplied as ammonium salts or nitrates; most algae can assimilate either but evidence suggests that the ammonium salt is preferred; especially is this so for colourless flagellates when no organic nitrogen is available. The chlorophyll-containing flagel-lates, *Euglena gracilis* group, *Trachelomonas abrupta*, *T. pertyi* and *Phacus pyrum* cannot utilize nitrates.[329] In solutions containing NH_4NO_3, ammonia is usually preferentially absorbed and the pH of the medium falls. Assimilation of nitrate ions on the other hand tends to raise the pH.

The normal requirement of nitrogen in cultures of Chlorophyceae was found to be 6·5–8·3 per cent of the ash-free dry wt., but under conditions of nitrogen starvation this level can be greatly reduced.[208] Figures for marine algae vary between 0·99 and 5·44 per cent of dry matter. Average values were, for *Enteromorpha* 1·57, *Macrocystis pyrifera* 1·28, *Laminaria saccharina* 1·80,

Fucus vesiculosus 1·64, *Rhodymenia palmata* 2·91, and *Chondrus crispus* 2·00.[405] Excessive absorption can be induced if the algae are grown in solutions deficient in manganese, boron or zinc; cells of *Scenedesmus obliquus* containing twice the normal nitrogen content were produced in this way.[271] Marine phytoplankton has been shown to contain nitrogen in proportion to carbon and phosphorus in the ratio 7:42:1.[103] Thus, next to carbon and oxygen, the element present in greatest amount in algal cells is nitrogen.

Elemental nitrogen is in abundant supply both in the air and in waters, but only a few algae of the Cyanophyta can utilize it under normal conditions. Proof that nitrogen is incorporated is deduced from the increase of the total combined nitrogen of species grown in the absence of other nitrogenous compounds. Nitrogen-fixing species are only found in groups forming heterocysts, e.g. amongst the genera *Aphanizomenon, Anabaena, Nostoc, Cylindrospermum, Gloeotrichia, Mastigocladus*. The absorption of elemental nitrogen is not a necessity for growth of most of these species, since in minimal media their nitrogen needs are supplied from other sources. Some species can grow and fix nitrogen in the dark if supplied with sugars; others appear to be obligate phototrophs. The fixation of nitrogen by these blue-green algae depends on a small but adequate supply of molybdenum. This is also necessary when the source of nitrogen is nitrate.[420] The path of nitrogen was traced by supplying ^{15}N to Cyanophyta and subsequently hydrolysing and analysing chromatographically; the highest ^{15}N concentration was in glutamic acid with the ammonia fraction next.

The assimilation of nitrogen is indirectly connected with photosynthesis since the energy source, hydrogen donors and carbon skeletons are ultimately derived from the latter process. Whatever the origin of the nitrogen, conversion to ammonia takes place, hence the need for hydrogen donors. This ammonia enters the organic carbon skeletons presumably via α-ketoglutaric acid derived from the tricarboxylic acid cycle.[106]

Nitrates accumulate in the vacuoles of marine algae, in *Valonia* to the extent of 2000 times and in *Halicystis* 500 times the nitrate value of seawater.[195]

Phosphorus

Phosphorus occurs in water as orthophosphate and in organic combinations. Soluble phosphate-phosphorus is present in small quantity in natural waters, except in some which are polluted by certain organic materials. Low concentration may limit the growth of some species, but others absorb phosphorus in excess and can exist for some time in waters which have become phosphate deficient. Phosphorus requirement of Chlorophyceae is 2–3 per cent of the dry wt.[208] Phosphate-deficient cells can be produced by growing successive generations in phosphate-free solutions; depleted cells can absorb phosphate in the dark whereas replete cells absorb it only in the light. The excess phosphate stored in the marine diatom *Asterionella japonica* can be removed by washing in seawater, but the minimal content is strongly bound.[133] The optimum requirements for phosphorus vary widely, e.g. 0·45 mg (P) dm^{-3} for the Cyanophyte *Coccochloris peniocystis*, 0·002 mg (P) dm^{-3} for *Asterionella formosa*, whilst 0·005 mg (P) dm^{-3} are reported to inhibit the growth of *Dinobryon* and *Uroglena*. Glycerophosphate is sometimes more effective than inorganic phosphates as a source of the element. Adenylic acid, monoethylphosphate, guanylic, cytidylic and yeast nucleic acids are utilized to varying degree by certain algae.[329] Phosphates are concentrated in a striking manner by algal cells, e.g. in White Oak Lake which receives low-level radioactive waste, the phosphates are concentrated by *Euglena* 100 000, *Volvox* 140 000, *Pandorina* 285 000, and *Spirogyra* 850 000 times.[224] Phosphate deficiency in algae results in the accumulation of large amounts of fat. Recent work on metaphosphates and polyphosphates has shown the presence of these in *Chlorella*, *Ankistrodesmus* and *Hydrodictyon*; there appears to be an increase in these compounds in the light, while in darkness they decrease and orthophosphates appear.

Sulphur

This element is generally present in small quantity in all plant cells but is probably not a limiting factor for many algae under normal conditions. The marine planktonic diatom *Ditylum brightwellii* did not grow in seawater collected during summer unless a divalent sulphur compound, such as sodium sulphide, cysteine, glutathione or thiamin was added.[154] In fresh and saline waters sulphur is present as sulphate, but under strong reducing conditions, e.g. in the hypolimnion of some lakes, it may collect as hydrogen sulphide. In some closed basins, sulphates may accumulate giving a highly mineral water. Sulphur is incorporated into numerous organic compounds and sulphates are present in the vacuoles. Evidence is mounting for a connection between divalent sulphur compounds and the assimilation of silica in diatoms, cf. *Ditylum* above. Stimulation of growth of other diatoms has been recorded, e.g. *Sceletonema costatum*.[281] It was shown that *Sceletonema* cultures required 3 mg $Na_2S.9H_2O$ per dm^3, if vigorously aerated, but none if left unaerated, which suggested that there may be a connection between thiols and redox potential of the cell surface. Silica uptake may depend upon water-soluble sulphydryl groups in the cell membrane of some diatoms;[238] uptake can be inhibited by the sulphydryl inhibitor, cadmium chloride, whilst even washing the cells may inhibit silica uptake. The substance washed from cells can be replaced partially by SO_4^{2-} ions and ascorbic acid, and completely by N_2S, Na_2SO_3, glutathione, l-cysteine, dl-methionine or a mixture of sulphate and ascorbic acid.

Silica

This is an absolute requirement for diatoms and for some species of Chrysophyceae and Xanthophyceae, but probably not for other groups.

Although silica is often present in appreciable amounts in natural waters it is one of the elements which has been definitely shown to be limiting at certain times. The concentration range of silicate-silica in seawater is from a trace up to at least 4·0 mg dm^{-3}; this is similar to the range in freshwaters of Europe, but in N. America and Japan values up to 27 mg dm^{-3} have been recorded and in tropical regions up to 77 mg dm^{-3}.[190] Low concentrations of silicate can be utilized by diatoms both in natural habitats and in culture. Owing to the fact that assimilation is directly connected with the formation of new walls, there is a definite low concentration of silicate below which a population cannot live, since cytoplasmic division will proceed without the formation of new walls, e.g. 0·5 mg dm^{-3} for *Asterionella formosa* and 0·8 mg dm^{-3} for the thicker walled *Melosira italica* subsp. *subarctica*.[253] Much higher quantities, at least 25 mg dm^{-3}, are required for optimum growth of *Fragilaria crotonensis*, and *Nitzschia palea*.[65] *Navicula pelliculosa* utilized only orthosilicate and the uptake is dependent upon aerobic respiration, probably involving high-energy phosphate, and, as mentioned above, is associated with sulphydryl groups in the cell membrane.[237] The cycle of silica in nature, unlike that of many other nutrients, is complicated by the almost complete removal of assimilated silica, since most diatoms are insoluble except in very alkaline solutions and under some as yet unexplained conditions (e.g. in peat). This is very noticeable in freshwaters where the silica frustules are deposited on the sediment and preserved (see Chapter 11); some of the more delicate species may however be dissolved (e.g. *Rhizosolenia*). Thus some silica is re-cycled from this source, though at least in freshwaters most is supplied by inflow of water which has taken up the silica during percolation through soil.

Calcium and magnesium

For many years calcium was not thought to be an absolute requirement for algae, but it is now certain that where it is required the amount is small and in many experiments it may have been supplied as contaminant, e.g. for *Cylindrotheca* (*Nitzschia*) *closterium* only 5·0 mg dm^{-3} is required.[191] The calcium requirement of many species is considerably less than that found in natural habitats. Calcium ions undoubtedly play a part in the maintenance of cytoplasmic membranes and in wall structures. Strontium can substitute for the small calcium requirement of *Chlorella*. Calcium is deposited as calcite or aragonite on and in the walls of many algae; in some, e.g. Cyanophyta such as *Gloeotrichia* and Charophyta such as *Chara*, it is deposited in the mucilage or on the cell wall, in others it is invariably present forming an integral part of the skeletal structure, e.g. in the desmid *Oocardium*, in the tropical *Halimeda*, *Neomeris*, *Acetabularia*, *Penicillus*, *Udotea*, etc., and in the Rhodophyta, *Corallina*, *Lithothamnion*, etc. In some species the absorption of CO_2 is assumed to lead to an increase in alkalinity and subsequent precipitation of calcium carbonate. However this is probably a simplification, since it is common to find uncalcified species alongside the calcified (for other details on calcification see p. 205).

Magnesium, since it is a constituent of chlorophyll is obviously an absolute requirement for pigmented algae of all groups and is also necessary for the formation of catalase. The minimum requirement of magnesium appears always to be greater than that for calcium (e.g. 40 mg dm^{-3} for *Cylindrotheca* (*Nitzschia*) *closterium*). Provided calcium and magnesium are present in sufficient amounts, many organisms are tolerant of a wide range of Ca/Mg ratios. The tolerance of algae to these elements is also bound up with their tolerance to different ratios of monovalent to divalent ions. Magnesium deficiency interrupts cell division in *Chlorella* and *Ankistrodesmus*, resulting in abnormally large cells.

Sodium and potassium

Sodium appears to be a requirement for blue-green algae only. Kratz and Myers [223] found that sodium was necessary to maintain logarithmic growth of *Anabaena variabilis*, *Anacystis nidulans* and *Nostoc muscorum*. The increase of blue-green algae when waters become eutrophic, may in part be associated with increase in sodium content. There is evidence that large amounts of sodium may be inhibitory, which may account for the lack of blue-green algae in marine environments. However, in inland saline lakes they are often abundant, e.g. *Spirulina* blooms in East African lakes. Potassium is a requirement for all algae tested and under low potassium conditions growth and photosynthesis are low and respiration high. Providing sufficient potassium is available the ratio of K to Na within the cell is independent of the ratio in the medium.[363] *Ankistrodesmus* can undergo mutative adaptation to rubidium, but it still requires potassium; the mutative effect is to increase the resistance of the cells to rubidium toxicity. In non-adapted *Ankistrodesmus* multinucleate giant cells are produced due to cessation of cell division, continuation of mitosis and the production of cytoplasm. When returned to normal rubidium-free media the cells split up to give normal cells.

Iron and manganese

Iron has long been known to be essential to algae. It is a key element in metabolism, being a constituent of the cytochrome molecule; the rate of photosynthesis is lowered by iron deficiency. Iron exists in ionic form in all natural waters although the amount in solution in alkaline waters is very small. However, it is suggested that colloidal iron can be utilized, e.g. Goldberg,[132] using radioactive iron, found that the marine diatom *Asterionella japonica* utilized only colloidal iron. Small amounts of manganese are present in all natural waters and owing to its role in nitrogen metabolism it is probably a requirement for all algae. Photosynthesis and growth are stimulated by the addition of manganese to algal culture solutions. In manganese-deficient cells photosynthesis is lowered but, unlike other mineral deficiencies, there is no immediate effect on respiration, nitrate reduction or the oxidative assimilation of glucose in darkness. *Chlorella* can grow in the dark in manganese-deficient solutions when glucose is supplied, but in the light manganese is essential.[319] The seasonal variation in manganese concentration in surface waters, and the different requirements of algae, may play a part in regulating the composition of the phytoplankton.[190] Both iron and manganese compounds are deposited on and in the cell walls of some algae, e.g. desmids such as *Penium* and *Closterium* and the thecae of *Trachelomonas*.

Trace elements

Molybdenum, copper, vanadium and cobalt have all been shown to be essential for algae. These elements are required in very small amount and the tolerance of algae to them may be very narrow. Thus although at extremely low concentrations copper is essential, at higher concentrations it is an algal poison (cf. its use in combating algal blooms, p. 227). The high copper concentration at the end of summer stagnation in lakes may conceivably lead to a disappearance of some members of the microflora.[190] Concentrations of the order of 30 mg m^{-3} in the trophogenic zone of lakes during autumnal circulation may affect species of *Coelastrum*, *Navicula* and *Uroglenopsis*. It is just possible that this, or a similar trace metal, may be responsible for the low cell numbers of algae recorded in the autumn on sediments of certain lakes.[345] Molybdenum is an essential element for the nitrogen-fixing Cyanophyta and cobalt, or cobalt combined organically in vitamin B_{12} (Cyanocobalamin), has been shown to be essential for a large number of algae. Molybdenum-deficient cells of *Anabaena cylindrica* absorb nitrate but further utilization is blocked; when the nitrogen source is ammonium chloride growth is normal. Molybdenum may also play a role in the inhibition of phosphatase activity.[108]

Boron deficiency produces a loss of pigment and reduction of growth in *Nostoc muscorum*, but more work is necessary to establish its essentiality for other algae.

Von Stosch [406] showed that the Rhodophyte *Asparagopsis armata* required iodine, arsenic and vitamin B_{12}. Arsenic deficiency did not appear when phosphorus was reduced to one-fifth of its normal concentration in the medium, suggesting a relationship between arsenic and the metabolism of phosphorus. Phaeophyta have been shown to concentrate trace metals even when these are present in minute quantity in the surrounding sea, e.g. *Pelvetia canaliculata*, *Fucus spiralis* and *Ascophyllum nodosum* concentrate titanium 1000–10 000 times, zinc 1000–1400 times, nickel 600–1000 times and strontium 8–20 times.

Organic factors

Three vitamins, cobalamin (B_{12}), thiamin (B_1) and biotin are required, either singly or in combination by a large number of algae. The first alga shown to require vitamin B_{12} was *Euglena gracilis* and this organism is frequently used in the bio-assay of vitamin B_{12}. Lewin [241] lists some 65 species requiring exogenous supply of vitamin B_{12}, distributed amongst the Chlorophyta, Chrysophyceae, Cryptophyceae, Bacillariophyceae, Dinophyceae, Euglenophyceae, Cyanophyta and Rhodophyta. Some algae can utilize vitamin B_{12} homologues, such as pseudocobalamin, 5:6-dichlorobenzimin-azole and others.[86] Two algae, *Phormidium persicinum* and *Amphora perpusilla*, are remarkable in being able to use cobalamin and all the homologues. *Euglena* assay methods have been used to demonstrate the presence of vitamin B_{12} in algal tissue and values up to and even over 100 μg/kg dry wt., have been recorded. Uptake of the vitamin has been shown in some brown and red algae whilst *Chlorella* and some Cyanophyta can synthesize it; these and bacteria may be the principal source of the vitamin in natural waters. It has been calculated that the B_{12} content of seawater is sufficient to support large crops of algae,[86] although it has been suggested that the assay method may have overestimated the available soluble cobalamin. The B_{12} content of sea-water has been shown to decrease over the period March–May/June coincident with the growth of phytoplankton, whilst there is evidence that 'blooms' of dinoflagellates are related to cobalamin being washed out into the sea from soils, which contain an appreciable amount of this vitamin. The B_{12} content of seawater is of the order of $0 \cdot 16$ mg dm^{-3} in Loch Fyne (a coastal water) and 0–$0 \cdot 026$ mg dm^{-3} in the N.W. Pacific (data collected by Lewin[241]) whilst in freshwaters higher amounts, comparable to that of coastal waters, are found.

Thiamin, a component of the coenzyme for carboxylase, is required in its entirety by *Ochromonas malhamensis* and by an ultraviolet induced mutant of *Chlamydomonas reinhardtii*, whilst at least 40 species require either the complete molecule or the thiazole or pyrimidine moiety.[241] The thiamin content of algae decreases with age; values ranging from 200–7700 μg/kg fresh wt. have been recorded for *Chlorella* and *Nitzschia*. In general the values are higher than those for vitamin B_{12}. Lewin and Lewin[242] found that strains of the same marine diatom species isolated from different sources had different requirements for thiamin and B_{12}, e.g. for *Amphora coffeaeformis* strains requiring neither vitamin, either, or both, were obtained.

Biotin is required by a much smaller number of algae, all of which require either vitamin B_{12} and/or thiamin. *Ochromonas malhamensis*, *Poterio-chromonas stipitata*, *Amphidinium klebsii*, *A. rhynchocephalum* and *Eutreptia* sp. require all three factors. Cells of *Scenedesmus obliquus* and *Chondrus crispus* have also been shown to contain biotin.

The requirement for these growth factors is strong in algal groups with well developed saprophytic and holozoic tendencies (e.g. the Dinophyceae) and weak in groups with strong vegetal tendencies (e.g. Chlorophyta).

Other growth factors occur in algae and some are necessary for the growth of mutant strains, e.g. niacin for strains of *Chlamydomonas reinhardtii* and para-aminobenzoic acid for strains of *C. reinhardtii* and *C. moewusii*. The growth of several algae is stimulated by folic acid, pantothenic acid and pyridoxine, all of which have been detected in algal cells. There is a seasonal variation in the content of these substances, e.g. 35 μg niacin/g dry wt.

were found in spring and 15 μg/g dry wt. in autumn in *Laminaria hyperborea*, *L. digitata* and *Ascophyllum nodosum*.[227] A very early summer maximum and winter minimum of ascorbic acid in *A. nodosum*, *Fucus serratus* and *F. vesiculosus* (although this is not a necessary factor for algae) was reported.[199] Droop [86] showed that glycine has a stimulatory effect on the growth of *Hemiselmis virescens* and histidine stimulates, and may be essential for *Chlamydomonas chlamydogama*, *Ochromonas malhamensis* and *Gyrodinium cohnii*.

7 Physiology: energy sources and pigments

The old concept of the algae as a simple phototrophic group has now to be modified. Photo-autotrophy, the synthesis of the essential metabolites from simple chemicals and light energy, is, however, still a feature of many algae (e.g. many Chlorophyta, diatoms and Cyanophyta) and is obligate. The use of simple inorganic sources and light energy with water as the hydrogen donor is termed photo-lithotrophy, whereas the use of organic sources and light energy is termed photo-organotrophy and is a characteristic of a few algae and some bacteria. Thus it has recently been demonstrated that *Chlamydobotrys*, a green alga, requires acetate which is photo-assimilated in red light but not green or blue. No details of the pathways have been worked out but oxygen is not required for the process; photosynthesis of carbon dioxide by this organism occurs at extremely low rates or not at all. Many algae, however, require vitamins or other growth factors in minute quantities; this type of nutrition is termed mixotrophy. Others are capable of photosynthesis, but in addition require organic compounds such as acetate or sugar as a source of energy; this is mixotrophy of a different degree. It is probable that these organisms (*Euglena*, *Chlorogonium*, etc.) use acetate in the same way as does *Chlamydobotrys*. Numerous Volvocalean flagellates have recently been shown to be mixotrophic, e.g. *Chlamydomonas*, *Gonium octonarium*, *Hæmatococcus pluvialis*, *Stephanosphaera pluvialis*, *Volvulina steinii*, etc. Mixotrophic organisms (e.g. *Euglena* spp.) have a tendency to metabolize phototrophically in the light and heterotrophically in the dark; these may be termed amphitrophic.[327] Of these, *E. gracilis* can multiply as rapidly in the light as in the dark on acetate. Some algae (e.g. *Ochromonas malhamensis*) possess pigments in such small amount that although they can photosynthesize this alone is not sufficient for growth.

Colourless algae have of necessity to be heterotrophic, i.e. external metabolites are an absolute requirement, and their nutrition is of an obligate chemotrophic nature as opposed to that of the acetate organisms which grow in the dark, and are facultative chemotrophic or facultative chemo-organotrophic since they use organic compounds.

Some heterotrophic organisms, e.g. *Ochromonas* and *Chrysochromulina*, are also phagotrophic, that is, they absorb particulate nutrients into vacuoles within the cell thus behaving in a similar manner to some protozoa.

The utilization of inorganic compounds as energy sources, known as chemolithotrophy, is common in bacteria but rare in algae, e.g. in hydrogen-adapted *Scenedesmus* and *Oscillatoria* utilizing H_2S. Obligate chemo-organotrophy is found in the colourless *Euglena* spp., *Polytoma* (a colourless

Chlamydomonas), *Polytomella* (a colourless *Tetrachloris*) and *Prototheca* (a colourless *Chlorella*).

In addition to inorganic and organic components, phototrophic algae require an external source of energy. This energy is provided by light of wavelengths between 400 and 700 nm and it is absorbed by the photosynthetic pigments located, usually, but not always, in discrete chromatophores (see p. 45). Apart from the pigments concerned in the photochemical reactions of photosynthesis, there are others which do not appear to be implicated, others which are confined to particular structures, e.g. carotenoids of the eyespots of the Chlorophyceae, Euglenophyceae and Dinophyceae, carotenoids dissolved in the reserve products (oil) of many cysts and dinoflagellate cells and the anthocyanins and tannins generally associated with the vacuole.

PIGMENTS AND LIGHT ABSORPTION

The bulk of algal pigments can be divided into three groups, differing widely in chemical composition. The highly labile, fat-soluble, chlorophylls are tetrapyrrolic molecules with a central magnesium atom and two ester groups. Five chlorophylls have been isolated but only one, chlorophyll *a*, is common to all algal groups. Table 4 shows their distribution in the algae and clearly demonstrates the similarity between Chlorophyeae and higher plants (which have only chlorophylls *a* and *b*) and the divergence between higher plants and the other groups. Chlorophylls are characterized by strong absorption of red (650–680 nm) and blue light (400–450 nm) and by their red (emission) fluorescence in fat solvents. The chlorophyll molecule is loosely associated with protein molecules in the plastids.

The other fat-soluble group of pigments comprises the yellow- or red-coloured carotenoids, consisting of carotenes, xanthophylls (oxycarotenes) and carotenoid acids. They absorb blue and green light (430–500 nm), transmit yellow and red, and are weakly fluorescent. Carotenes are unsaturated long-chain hydrocarbon molecules. The structure is a polyene chain, i.e. having alternate double and single bonds; light absorption is due to these bonds and the greater the number of double bonds the redder the colour. The ends of the chains of molecules are coiled into rings and like the chlorophylls they are loosely bound with proteins in the plastids. β-carotene is present in all algal groups, but in the Bryopsidophyceae it is subordinate to α-carotene. The β-carotene content of algae is generally less (5–20 per cent) in the Chlorophyta than in higher plants (30 per cent of total pigment). In fruiting margins of *Ulva* the carotene content is increased over that of the remaining thallus, whilst the xanthophyll content remains the same.[166] The gametes have a still higher content of carotenes and also of xanthophylls (α, β, γ and an unknown carotene in the proportions 3, 32, 43 and 22 per cent). Large amounts of γ-carotene have also been recorded from antheridia of *Chara* and *Nitella*. The xanthophylls are long-chain hydrocarbons of the carotene type but with oxygen atoms forming hydroxyl (—OH), carbonyl (C=O), or ethylene oxide structures:

$$\begin{array}{c} \diagdown \quad\quad O \quad\quad \diagup \\ \diagup\diagup\quad \diagdown\quad\diagdown\quad\diagup \\ C\text{———}C \\ \diagup\quad\quad\quad\quad\diagdown \end{array}$$

The nature of the oxygen bonding determines the spectral absorption bands. The separation of xanthophylls from carotenes is by partition between petroleum ether and 90 per cent methanol, the carotenes remain in the former and xanthophylls in the latter. Mutants of *Chlorella* are known, in which the normal carotenoids are replaced by hydrogenated lycopene derivatives, and carotenoid-deficient mutants of *Chlamydomonas reinhardtii* have also been produced. Unlike the chlorophylls and carotenes, there is no one xanthophyll common to all algal groups and in addition they are present as a smaller fraction of the total pigments (Table 4). In the Bryopsidophyceae a xanthophyll ester (siphonein) occurs.

A group of water-soluble pigments (phycobilins) are found in the Rhodophyta, Cyanophyta and Cryptophyta. Chemically they are tetrapyrrolic structures linked to globulin-like proteins. Two types occur, phycocyanins, transmitting blue light and absorbing green, yellow and red light, and phycoerythrins, transmitting red light and absorbing blue, green and yellow. Both are strongly fluorescent (emitting orange/red light) and they are of slightly different composition in the algal groups. In the Rhodophyta, phycoerythrin is dominant and phycocyanin present in small amounts and the reverse in the Cyanophyta; phycoerythrin is also present in the Cryptophyceae.[167] *Porphyra naiadum* contains β-phycoerythrin, which differs from R-phycoerythrin normally found in the Bangiales. It has a single absorption maximum at 545 nm. This and other Rhodophyta also contain allophycocyanin with a single absorption peak at 650–654 nm compared with the double peak of R-phycocyanin.

The chlorophyll content of algae is usually about 0·5–1·5 per cent of the dry wt. but increased amounts, up to 6 per cent of dry wt., have been recorded in algae cultured in weak light. Spoehr and Milner[376] record extremes of 6 per cent and 0·01 per cent for the pigment content (as per cent of dry wt.) for *Chlorella* grown under different conditions. The content is affected by light intensity (weak light increases the pigment content and intense light may cause photochemical breakdown of pigment), the supply of carbon dioxide, and nitrogen content of the medium. There is also considerable variation in nature. Table 5 shows this for samples of *Ulva lactuca* from the upper littoral. Although there is considerable variation in the content of chlorophylls *a* and *b* in Chlorophyceae, the former is the dominant; in other groups containing only chlorophyll *a*, it is present as less than 1 per cent of the dry wt. (most frequently the analyses range between 0·1–0·3 per cent). Within the chloroplast itself, it is suggested that the concentration of chlorophyll reaches

Table 4. The distribution of pigments in the algal groups. ● = major pigment(s) of the group; ◑ = a pigment comprising less than half the total pigment content; ○ = present in small amounts. The data given by earlier authors varies considerably and the present table is compiled from tables in Fogg (1953), Strain (1958), Goodwin (1960), Egle (1960) and Haxo and O'Heocha (1960) with additions from their discussions.

Pigments	Chlorophyta	Bryopsidophyceae	Euglenophyta	Xanthophyta	Chrysophyta	Bacillariophyta	Phaeophyta	Dinophyta	Rhodophyta	Cyanophyta	REMARKS
Chlorophylls											
Chlorophyll a	●	●	●	●	●	●	●	●	●	●	
Chlorophyll b	◑	◑	○								
Chlorophyll c[5]				○	○	○	○[5]				
Chlorophyll d									○*		*But not in all genera
Chlorophyll e				○	○						
Carotenes											
α-Carotene	±○	●			±○	±○			±○		
β-Carotene	●	○	●[4]	●	●	●	●	●	●	●	
γ-Carotene	○					○					Not in higher plant
ε-Carotene	?	○				○*					*In *Navicula torquatum*
Flavacene										○	
Xanthophylls											
Lutein	●	○?	●[4]	○	○	?	±○	◑	±○	±○	
Zeaxanthin	○	○?						±○	±○	○	
Violaxanthin	○	○		○			○		○*		*Taraxanthin?
Flavoxanthin							±○				
Neoxanthin	○	○	○	○			○				
Siphonein		◑									
Siphonoxanthin		○									
Fucoxanthin					○	◑	●[1]				Occurs as a chromoprotein
Neofucoxanthin (A and B)					○	○					
Diatoxanthin					○	○					
Diadinoxanthin					○	○					
Neodiadinoxanthin								○			
Dinoxanthin								○			
Neodinoxanthin								○			
Peridinin								◑			
Neoperidinin								○			
Myxoxanthin(=Echinenone)										◑	Also syn. Aphanin and Calorhodin
Myxoxanthophyll										◑	
Oscilloxanthin										○	
Astaxanthin	○*		○								*In *Haematococcus, Brachiomonas* and *Protosiphon*
Unknown xanthophyll			○								
Phycobilins											
R-phycoerythrin									●		
R-phycocyanin									○		
C-phycoerythrin										○	Also in Cryptomonads
C-phycocyanin										●	Also in Cryptomonads, but absorption peaks not the same
β-phycoerythrin									○*		*In *Porphyra naiadum*
Allophycocyanin									○*		*In *Porphyra naiadum*

1. 5–8 times the content of β-carotene and lutein, but gametes of *Fucus* almost entirely β-carotene.
2. Sometimes in greater amount than β-carotene.
3. In large amounts possibly in the cytoplasm.
4. Dominant in some species. The carotenoid contents of *Euglena* spp. are higher than other algae.
5. Consists of two spectrally different forms (C_1 and C_2) in Crysophyta, Bacillariophyta and Phaeophyta, but in Cryptophyta and Dinophyta only C_2 occurs.

10–15 per cent of dry wt. The amounts of carotenes and xanthophylls present in the cells are much less than those of chlorophylls; the ratio of xanthophylls : carotenes, is usually between 4 and 6, although much higher ratios have also been found. There are many reports of algae showing chromatic adaptation, that is the development of pigment complementary to that of the light transmitted by the medium. It is a fact that the Chlorophyta tend to be confined to shallow water, the Rhodophyta to deep water, whilst the Phaeophyta occupy an intermediate position. Argument has centred on

Table 5. Pigment content of different thalli of *Ulva lactuca*
(Adapted from Egle, 1960)

Date	Sample No.	mg Pigment in 10 g fresh wt.					
		a	b	$a + b$	c	x	$x + c$
12·8	96	12·6	5·7	18·3	0·54	2·07	2·61
13·7	22	11·6	4·8	16·4	0·52	2·80	3·32
10·7	14	10·3	3·8	14·1	0·48	2·31	2·79
28·7	64	10·4	5·1	15·5	0·50	2·74	3·24
8·8	88	5·6	2·3	7·9	0·33	1·78	2·11
12·8	97	5·1	2·5	7·6	0·25	1·41	1·66
	Average	9·3	4·1	13·4	0·44	2·18	2·62

a and b = chlorophyll a and b
c = carotene
x = xanthophyll

the relative role of light intensity and light colour in determining this zonation. Engelmann in the 1880's maintained that colour was the important factor, whilst Oltmanns at the turn of the century maintained that intensity was responsible. Harder [147] suggested that both factors play a part. Whether or not intensity and/or colour have played an important part in the phylogenetic development of pigmentation, does not seem to have been proven one way or the other. On the other hand chromatic adaptation of individual algae to light of different intensity and colour does occur (ontogenetic adaption of Rabinowitch [331]). Early work of Gaidukov showed that the colour of Cyanophyta can be changed by illumination with light of different colour, thus *Oscillatoria sancta* became green in red, blue in green, yellow in blue-green and blue in yellow light. This variability is obvious when studying the same species collected from different habitats and hence different colour regimes, and is not confined to the laboratory. Gaidukov originally thought that these changes were due to changes in the nature of the pigments, but Boresch later showed that they were due to changes in their relative concentration. In the planktonic diatom *Chaetoceros*, Mothes and Sagromsky,[288] found that changes from dark brown in green light to yellow in red light was caused by a shift in the chlorophyll: carotenoid ratio. This is seen in nature; for instance diatoms living on the beach and in shallow water at La Jolla, California were yellow in colour, whilst at lower depths they were deep brown, and a marine *Holopedia* (Cyanophyta) clearly

Table 6. The percentages of chlorophylls and carotenoids in some algae

| | Chlorophyll | | a : b | Carotenoids | | x : c | $\dfrac{a + b}{x + c}$ |
	a	b		Carotenes	Xanthophylls		
Ulva lactuca	0·33	0·15	2·2	0·016	0·077	3·1	2·6
Chlorella pyrenodosa	2·00	0·55	3·6	0·45	0·268	6·0	7·9
Fucus serratus	0·45	—	—	0·016	0·067	4·2	5·4
Dictyota dichotoma	0·78	—	—	0·028	0·163	5·8	4·6
Porphyra lacinata	0·44	—	—	0·029	0·100	3·4	3·4

Data from Rabinowitch (1945). Values are per cent of dry wt.

took on a more intense pink coloration at the lower depths (Round—unpublished).

From the earliest recognition of the photosynthetic process in plants, it has been realized that it was the pigmented regions which were involved in the conversion of light energy to chemical energy. The exact relationship between light absorption by the pigments and photosynthetic activity is however still the subject of many investigations. The percentage absorption of light of different wavelengths, when light scatter, reflection, etc., is reduced to a minimum, can be measured most easily in a dilute suspension of algae or across a thin membranous alga (e.g. *Ulva*, *Porphyra* or *Delesseria*). The resulting curve is known as the absorption spectrum and is usually measured for wavelengths between 400–760 nm.

This gives a measure of the percentage absorption by the combined pigment complement, and comparison of this with similar absorption spectra of extracted individual pigments, yields data on the percentages attributable to them separately. If these absorption spectra are combined with relative photosynthetic rates (action spectra), measured by the output of oxygen either by the Winkler method or by modern polarographic techniques, the relationship between absorption and utilization can be followed.[165] A technique which yielded data, later proved correct by modern methods, was the illumination of algae (*Spirogyra*) by a microspectrum in the presence of bacteria; the bacteria congregated in the blue and red region of the spectrum where the oxygen output was greatest.[92] An example of the correlation between an absorption spectrum and an action spectrum is given for *Ulva taeniata* (Fig. 49).

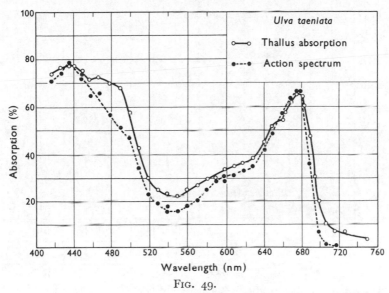

FIG. 49.

The absorption and action spectra of the Chlorophyte *Ulva taeniata*.

(From Blinks, 1954.)

The parallel between absorption of light energy and photosynthesis is striking; only in the region 460–500 nm, around 540 nm and above 700 nm is there a slight deviation. The absorption maxima of extracted chlorophyll *a* fall at approximately 435 nm and 670 nm, very close to the peaks of absorption and photosynthesis on the graph for *Ulva taeniata*.[25] Comparison of the absorption curve for extracted chlorophyll *a* in methanol shows a very abrupt fall from 440 nm to 470 nm, whilst over this range thallus absorption by *Ulva* is high and the action spectrum only slightly depressed. This is a region where carotenoids contribute nearly 50 per cent to the absorption (determined by extraction), which means that these pigments must be effective in photosynthesis, at least as accessory pigments absorbing light energy and transferring this to chlorophyll *a*. Various mechanisms for this energy transfer have been suggested, e.g. internal resonance between carotenoid and chlorophyll molecules situated close together in the chromatophore, direct electron transfer, fluorescence, etc. Above 550 nm, except in red and blue-green algae, the absorption is by chlorophylls alone. In diatoms and brown algae, fucoxanthin acts as an accessory pigment with its absorption maximum at about 540 nm. The quantum yield of photosynthesis of *Navicula minima* (Fig. 50) was measured at different wavelengths and this

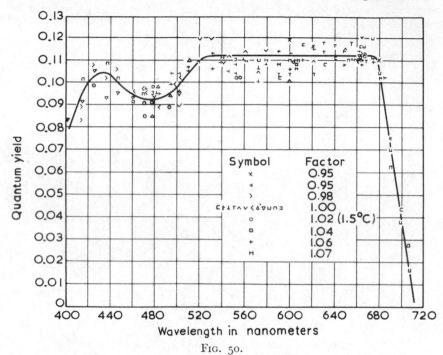

FIG. 50.

The quantum yield of photosynthesis by *Navicula minima* as a function of wavelength.
(From Tanada, 1951.)

was compared with the absorption of light by the chlorophylls, fucoxanthin and other carotenoids.[392] Since there are shifts in the absorption bands between extracted pigments and *in vivo* pigments, a correction must be applied. Fig. 50 gives the quantum yield of photosynthesis as a function of wavelengths between 400 nm and 700 nm. The straight part of the curve between 520 nm and 680 nm shows that the light absorbed by fucoxanthin is utilized in photosynthesis with about the same efficiency as that absorbed by chlorophyll *a*. The same applies to the fucoxanthin of the Phaeophyta. In the Cyanophyta the energy absorbed by phycocyanin, but not by the carotenoids, is effective in photosynthesis.[95] In the Rhodophyta, Haxo and Blinks [165] showed that the action spectrum ran parallel to the absorption by the phycobilins, whilst the chlorophylls and carotenoids were relatively inactive—cf. the extremely low photosynthesis of *Delesseria decipiens* (Fig. 51) at 420–445 nm and at 680 nm where chlorophyll *a* has its maxima. The action spectrum clearly follows the absorption curve for aqueous extracts of pigments, i.e. the phycobilins. The energy absorbed by phycoerythrin is passed via phycocyanin to chlorophyll. The transfers and the concomitant fluorescence are shown in the following diagram.[113]

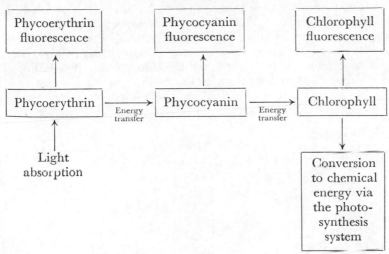

Thus there is overwhelming evidence that the carotenoids and phycobilins act as accessory pigments and absorb energy which is then passed on to chlorophyll. The early view of chromatic adaptation is borne out, since light energy in passing through water is differentially absorbed, the red first then green and finally blue, so that the Rhodophyta, living generally at the

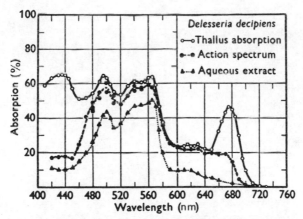

FIG. 51.

The absorption and action spectra of the Rhodophyte *Delesseria decipiens* and of an aqueous extract (phycobilins).

(From Blinks, 1954.)

greatest depth, have their maximum absorption in the green, which is the only light energy available in any quantity at such depth; the intermediate Phaeophyta absorb in the green-yellow-orange, which penetrates to intermediate depths and the Chlorophyta in the blue and red, both of which are available at the surface. The relative inactivity of chlorophyll *a* in the Rhodophyta, in directly absorbing light, is probably due to a deactivation of the chlorophyll *a* in green light. Yocum [427] found that *Porphyra* could be adapted by exposure to red light to use the chlorophyll *a* it contains, whilst this was rapidly lost and a return to the 'wild' type occurred after a few hours in green light. It is suggested that the absorption of light energy by phycoerythrin deactivates the chlorophyll ('competitive inhibition'). [25]

8 Physiology: energy relationships

PHOTOSYNTHESIS

Photosynthesis can be split into three stages:

1. Absorption of light energy by the photosynthetic pigments located in the chromatophores.

2. The transference of this energy, partly to pyrophosphate bond energy of ATP,* in a process of 'photosynthetic phosphorylation' and partly to oxidation/reduction energy, in which $NADPH_2$ is formed and oxygen released.

3. The assimilation of carbon in a series of dark reactions involving ribose-5-phosphate, ribulose diphosphate and utilizing the reducing power of $NADP_2$ and the phosphorylating action of ATP.

The first stage, the absorption of light, has been discussed above. A scheme for the second stage has been proposed by Arnon,[13] Fig. 52. Two cyclic photophosphorylation pathways were discovered, catalysed either by vitamin K or by riboflavin phosphate together with triphosphorpyridine nucleotide. The only product of these cyclic pathways is ATP and neither oxygen nor a reductant is formed; light energy is converted by this process into chemical energy in the form of 'high energy' pyrophosphate bonds. The 'excited' chlorophyll molecules acquire a tendency to expel electrons which are raised to a high energy potential at the expense of the absorbed quanta of light energy. This energy is transformed into chemical energy through a series of enzymatic reactions, the first, in which oxidized vitamin K is reduced and is in turn re-oxidized by cytochrome I; the reduced cytochrome I is itself re-oxidized by passing electrons to the chlorophyll which is thus returned to its unexcited ground state; this process is coupled with a phosphorylation process converting ADP to ATP. Likewise the electrons may travel via the riboflavin phosphate pathway; this pathway is also dependent on a reductase, needed for the reduction of NADP and on chloride ions which are presumed to catalyse the electron transfer in the cytochrome chain. The evolution of oxygen is associated with a non-cyclic

---

* The following symbols are used. ATP, adenosine triphosphate; ADP, adenosine diphosphate; NADP, triphosphopyridine nucleotide; $NADPH_2$, reduced form of triphosphopyridine nucleotide.

photophosphorylation, in which the hydrogen ion of water is used to form reduced triphosphorpyridine nucleotide and the OH⁻ moiety yields molecular oxygen and donates electrons via the cytochrome chain to chlorophyll.

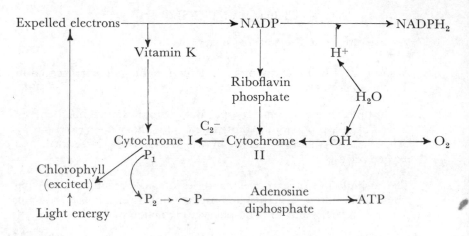

Fig. 52.

Scheme of stage 2 of photosynthesis.

(Adapted from Arnon, 1959.)

The overall equations for these reactions are:

$$ADP + 2H_2O \rightarrow ATP \text{ (cyclic photophosphorylation)} \qquad (1)$$

$$NADP + 2H_2O^* + 2ADP + 2P \rightarrow NADPH_2 + O^*_2 + 2ATP$$
$$\text{(non-cyclic photophosphorylation)} \qquad (2)$$

The assimilation of carbon dioxide in the dark, stage 3, utilizing the energy and reducing power of ATP and $NADPH_2$ formed in stage 2, is represented by the following equation:

$$CO_2 + 2NADPH_2 + n.ATP \rightarrow (CH_2O) + H_2O +$$
$$2NADP + n.ADP + n.P \qquad (3)$$

The sum of equations (1), (2) and (3) is the well known basic equation (4) of photosynthesis:

$$CO_2 + 2H_2O^* \rightarrow (CH_2O) + O^*_2 + H_2O \qquad (4)$$

The pathways indicated above have been worked out using a variety of plant material amongst which the algae *Chlorella* and *Scenedesmus* have figured. The second stage involving phosphorus as the keystone in the conversion of light energy into chemical energy has mainly been based on studies of isolated chloroplasts and on bacteria. However, many of the chemicals, e.g. vitamin K and cytochrome *f* have been identified in *Chlorella* and there is no reason to suppose that any other pathway is implicated.

Exclusion of carbon dioxide enhances the uptake of phosphate by *Chlorella* in the light, whereas *Chlorella* grown in the dark and supplied with glucose, stores 93 per cent of the glucose taken up which in nitrogen is not assimilated. However, if light is supplied at too low an intensity for photosynthesis, the *Chlorella* can utilize the glucose, indicating the photosynthetic phosphorylation potential in algae.

The dark reaction pathway is largely documented from studies on algae. Early work with $^{11}CO_2$ showed that radiocarbon was taken up by algae, but it was only when the longer half-life isotope ^{14}C was used that the path from $^{14}CO_2$ to numerous organic products was confirmed. The uptake occurred after only one minute exposure of *Chlorella* to $^{14}CO_2$, in the dark, following pre-illumination. Continuous dark uptake of $^{14}CO_2$ was also demonstrated. The products of $^{14}CO_2$ assimilation were separated by two-dimensional paper chromatography, combined with autoradiography resulting in the isolation of a large number of labelled compounds. Very short exposure (5 s) of *Chlorella* to $^{14}CO_2$ resulted in the predominant labelling in the carboxyl group of 3-phosphoglyceric acid, together with sugar phosphates, malic acid and traces of amino acids. Using algal material and $^{14}CO_2$ two important sugar phosphates (ribulose diphosphate and sedoheptulose monophosphate) involved in the carbon assimilation cycle were identified.[20] Further experiments with unicellular algae in which all the intermediate compounds in carbon assimilation were labelled (^{14}C saturation experiments), have been used to show the changes in compounds on transfer from light to dark when for example phosphoglyceric acid increases and ribulose diphosphate decreases. Cutting off the CO_2 source resulted in the opposite effect.

Algal chloroplasts, isolated from the cells and suspended in solutions of artificial oxidants, show residual photosynthetic activity with the formation of oxygen (Hill reaction), this carbon dioxide uptake and oxygen evolution has been demonstrated in chloroplast fragments of *Spirogyra*;[398] these were suspended in phosphate buffer at pH 7·2 without the addition of cofactors or enzymes and rates comparable to those of intact cells were recorded. Chloroplasts squeezed out of *Nitella* cells are also capable of assimilating carbon dioxide for a short time.

Factors affecting photosynthesis

LIGHT. Numerous curves have been plotted of light intensity against Q_{O_2} showing a linear increase levelling off at high intensities, i.e. when light saturation occurs (Fig. 54). This well known effect shows the limitation of the 'dark' reactions. Algae differ considerably in their light saturation

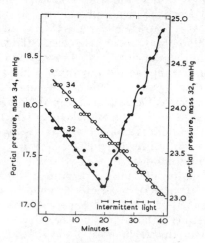

FIG. 53.

The respiration of *Chlorella* measured by the pressure change of O^{34} during dark and light and the simultaneous photosynthesis measured by the pressure change of O^{32}, both recorded with a mass spectrograph.

(From Brown, 1953.)

values and these can be varied by the temperature, concentration of CO_2, enzymes, etc. High light intensities eventually result in irreversible photo-oxidation. *Ochromonas malhamensis* is interesting in that it contains so little chlorophyll that its photosynthesis hardly compensates for respiration.

Cells of some algae (e.g. *Chlorella*) grown in high light intensities adapt, by the formation of greater amounts of chlorophyll, whilst others maintain the same chlorophyll content but the rate of photosynthesis is increased presumably as a result of increased enzyme concentration (e.g. in *Cyclotella*).

TEMPERATURE. At light intensities over which the photosynthesis/light intensity curve is linear, increase in temperature has very little effect since photochemical processes are relatively insensitive to temperature. However, in high light intensities, increase in temperature will raise the point at which light saturation occurs. High temperature strains of *Chlorella* have been isolated which will tolerate 32 294 lux at 39°C, whilst at 25°C photosynthesis is inhibited by intensities above 10 764 lux.[375]

CO_2 AND O_2 SUPPLY. There is a considerable range over which carbon dioxide can be utilized but excess can lead to inhibition. Cultural work is usually done with enriched air of 4–5 per cent CO_2 content which is much greater than is normal under natural conditions. Oxygen concentration operating via respiration can affect photosynthesis since the enzymes and metabolites of the two processes are the same. There is evidence that at high light intensity the decarboxylations involved in respiration cannot proceed owing to the reduced state of the pyridine nucleotides and so in a sense photosynthesis blocks respiration. Brown [38] using oxygen enriched in mass 34 and a recording mass spectrometer, found no inhibition of oxygen uptake in *Chlorella* during photosynthesis except at extremes of oxygen tension and at the highest photosynthetic rates (Fig. 53). The two facts are however compatible since oxygen uptake can proceed independently of the respiratory breakdown of organic compounds.

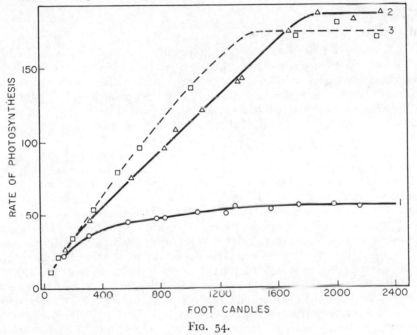

Fig. 54.

Rates of apparent photosynthesis in mm³ (O_2) mm⁻³ packed cells h⁻¹ of *Chlorella*. Curve 1 of cells grown under 60 ft. candles (645 lux) and 39°C; curve 2, cells grown under 400 ft. candles (4305 lux) and at 39°C; curve 3, cells grown under 60 ft. candles (645 lux) and at 25°C. All measured at 39°C.

RHYTHM. As in respiration an endogenous photosynthetic rhythm can be set up, e.g. in *Hydrodictyon* (Fig. 56) by alternating light and dark periods. This continues when cultures are transferred to continuous light. It also occurs in *Acetabularia* (see p. 198). The peak of photosynthesis in some 4 hours after onset of illumination. The rhythm is induced in red and blue light but not in green light of similar energy.[320] A rhythm can also be induced by intermittent CO_2 supply. Since cell size and metabolic activities change during the life history of *Chlorella*, for certain experiments it is necessary to obtain cultures in which the division of all the cells is synchronized; this is done by growing them in intermittent light and dark periods. After such treatment is was found that in the high temperature strain of *Chlorella* the lowest apparent photosynthetic rate was in the young and old cells and the highest in cells 3–4 h old (cf. *Hydrodictyon*).[374] Pretreatment affects the photosynthetic system and plants grown at low temperature and low light, behave as shade plants and those grown at high temperature/high light, as sun plants; in these experiments pretreatment at 645 lux and 39°C gave lower photosynthesis that 645 lux at 25°C or 4305 lux at 39°C (Fig. 54).

Alternative hydrogen donors

In the above scheme for normal photosynthesis, water acts as the hydrogen donor, but some algae are capable of utilizing elementary hydrogen and others hydrogen sulphide. *Scenedesmus* and *Raphidium* incubated in the dark with hydrogen will absorb this gas and when transferred to light will reduce carbon dioxide without release of oxygen; instead an equivalent amount of hydrogen is absorbed, the overall equation being

$$CO_2 + 2H_2 \rightarrow (CH_2O) + H_2O.$$

This is an adaptive process, not normally found in nature and is dependent on the presence of a latent hydrogenase enzyme, which is activated under dark anaerobic conditions. It has so far been found only in bacteria and algae (*Scenedesmsus, Ankistrodesmus, Raphidium, Chlamydomonas moewusii, Ulva, Ascophyllum, Porphyra, Porphyridium, Synechococcus* and *Synechocystis*). The length of time taken to adapt is very variable, short or non-existent in *Chlamydomonas* to several hours for *Ascophyllum*. The continuation of this photoreduction process is possible provided that light intensity is kept low; raising the intensity leads to diminished hydrogen absorption and a return to normal photosynthesis. The fundamental metabolic pathways seem to be maintained with the formation of the same intermediates as in normal photosynthesis, except that the malic acid content may rise. Adaptation of *Scenedesmus* to hydrogen was found to reduce, but not completely inhibit, oxygen evolution. However treatment of hydrogen-adapted *Scenedesmus* with inhibitors, so that oxygen would not be evolved even under normal aerobic conditions, stabilizes the photoreduction which can then continue with higher light intensity and subsequent increase in the rate of hydrogen uptake. Manganese deficiency inhibits normal photosynthesis but not photoreduction using hydrogen, thus manganese is not essential when the oxygen evolution system is out of operation.

When a little oxygen is introduced into the gas mixture supplying hydrogen-adapted *Scenedesmus*, it is absorbed in a reaction which differs from normal respiration (Oxyhydrogen reaction). In addition, two molecules of hydrogen are taken up for each molecule of oxygen and if carbon dioxide is also present still more hydrogen is used for the reduction of carbon dioxide. Anaerobic incubation of these algae in nitrogen, which are capable of adaptation to photoreduction, results in a similar activation of the hydrogenase system and fermentation occurs, first with the release of carbon dioxide and then with evolution of hydrogen.

The utilization of hydrogen sulphide as a hydrogen donor by *Oscillatoria*, results in sulphur deposition in place of oxygen evolution according to the equation

$$CO_2 + 2H_2S \rightarrow (CH_2O) + H_2O + 2S.$$

Facultative chemotrophy

A few algae can be adapted to utilize inorganic compounds (chemolithotrophy) as a source of energy, e.g. *Scenedesmus* and *Chlamydomonas moewusii*. A more widespread phenomenon is the utilization of organic compounds as a source of energy (chemo-organotrophy). These algae possess pigments and can photosynthesize in the light and chemosynthesize in the dark; in addition, photosynthesis may be stimulated by the presence of the organic compounds. The commonest organic sources are hexose sugars and acetic acid but alcohols, amino acids, peptones and proteins have also been utilized. The ability of many organisms, from the unicellular Dinophyceae and diatoms to the larger seaweeds, to grow at depths where light intensity is very low, may be due to this facultative chemotrophy. Utilization of organic sources of energy is now known to be widespread but still little is known about the nutrition of multicellular algae. Sixteen marine littoral diatoms have been grown in the dark, utilizing glucose (but not acetate or lactate), whilst eight used glucose or lactate, one glucose or acetate, one glucose, acetate or lactate and two, only lactate.[242] It was also found that different strains of a single species could behave differently, either not growing on organic sources or growing on different sources. However, another 16 species could not be cultured in this manner.

Until recently the Euglenophyceae was the group best known for chemotrophic assimilation of acetate (so-called 'acetate organisms') and under certain conditions butyric or succinic acid can be utilized. Few flagellates are capable of photo-autotrophy, most require exogenous sources of vitamins, and many require in addition sugars or acetate. Unexpectedly many of the colonial Volvocales can be cultivated on acetate or are stimulated by acetate; a few, e.g. *Gonium quadratum* and *Stephanosphaera pluvialis* cannot multiply in the light in the absence of organic nutrients.[327] These organic substrates are apparently partly utilized in respiration and partly synthesized into cell material, since under aerobic conditions the algae do not consume as much oxygen as would be required to oxidize the whole of the substrate. This type of nutrition has been termed *oxidative assimilation*. Acetate may undergo condensation with oxalacetic acid to form citric acid, a fact suggested by the appearance of radioactive citric acid in *Scenedesmus* fed with ^{14}C-labelled acetate; alternatively it may undergo condensation to form succinic acid.[50] Thus acetate probably enters the tricarboxylic acid cycle and is then built up into carbohydrates or proteins, e.g. ^{14}C-labelled acetate fed to *Nostoc muscorum* led to labelling of glutamate,[9] whilst in *Scenedesmus* it was assimilated into lipids.[50] The fatty acids with even numbers of carbon atoms are assimilated, whereas those with odd numbers are not, presumably since assimilation involves C_2 fragments. Although the organic acids are utilized in the dark, when supplied in the light little of the CO_2 assimilated is derived from the acids, which tend under these conditions to be converted into lipids. The green flagellate *Chlamydobotrys* cannot grow in the dark when supplied with acetate, but can grow in red light, but not green or blue.[328] Also this assimilation proceeds in the absence of CO_2 and oxygen, under which conditions normal photosynthesis is absent or negligible and certainly insufficient for growth. This process is termed photo-assimilation of acetate and is an example of obligate photochemo-organotrophy. Another interesting case is that of *Ochromonas malhamensis* which, as mentioned above, is photosynthetic, but does not possess enough chlorophyll to allow photosynthesis to proceed at a rate sufficient for growth and must be supplied with acetate, palmitate or glucose.

Products of photosynthesis

Cell wall material and many storage products are composed mainly of polysaccharides. The major wall polysaccharides are pectin, uronic acid, glucans, xylans, mannans and galactans; some of these are laid down as microfibrils in a matrix of sugar residues (see p. 37). In the Phaeophyta, alginic acid is present in the wall and in the Rhodophyta agar and carrageenin (see p. 218). The algae are the only group in the plant kingdom in which sulphated polysaccharides are formed; from *Porphyra* a mixture of D- and L-galactose and 3,6-anhydrogalactose, with both sulphate and methyl residues has been isolated. These sulphated polysaccharides and alginic acid are more in the nature of mucilages than structural elements. A common mucilage in the Phaeophyta is fucoidin, composed of L-fucose residues (i.e. a fucan), which are heavily sulphated probably with one sulphate ester group per fucose residue.[181] Mucilages from the red algae *Dilsea* and *Dumontia* consist mainly of D-galactose, uronic acid residues and sulphate esters.

Many of the algal carbohydrates tend to be liberated into culture media, for example Lewin [240] found that 18 species of *Chlamydomonas* released extracellular polysaccharide. In one species, *C. mexicana*, 25 per cent of the total organic carbohydrate production was liberated. There was considerable similarity of structure in these extracellular products, galactose and arabinose being the main sugars; one species differed in forming glucose and xylose, whilst fucose, rhamnose, mannose and uronic acids were also detected. Extracellular mucilage is part of the morphology of many algae, e.g.

Dictyosphaerium, desmids, *Uroglena* and the sheaths and stalks of colonial diatoms. The diatom *Navicula pelliculosa* forms a mucilage capsule when division stops, which may occur when silica, phosphorus or nitrogen are limiting in the media. This capsule is composed of glucuronic acid residues; these may also be formed in the dark if the diatom is supplied with glucose, but hydrolysates of the capsule are not metabolized, neither are extracellular enzymes formed which can act on the capsule.[238]

All these wall and storage carbohydrates originate from the photosynthetic processes in the algae and must be built up from the simple sugar residues which themselves can be found in minute quantity in algal cells. Small amounts of free glucose and fructose were found in *Laminaria digitata* and slightly more free glucose in *Fucus serratus* (0·5 g/100 g dry alga).[198] Galactose, mannose, fructose, arabinose and traces of ribose also occurred free in *Fucus*. Simple sugars have been recorded from most groups of algae, but it seems unlikely that any alga will contain much free sugar.

Polyhydric alcohols (sugar alcohols) occur in algae, e.g. erythritol in *Trentepohlia*,[29] galactitol (dulcitol) in *Iridaea* and *Bostrychia* (together with sorbitol), D-mannitol, which is the most frequently recorded in the plant kingdom, in almost all Phaeophyta and some Rhodophyta (*Pelvetia* is an exception and contained D-volemitol).[248] Certain sugar alcohols seem to be confined to species living high on the shore, e.g. sorbitol in *Bostrychia*, D-volemitol in *Pelvetia* and *Porphyra*. The simplest sugar alcohol, glycerol, was found in all Rhodophyta which also formed floridoside (glycerol α-D-galactoside). Mannitol may form up to 20 per cent of the dry wt. of *Laminaria digitata* fronds; a conspicuous seasonal variation was found, with minimal values of mannitol (5 g/100 g dry matter) in February/March and maximum (15/100 g) July/August/September (Fig. 55). The mannitol content of *Laminaria* stipes is somewhat lower than that of the fronds and the concentration is highest from September–January, that is later than for the fronds. The mannitol content also varies with habitat and was less abundant in samples of *Ascophyllum nodosum* growing where freshwater contamination occurred.[228] Cyclic sugar alcohols are also recorded, e.g. lamitol (C-methylinositol) in *Laminaria*, and this and scyclitol in *Porphyra*.[248] Glycosides are also present in brown algae, e.g. 1-D-mannitol, β-D-glucopyranoside, whilst *Pelvetia* also contains the corresponding β-glucoside of D-volemitol. In the Rhodophyta, floridoside is generally distributed, this is 2-glycerol α-D-galactopyranoside.[248]

The principal storage products are mainly glucose polymers. Starch (a mixture of amylose and amylopectin) is common in the Chlorophyta and starch-like compounds are found in Cryptophyceae and Dinophyceae and are similar in chemical structure to starch of higher plants. In the Rhodophyta the major storage compound is Floridean starch, which consists of glucose residues, although that from *Dilsea* differs from ordinary starch in consisting mainly of amylopectin units and being more resistant to amylase than amylopectin from other sources.[137] Cyanophycean starch may also be similar to this; it gives maltose on treatment with dialyzed malt extract, but, it has also been suggested that like Floridean starch it may be nearer glycogen. The substance termed paramylum in the Euglenophyta also consists of glucose residues and may be yet another form of starch. In the

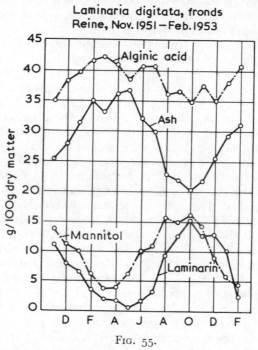

FIG. 55.

The seasonal variation of some chemical constituents of *Laminaria digitata* fronds. (Haug and Jensen, 1956.)

Phaeophyta, starch has not been detected, its place being taken by laminarin, which is built up of chains of 1,3-linked β-D-glucopyranose residues, with some branched molecules interlinked by β-1-6 glucosidic linkages and with mannitol combined as an end group on some of the molecules.[12] The enzyme laminarase can be extracted from some algae. A seasonal variation in laminarin occurs similar to that of mannitol.[162] The characteristic reserve product of the Chrysophyta and Bacillariophyta is also a glucose polymer (leucosin, chrysolaminarin, chrysose) and a crystalline sample obtained from diatoms consisted of 99·5 per cent glucose residues.[16] Methylation proved the presence of branched chains, 1–6 and 1–3 linkages. This compound appears to be very similar to laminarin, differing only in the absence of mannitol molecules at the reducing end of the chains.

From extracts of minced seaweeds, enzymes showing carbohydrase activity have been recorded;[89] they will hydrolyse α-glucosides (e.g. maltose and sucrose), β-glucosides (e.g. cellobiose, laminarin), lactose and xylans. The 'maltase' present in the crude extracts also showed synthetic activity. *Cladophora rupestris* has yielded an enzyme capable of synthesis of higher oligosaccharides from maltose.[88]

Organic acids are present in some quantity in certain seaweeds, whilst many of the Krebs cycle acids are found in small quantities in algae. Citric acid has been found in species of Chlorophyta in amounts varying from 6–145 mg/100 g dry wt., from 24–747 mg in Rhodophyta and from 15–1470 mg in Phaeophyta.[72] An extremely acid alga is *Desmarestia*, which turns blue on injury owing to the effect of its acid on the carotenoid pigments. Extracts of *Desmarestia* have been found to have pH values around 1·0;[24] this acidity may be due to malic acid but other acids have also been reported, including free sulphuric acid.[283] In *Porphyra* and *Alaria* there is a high concentration of ascorbic acid comparable to that in lemons. Unlike bacteria and fungi, algae liberate only small amounts of extracellular acids, e.g. glycollic, oxalic and pyruvic acid from *Chlamydomonas* spp.

Fat as a reserve product occurs in the Chlorophyta, Cyanophyta, Phacophyta and Rhodophyta, but is particularly common in the Chrysophyta, Bacillariophyta and Dinophyceae. *Chlorella, Scenedesmus* and diatoms have been used experimentally for the production of fats. In cultures of *Chlorella* in which cell division had ceased owing to lack of nitrogen in the medium, the fat content of the cells increased from 28 to 70 per cent, coincident with a decrease in protein content from 30 to 8 per cent (Aach[1]). The Rhodophyta and Cyanophyta differ from other algae in that fat accumulation is not associated with low cell nitrogen contents.[69] Lack of water appears to be a factor which increases fat content of algal cells. Both saturated, particularly palmitic acid, and unsaturated fatty acids occur, the latter however are predominant. Sterols (sitosterol, fucosterol, ergosterol and chondrillasterol) are found in the fat solvent extract of algae.

Recent work has shown that the wavelength of light affects the products of photosynthesis—equal quanta of blue rather than red light decreases the amount of carbohydrate formed but increases the protein content and enhances the production of RNA.

RESPIRATION

The essentials of algal respiration, the breakdown of complex molecules with or without the uptake of oxygen and the all important release of energy, probably follows metabolic pathways similar to those of other organisms.

Proteases and lipases have been shown to exist in algae and glucose-1-phosphate has been detected, so the breakdown of reserves such as proteins to peptides and amino acids, and of polysaccharides by phosphorylation to yield the initial substrate for the Embden Mayerhof Parnas glycolysis pathway, can occur. As already mentioned ADP and ATP have been demonstrated in *Chlorella, Ankistrodesmus* and *Euglena* and these together with the phosphorylated sugars (fructose-6-phosphate, frustose-1,6-diphosphate) and phosphoglyceric acid, point to the operation of this pathway. Aerobic breakdown of glucose in *Ochromonas malhamensis*, stopped by addition of arsenite, caused pyruvic and lactic acid to accumulate and labelling of the glucose in the 1 or 2 position yielded labelling of the pyruvate, which is expected in the EMP pathway operates.[332] These reactions and the yield of high-energy phosphate groups and reduced NAD can be summarized thus:

$$1. \quad C_6H_{12}O_6 + 2NAD + 2P_i + 2ATP + 2ADP \rightarrow 2CH_3CO.COOH + 2NADH_2 + 4ATP$$

Further oxidation of pyruvic acid via the tricarboxylic acid cycle in algae, is deduced from the presence of tricarboxylic acids in *Chlorella* and *Scenedesmus*, which when supplied with $^{14}CO_2$ produce the labelling in malic, succinate, glutamic and alanine.[21] The overall result of this cycle can be summarized thus:

$$2. \quad CH_3.CO.COOH + 4NAD + FAD + P_i + ADP + 3H_2O \rightarrow 3CO_2 + 4NADH_2 + FADH_2 + ATP$$

However, the enzymes involved in this cycle have not been identified with certainty. Organic acids added to cultures of algae are taken up if the pH of the solution is such that undissociated molecules predominate and these are then used as respiratory substrates. *Chlamydomonas moewusii* can oxidize acetate, pyruvate and succinate (Lewin [236]), the Xanthophycean alga *Monodus subterraneus* oxidizes acetate and propionate,[286] the respiration of the diatom *Navicula pelliculosa* is stimulated by lactate, citrate and succinate, whilst *Euglena gracilis* v. *bacillaris* is stimulated by a range of these acids. These facts point to the operation of the Krebs cycle, although the evidence is still only fragmentary.

The respiration of *Chlorella*, *Scenedesmus*, *Anabaena*, *Nostoc* and many other algae is stimulated by the addition of glucose to the medium. This and other added substrates are not entirely broken down to carbon dioxide, but assimilated into cellular material.

The respiratory activity of algae is measured by the usual methods, involving oxygen uptake or carbon dioxide production. Rates between 0·14 and 0·93 μl/mg dry wt./h are given for some Chlorophyta, Phaeophyta and Rhodophyta, with R.Q. values between 0·53–1·28.[418] The rate for fruiting thalli of *Ulva lactuca* is higher (3·53 μl/mg dry wt./h for female thalli and 4·18 for male thalli) than the vegetative thalli (1·8 μl/mg dry wt./h), whilst for the gametes, the rise is to 26·2 μl/mg/dry wt./h for the female and 35·2 for the male.[166] The respiration levels of thalli will vary considerably for any one species according to the level of respiratory substrates and variety of cultural conditions.

Decrease in oxygen tension results in decreased respiration in algae of fast-flowing aerated waters, e.g. *Hydrurus* and *Batrachospermum* are more affected than algae of standing waters (e.g. *Cladophora*).[125] The reduction was observed as soon as the oxygen content dropped below 100 per cent, suggesting that in natural habitats, oxygen lack may be a more important factor than previously thought. Supersaturation with oxygen increased the respiration of *Pithophora* up to 300 per cent supersaturation, but at 400 per cent it was decreased again, although still higher than at 100 per cent. Unicellular planktonic algae such as *Asterionella formosa* and *Fragilaria crotonensis* also exhibited the same phenomenon. Supersaturation with oxygen does occur in algal habitats, e.g. in sewage ponds. Decrease in temperature decreases the respiration rate of algae but the decrease is much greater than the decrease in photosynthesis, so that at low temperatures the quotient assimilation/respiration is higher, a fact which may explain the enormous growth of large brown algae in polar waters. The effect of pH of the medium is clearly shown in work on *Ochromonas*, which has a peak of oxygen consumption at 5·0 and falls to nil at 3·5 and 8·5.[332] pH also affects the penetrability of endogenous respiratory substrates, some of which enter only at physiologically unsuitable pH values, hence the use of dry cells in some experiments.[285]

Rhythmic respiratory activity is reported in *Hydrodictyon* and *Fucus*. The former, if grown through alternating light and dark periods, continues to show peaks of oxygen uptake when transferred to continuous dark, the peaks coinciding with the previous dark time intervals[359] (Fig. 56). This graph also shows that the peak of oxygen consumption in the dark period is reached some 6 hours after transfer to the dark and subsequently decreases. Addition of glucose to the culture increased the oxygen consumption by a factor of 3, but during the subsequent continuous dark period, no rhythm occurred, merely a slow decrease in oxygen consumption.

Anaerobic respiration (fermentation)

Acid fermentation has been demonstrated in a number of algae. The colourless alga *Prototheca zopfii*, supplied with exogenous glucose, produces large amounts of lactic and some succinic acid. *Chlorella* produces little carbon dioxide under anaerobiosis, but the addition of glucose, fructose, mannose or galactose increases the CO_2 production and alcohols and acids, including lactic, are formed. Fermentation by *Scenedesmus* leads to CO_2 production, followed by hydrogen production together with slight formation of lactic acid; added glucose again increases the reaction.[117] Anaerobic culture in hydrogen, results in a net uptake of hydrogen whilst carbon dioxide production remains constant. Studies by Reazin (1956) with *Ochromonas malhamensis* anaerobically cultured with labelled glucose, showed that either the methyl group or the carbonyl group of pyruvate respectively could be labelled when either the 1-^{14}C or 2-^{14}C compound was used, which is evidence of the EMP pathway in anaerobiosis; ethanol, carbon dioxide and lactic acid were formed.

Endogenous respiration of *Chlorella* is not blocked by cyanide but glucose respiration is, suggesting that endogenous and exogenous respiration systems exist independently. This hypothesis is supported by the fact that glucose respiration in *Chlorella* is more susceptible than endogenous respiration after treatment with ultraviolet radiation.[182]

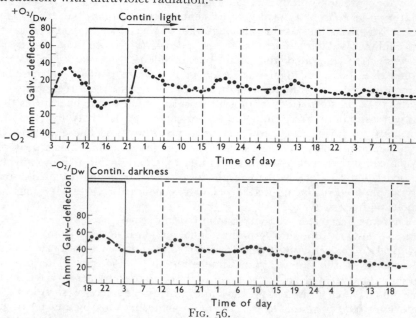

FIG. 56.

The photosynthesis (*above*) and respiration rhythm (*below*), of *Hydrodictyon* during a 9 hours light/9 hours dark regime followed by continuous light or dark. Dashed lines indicate the times of the light/dark periods if they had continued. O_2/DW = Oxygen evolution per unit dry wt. per hour measured as deflections on the galvanometer linked to a dropping mercury electrode.

(After Pirson, 1957, in Sweeney, 1963.)

Cells of *Chlorella* dried *in vacuo* over P_2O_5 were able to oxidize Krebs cycle acids more readily than intact cells.[285] The effect of dry g was thought to increase permeability, whilst endogenous oxygen uptake of the dried cells was also stimulated.

Algae utilizing acetate, may either assimilate (see p. 177) or respire this, in the latter case, via the tricarboxylic acid cycle. Thus it was found that ^{14}C-labelled acetate fed to *Scenedesmus* resulted in labelling of citric acid.[50]

Since lipids are conspicuous reserve products in many algae, it is likely that they also are respired, probably following the pathways known in higher plants, i.e. via glycerol, fatty acids and the fatty acid spiral.

PLATE 9 **A**: A cell of *Cyclococcolithus leptoporus*. Mag. × 4300. **B**: A cell of *Syracosphaera mediterranea*. Mag. × 6000. These are both genera of the widespread group Prymnesiales and show the delicately sculptured calcareous coccoliths which coat the outside of these flagellates. (Scanning electron micrographs kindly provided by Dr. K. Gaarder.)

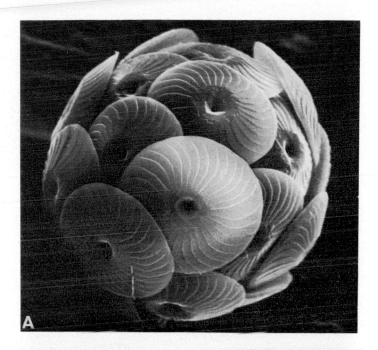

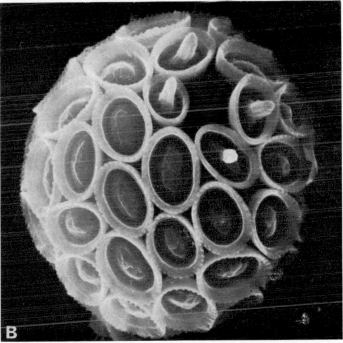

Plate 9

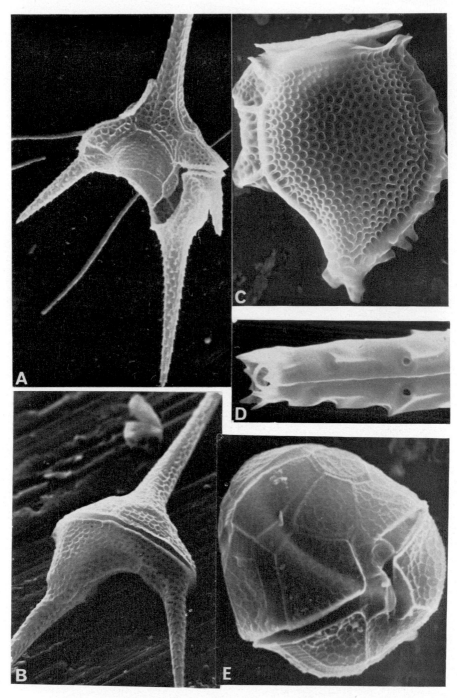

Plate 10

NITROGEN METABOLISM

The sources of nitrogen for algae are discussed on p. 183 where it is noted that nitrate, ammonium salts and organic nitrogen compounds are all utilized. That nitrates can be reduced by algae has long been known. Recently cultures of *Ankistrodesmus* have been shown to accumulate nitrite when transformation to ammonia is blocked by low pH values.[205] In *Chlorella* grown in the light, in solutions containing glucose and nitrate, but without CO_2,[409] oxygen is given off indicating nitrate reduction.[76] Similar cultures in the presence of CO_2 and at high light intensities, evolve more oxygen in the presence of nitrate than in its absence, but the rate of CO_2 assimilation is approximately the same.[402] At low light intensity the oxygen production is unaffected by the presence of nitrate, but the rate of CO_2 assimilation is lower. These results suggested that nitrate acts as an alternate hydrogen acceptor in photosynthesis. The reduction of nitrite in *Ankistrodesmus* can be stopped by 2,4-dinitrophenol, and also by arsenate, suggesting that this process may be dependent on photosynthesis not only for hydrogen donors but for high energy phosphate.[206] The assimilation of elemental nitrogen by Cyanophyta appears to proceed via ammonia; the first products, when ^{15}N is supplied to *Nostoc muscorum*, being ammonia, glutamic and aspartic acids.[419] Nitrogen supplied as organic compounds is first deaminated;[6]

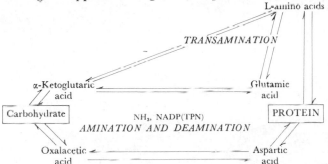

some species appear to have an excessive capacity for deamination, resulting in the release of ammonia into the medium, e.g. *Scenedesmus*, *Haematococcus*, *Ankistrodesmus* and *Hormidium*, whilst others have a much lower capacity, which may be a limiting factor in nitrogen assimilation, e.g. *Chlorella* and

PLATE 10 **A, B** & **D**: The freshwater planktonic dinoflagellate *Ceratium hirundinella*, A & B show the ventral and dorsal surfaces with the sculptured plates covering the cell and the transverse furrow in which one flagellum runs. D is an enlargement of the spine on the epicone showing the sculpturing and pores in the plate. *C. Dinophysis caudata*, a very common marine planktonic dinoflagellate of the section Desmophyceae. The furrow in which one flagellum runs is at the apex and the other trails out from the left hand side. *E. Peridinum cinctum*, a freshwater planktonic dinoflagellate showing the plates of both epicone and hypocone, transverse furrow and lateral furrow system. (All scanning electron micrographs kindly provided by Dr. J. D. Dodge. Mag. A & B × 32 000, C × 4800, D × 25 200, E × 7700.)

Zygnema. It is interesting that the former group tend to live naturally in habitats where high concentrations of organic nitrogen occur and as suggested by Algéus, they may contribute to purification by conversion of organic nitrogen compounds to ammonia. Whatever the source, it appears that it is in the form of ammonia that the nitrogen is accepted into the metabolic pathways. Little data are available regarding the mechanism of formation of amino acids, amides, peptides and proteins. It was shown that nitrogen-starved *Chlorella*, supplied with ammonium salts initially increased their respiration rate, whilst α-amino nitrogen and amides (glutamine) were rapidly formed.[387] This was thought to be connected with respiration through phosphorylated compounds as in higher plants. Transaminases have also been detected in cell-free preparations of *Chlorella* [285] involving principally, aspartic acid, glutamic acid and alanine. Similar systems are reported in *Ulva lactuca* [193] and the following scheme for amino acid pathways

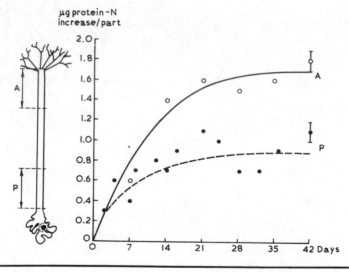

| μg N/part ± 3 m | | | |
	0 days	42 days	Increase %	Maxim. %
A	1·2 ± 0·2	3·0 ± 0·2	150	>270
P	1·9 ± 0·1	3·0 ± 0·1	58	77

Fig. 57.

The increase in protein nitrogen content of enucleate anterior segments (A) and enucleate posterior segments (P) of *Acetabularia* grown in the light. The diagram on the left shows the position from which the segments were taken.

(From Hämmerling *et al.*, 1958.)

in *Ulva* has been proposed, although it is likely that the major pathway is via glutamic and the lesser via aspartic acid. In the nitrogen-fixing Cyanophyta it would seem from studies with labelled nitrogen, that there is a similar entry of ammonia into the metabolic cycles by amination of α-ketoglutaric acid. In *Scenedesmus* it has been shown that aspartic acid is a very poor nitrogen source and that glutamic acid occupies the key position;[7] however, *Stichococcus* and *Hormidium* grew well when supplied with aspartic acid [8] and it may be significant that they belong to the same algal group as *Ulva*.

Peptides are reported from several algae and polypeptides have been detected as extracellular products of blue-green algae.[104]

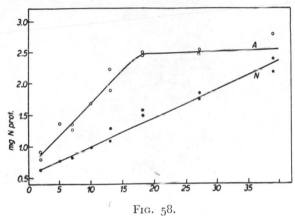

FIG. 58.

The formation of protein nitrogen in nucleate (N) and enucleate (A) segments of *Acetabularia* over a period of 40 days.

(From Brachet *et al.*, 1955.)

Little has been achieved in the way of isolation of proteins from algae. Bulk proteins have been extracted and their amino acid content determined,[110] showing that the different amino acids are present in roughly comparable amounts in the proteins from Chlorophyta (*Chlorella*), Cyanophyta (*Anabaena*), Xanthophyceae (*Tribonema*) and Bacillariophyceae (*Navicula*); the values are comparable to those for higher plants. The sites of protein synthesis are numerous; they are not necessarily associated with the nucleus, since in *Acetabularia*, synthesis continues in enucleate plants, both in the cytoplasm and chloroplasts.[33,36,66,412] Fig. 57 shows that protein synthesis is least in the basal region of the stalk, i.e. the region of least regenerative power (see p. 201). Non-growing enucleate fragments also form protein,[412] suggesting that protein increase can be independent of growth, although in growing fragments there is a strong correlation between growth and synthesis. In enucleated (and nucleated) fragments, the rate of protein synthesis is related to the energy production in the cytoplasm, e.g. in weak illumination it is lower than in high illumination and further, both enucleate and nucleate fragments, under the same light conditions, have a similar rate, suggesting that the nucleus is not involved in the regulation of the process. Initially the speed of protein synthesis may be greater in enucleate than in nucleate fragments but later it slows down (Fig. 58, Brachet *et al.*[33]), suggesting an inhibitory effect of the nucleus. The process in enucleated fragments is not merely a consumption of the nitrogen pool, since this itself increases.[33]

9 Physiology: movement and rhythm

Many algae are capable of movement which is often associated with positive phototaxis and sometimes with an endogenous rhythm. Other physiological rhythms have been recorded associated with light/dark stimulus and even tidal periodicity.

Movement of algae is accomplished by means of flagellar action, or by extrusion of mucilage; movement of cytoplasm and plastids also occurs, the actual mechanism of these motions is unknown. Parts of an otherwise attached alga, may move towards or away from stimuli, e.g. light (phototropism).

Phototaxis may be separated into two distinct reactions, phobo-phototaxis, which is the movement induced by 'shock reaction' to changes in light intensity and not to direction of the light, and topo-phototaxis, which is movement towards or away from the light source. In the case of flagellate phototaxis, it is not clear whether this is a series of phobic reactions, as the photoreceptor is alternately shaded and lighted, or a constant topic reaction. Phototactic flagellates in most cases possess an eyespot, but the term eyespot is unfortunate as it implies a photosensitive nature which it may not possess. The concept of the eyespot as a cup-shaped pigmented layer and a lens which concentrates the light[280] is not borne out by electron microscope studies. In *Chlamydomonas* the eyespot is embedded in the chromatophore and may be in any position but is most commonly somewhere near the apex of the cell; likewise the eyespot in *Euglena* is not always in the anterior region and in some species, numerous 'eyespot'-like granules occur in the cytoplasm. However many non-flagellate algae, without any trace of an eyespot, react phototactically, e.g. the motile diatoms. It is nevertheless a fact that most species with eyespots are motile; exceptions being species of *Astasia* and *Polytoma*[324] and sessile genera of the Tetrasporales. Exposure of the apical region of *Euglena* to ultraviolet light resulted in lack of motility, whereas exposure of the basal part did not;[395] the detrimental effect may however have been on organs other than the eyespot. 'Eyespotless' mutants of *Chlamydomonas reinhardtii*, still showed a phototactic response although this was less rapid and less uniform than that of the wild type,[152] which suggests that the view put forward some ninety years ago by Strasburger, that the whole protoplast is sensitive to light, is true but the presence of an eyespot accentuates this sensitivity. Reviewing the evidence for the functioning of the eyespot Halldal concluded that the 'photosensitive spot in topo-phototactic algae is situated at or near the flagellar base, but is not the stigma (eyespot) or any organ connected with it.[141] It is believed that shading of the photosensitive spot is important, but that this can be achieved by the

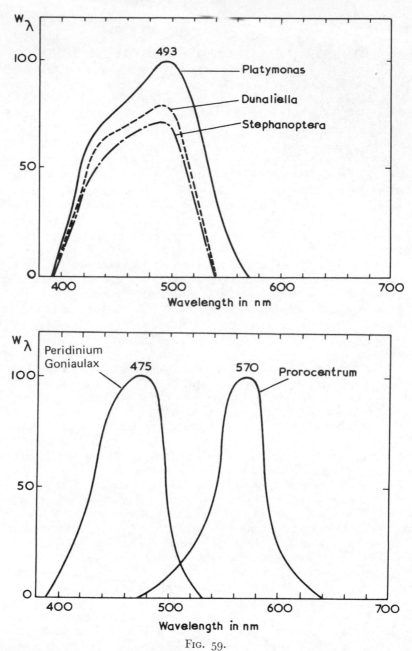

Fig. 59.

The action spectra of phototaxis in some Volvocales (top graphs) and some Dinophyceae (lower graphs).

(From Halldal, 1958.)

chromatophore, and that the eyespot 'may act to improve the reaction to a high degree.' The electron microscope has shown the presence of a swelling at the base of the long flagellum in *Euglena* (see Plate 5); this organelle is possibly associated with photo-reception.

Low light intensities in general induce positive phototactic reactions and high light, negative.

The pigments which are active in phototaxis are not known, although as early as 1882 Engelmann found that the phototactic action spectrum of *Euglena* was at a maximum at 480 nm and later other algae were found to be similar. Maxima for the phototactic action spectra of Volvocales is at 493 nm (Fig. 59), of *Ulva* gametes at 485 nm, both with shoulders at 435 nm, whilst the dinoflagellates *Gonyaulax* and *Peridinium* have maxima at 475 nm and *Prorocentrum* at 570 nm. These action spectra were identical for both positive and negative phototaxis (Fig. 59).[141]

In *Euglena gracilis* the absorption spectrum of the eyespot has the same series of peaks as the phototactic action spectrum, suggesting that there is a link between light absorption by the eyespot and motility (Fig. 60).[422] The

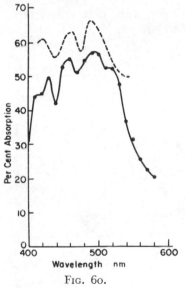

FIG. 60.

The phototactic action spectra (— — —) and the absorption spectrum of the *Euglena gracilis* eyespot (—·—).
(From Wolken, 1961.)

action spectrum of a colourless and eyespotless mutant of *E. gracilis* has quite a different form, with maxima at 410 and 425 nm as opposed to maxima at 425, 450, 475 and 495 nm for the coloured wild type. In *E. gracilis* the negative phototaxis is considered to be of a phobo-phototactic nature and its action spectrum is unlike that for positive phototaxis.[43] A similar action spectrum is given by a colourless form with or without a stigma, but the strongest response is shifted slightly from 415 nm for the green mutant to 410 nm for the colourless. This result for *Euglena* is in contrast to that obtained for Volvocales, etc., by Halldal. Colonial species are also phototactic, with maxima around 490 nm for *Volvox* and *Gonium* and around 530 nm for *Pandorina* and *Eudorina*.

A negative or positive phototactic reaction is not only dependent on light intensity; *Platymonas* was positively phototactic at all light intensities when the ratio of Mg to Ca ions was greater than 6 : 1 and negative when the ratio was less than 6 : 1.[141] A change from positive to negative phototaxis often occurs after copulation of gametes when the zygote is motile (planozygote), e.g. planozygotes of *Cymopolia* collect on the dark side of culture vessels, 2 minutes after mixing of the gametes. The desmid *Micrasterias* loses most of its phototactic response shortly before division and regains it only when the daughter cells are completely reorganized, which may be some time after they appear to be complete.[19]

A daily periodicity of phototactic response has been recorded for *Euglena gracilis* with a peak reaction around mid-day (Fig. 61); this was maintained albeit at a lower level when the *Euglena* was transferred to permanent darkness.[322]

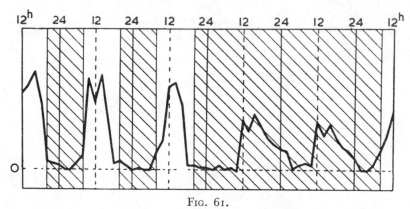

FIG. 61.

The phototactive sensitivity of *Euglena gracilis* in alternating 12 h light/12 hr dark periods and in constant dark. Dark periods are cross hatched.

(From Pohl, 1948.)

Diatoms are also conspicuously phototactic, positive phototaxis occurring at wavelengths below 550 nm at light intensities from 3–10 000 lux.[296] The movement of diatoms is complicated by the shape of the cells and the position of the raphe slits, e.g. in *Nitzschia* the cell moves along a curve and swings from side to side as the cell turns over (Fig. 62). Three main forms of movement have been recognized for *Navicula*, *Amphora* and *Nitzschia* (Fig. 62).

Many Cyanophyta are phototactic, positive in weak light and negative in high light intensities, but *Oscillatoria jennensis* is reported to be always negatively phototactic. The action spectra of *Phormidium uncinatum* is from 400–610 nm, but *Anabaena variabilis* and *Cylindrospermum licheniforme* only react between 500–670 nm.[83] In *Oscillatoria*, it was found that only the filaments pointing towards the light were phototactic and that light did not have an orientating effect on filaments lying outside a 45° arc from the light source.

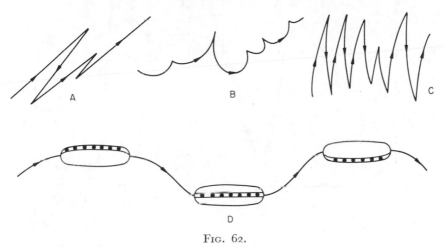

FIG. 62.

Diagrams illustrating the path of movement of *Navicula* (A), *Amphora* (B) and *Nitzschia* (C) and the corkscrew motion of *Nitzschia* (D).

(Adapted from Nultsch, 1956.)

Contrary to this, light had a distinct orientating effect on *Anabaena*, which creeps towards the light either with its filaments directed forwards or bent in a U-shape, with the bend in the U towards the light source.[83] *Phormidium autumnale* is topo-phototactic from 5–10 000 lux with an optimum at 200 lux.[297] The action spectrum of this species was determined (Fig. 63) and the second maximum (490–500 nm) was shown to be the principal absorption region of the carotenoids and the third maximum (560–570 nm) to be that of phycoerythrin. The tactic reaction is proportional therefore to carotenoid and phycobilin absorption, but is not related to chlorophyll absorption.

Photo-phobotaxis occurs in all these algal groups. In flagellates it may take the form of a sudden change in the direction of beat of the flagella resulting in a rapid turn. Cyanophyta and diatoms aggregate after sudden light changes, whilst diatom cells moving out of the dark into the light can often be seen to retreat back into the dark as a shock reaction.

The rate of movement of many species differs in different light intensities, this phenomenon is known as photokinesis. *Ulva* gametes rapidly increase their rate of linear movement between 0–1076 lux, but above this the increases are very slight.[166] The maximum rate of swimming of *Euglena* is reached at 430 lux and above this it decreases.[424]

Growth movements associated with light (phototropism) have long been recognized in algae and examples of phototropic growth and orientation of

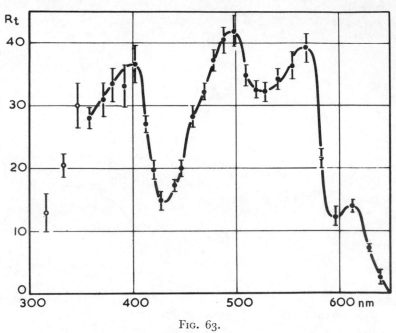

FIG. 63.

The action spectrum of phototactic movement of *Phormidium autumnale*.
(From Nultsch, 1961.)

the cleavage plane in egg cells is given on p. 199. A favourite alga for tropic studies is *Bryopsis*, in which the side branches grow towards blue, but not red light. Filaments of *Spirogyra* and of *Tolypothrix* are positively phototropic. It is considered that β-carotene is involved in *Tolypothrix*[266] and carotenoids in general have been implicated in phototropic responses.

Phototaxis is responsible for the vertical movement of some planktonic organisms. The dinoflagellates *Ceratium fusus* and *C. tripos* migrate downwards during the day and rise again at night in the inner Oslo Fjord, whilst *Gonyaulax polyedra* and *Prorocentrum micans* behave in the opposite manner.[155] Similar migrations have been recorded in freshwaters where many flagellates are believed to settle on to the sediments during darkness and rise into the water mass during daytime.

Phototactic movements of chloroplasts have been more fully studied in higher plants, however, desmids have long been known to undergo chloroplast movements. In *Mougeotia* the plate-like chloroplast (Fig. 6J, p. 14) can rotate; the movement from a profile position to a flat position is complete in 30–40 minutes after the filaments are transferred from light to darkness and the percentage of filaments showing this, increases at higher light intensities.[164] At high light intensities the response occurs after a very short exposure, e.g. a single electronic flash (1/1000 s). The action spectrum has a strong maximum between 600–700 nm and a weaker one below 400 nm. The induction in red light can be reversed by irradiations with far-red, provided the time interval between the two irradiations is less than 1 minute. Polarized light also induces the reaction, but only when the light is vibrating perpendicularly to the long axis of the cell; vibration parallel to the long axis is ineffective and also antagonizes the induction by light vibrating in the perpendicular plane. Equal energies of polarized light are more effective than unpolarized light. Similar results were obtained with *Mesotaenium*, but the shortest period of irradiation necessary was 30 min; this could however be replaced by a series of flashes. In the diatoms *Striatella* and *Biddulphia* the chromatophores move to the centre and cluster around the nucleus in high light intensity whilst in low light intensities they remain in a peripheral position.

Rhythms induced by phototactic responses have been mentioned above for *Euglena*. In nature *Euglena* burrows into the mud as high tide approaches and emerges again when the mud is exposed,[31] and this rhythm is maintained for many days in the laboratory.[308] A phototactic rhythm in *Chromulina psammobia* was maintained in the laboratory for 8 days.[99] The positive phototaxis was associated with low tide whilst a negative phototaxis and positive thigmotaxis produced burrowing at high tide similar to that of *Euglena*.[99] *Euglena* cells maintained in the dark become phototactically inactive, and the phototactic rhythm which continues in the dark is temperature independent and persists even when the cells divided more frequently than once every 24 hours.[40] Diatoms also have an endogenous rhythmic movement, e.g. *Hantzschia amphioxys*[100]* moves up to the sand surface during low tide and continues to do so when transferred to the laboratory. This reaction also seems to be associated with an agglutination of the cells during the phototactic phase, a feature which Faure-Fremiet thought may prevent their displacement when the tide again covers them. The vertical migration rhythm of this diatom maintained in the laboratory follows that of the cells in nature i.e. its timing follows approximately the tidal changes. Such a tidally linked rhythm is rare in plants.[308b]

A few marine algae are luminescent, e.g. the dinoflagellate *Gonyaulax polyedra*, which on stimulation by agitation (waves, or movement of fish, etc.) gives off a flash of light of 0·1 s duration. The luminescence is dim during the day and about sixty times brighter at night, i.e. it has a diurnal periodicity. If *Gonyaulax*, cultured in constant light, are placed in the dark they continue to exhibit a rhythm of luminescence, with peaks at 23 hour intervals (Fig. 64).[160]

---

* Now known to be *H. virgata* v. *intermedia*.[350b]

The gradual decrease in height of the peaks is due to energy exhaustion since this is a photosynthetic organism.[384] The diurnal rhythm is not dependent upon prior growth in alternating light to dark conditions, since cultures grown in bright light for one year show a diurnal periodicity of luminescence when placed in the dark. This and other evidence suggests that the rhythm is a 'basic oscillatory mechanism inherent to the cell.'[161] The amount of luminescence at night is directly related to the amount of light received during the day, probably being related to photosynthesis. Extracts of *Gonyaulax* have yielded a crude cell-free preparation which is luminescent in the presence of sodium chloride.[161] Oxygen is required and

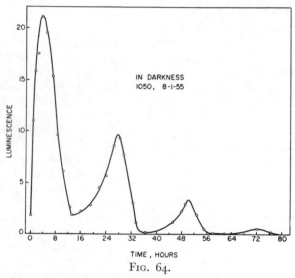

FIG. 64.

Rhythmic luminescence of *Gonyaulax* cells grown in constant light and placed in constant darkness. Time in hours after placing in darkness.

(From Sweeney and Hastings, 1957.)

activity is at an optimum at pH 6·6 and 24°C. The light emitted is blue-green with a peak at 478 nm (Fig. 65). The reaction appears to be an oxidation of a substrate, luciferin, in the presence of an enzyme, luciferase. This results in an excited molecule (L*) which emits a quantum of light and returns to the ground state.

$$LH_2 + \tfrac{1}{2}O_2 \xrightarrow{\text{luciferase}} L^* + H_2O$$
$$L^* \longrightarrow L + \text{Light (max} = 470 \text{ nm)}$$

In addition to the rhythm of luminescence a rhythm of cell division was also found, in which the majority of cell divisions occurred in a 5 hour period, spanning the end of the dark and beginning of the light period.[384]

This rhythm was lost after 4–6 days in continuous bright light, but persisted for fourteen days in continuous dim light. The maximum number of paired cells, that is those just divided, occurs an hour or two before the maximum of luminesence. Cell division rhythms are recorded for other algae, e.g. a mitotic rhythm has been found in *Oedogonium* which continues after the filaments are transferred to continuous light.[42] The formation of zoospores

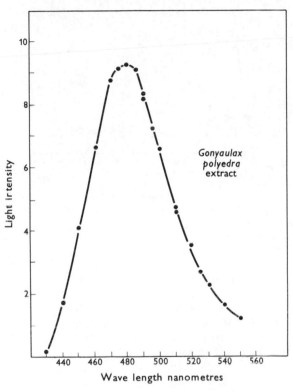

Fig. 65.

Spectrum of luminescence of *Gonyaulax* extracts.

(From Hastings and Sweeney, 1957.)

in *Oedogonium* is also a rhythmic process controlled by the prior dark/light period. The sporulation maxima of the material when transferred to continuous light is a little less than 24 hours. This rhythm was not altered by the addition of metabolic poisons, narcotics or growth substances, although the intensity of sporulation was affected.

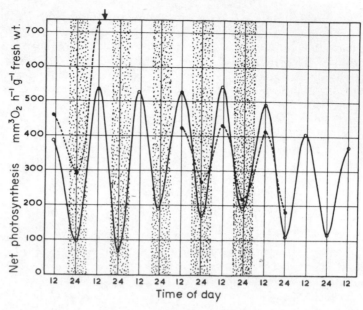

Fig. 66.

Diurnal photosynthetic rhythm of *Acetabularia* in alternating day and night (shaded) and in continuous light. Dotted line shows the oxygen production by ten young plants whose caps have yet to form and solid line is for one plant having a cap, i.e. relatively mature. The arrow indicates the time at which the nucleus was removed by amputating the rhizoids.

(From Sweeney and Haxo, 1961.)

Rhythms of photosynthesis and respiration have been mentioned on p. 175 and 183. Of particular interest is the study of the photosynthetic rhythm of *Acetabularia* by Sweeney and Haxo[284a] since the pronounced rhythm of oxygen production in alternating light and dark not only continues in continuous light but does so even after removal of the nucleus (Fig. 66). Thus the maintenance and time-keeping of the rhythm is outside the immediate control of the nucleus.

10   Physiology: polarity and morphogenesis

On the widest interpretation, almost all algal cells and thalli exhibit polarity. At the morphological level this is exemplified by the polar insertion of flagella, the orientation of chromatophores, the mode of branching of filamentous genera and the organization of more complex thalli, e.g. the apical formation of sporangia in *Acetabularia*. These are probably all reactions to polarity gradients of chemicals and particularly of morphogenetic substances.

The simplest experimental material is that of a spherical unicell which one might expect to be unpolarized. *Fucus* eggs have been used, since on germination these display a morphological polarity; a protruberance develops on one side and grows out into a filamentous rhizoid, whilst the remainder of the egg divides to form the embryo thallus. The first division is transverse to the rhizoid and so determines the polarity of cell division; it is affected by factors such as unilateral illumination, electric current, pH gradient and the presence of other eggs. In unilateral illumination, the rhizoid develops on the side away from the light; blue but not red light orientates the cleavage.[186] The susceptibility to light starts about 3–4 hours after fertilization and ends after 16–18 hours. The light is effective before rhizoid formation commences. From 5–9 hours after fertilization unilateral illumination produces most of the rhizoids in the 90° arc furthest away from the light, whilst in the 9–12 hour interval, the cell has become less plastic and rhizoids form in the 180° arc away from the light.[417] Eggs lying close together form rhizoids growing in towards the centre of the mass; this was clearly shown by placing eggs around the edge of, but not touching, a central mass of eggs, when the rhizoids grew inwards.[414] Eggs of *F. evanescens* grew in towards a mass of unfertilized *F. vesiculosus* eggs; thus the effect is shown between different species and is unrelated to fertilization, although the effect is still present if all the eggs are fertilized. This tendency to form rhizoids directed towards neighbouring egg cells is strong enough to overcome the polarizing effect of light if the eggs are within 2–3 egg diameters apart; two fertilized eggs lying adjacent do not exhibit this effect, the rhizoids growing out at random. It was found that 10 or more eggs were necessary to produce the effect of 'mutual induction.' If however the seawater is acidified to pH 6·0, then even two fertilized eggs are sufficient to induce polarized rhizoid formation towards one another. This may explain why in normal seawater (of pH around 8·0–8·4) a larger number of eggs are necessary to induce the polarity, i.e. by lowering the pH.[415] Eggs placed in a gradient of hydrogen ion concentration have also been shown to produce rhizoids only on the acid side. Centrifuging *Fucus* [416] and *Cystoseira* eggs,[214] resulted in rhizoid formation at the centrifugal pole. Elongated eggs formed by passing the egg cells through capillary tubes, form a rhizoid at a pole; this rhizoid formation precedes nuclear division and thus the polarity is not established by division. Small temperature gradients across the egg cells induced rhizoid formation on the warm side. Rhizoids grow towards concentrations of β-indolyl acetic acid, although an external source of this is not necessary, presumably because the eggs themselves contain growth substances.[303]

In the red alga *Griffithsia bornetiana*, the thalli produce rhizoids from the base of the basal cells of the plant, but late in the year the rhizoids may form in other positions. Spores of *Griffithsia* are also polarized in that the first rhizoid and first shoot appear at opposite poles. Sections of the plant can be induced to form rhizoids by placing them in a solution through which an electric current of 10–40 μA is passed, when rhizoids form on the anodal side of the thallus.[358] Increasing the current increases the number of rhizoids formed but decreases their size, and plants with their apices pointing towards the anode produce more rhizoids. There is also an aggregation of cytoplasm on the anodal side and presumably a concentration of morphogenetic substances there. Centrifuging of cells, causing the cytoplasm to aggregate in the apices, enhances branch formation and decreases rhizoid formation, whilst aggregation at the base of cells causes shoot formation there. Thus polarity can be reversed by movement of the cytoplasm either in an electrical field or by centrifugation. Normal cells produce shoots at the morphological apex whatever the orientation of the plant.

In *Enteromorpha*, cell division is polarized starting in the tip and moving downwards through the thallus as growth proceeds, with the result that plants a few centimetres or more in length have the meristematic zone localized just above the holdfast. This alga has considerable powers of regeneration. Apical sections cut from the thallus produce papillae on the morphological upper cut surface and papillae and small rhizoids on the lower cut surface. Sections from the middle of the thallus form papillae up to 65 μm long on the upper cut surface and numerous rhizoids 85–120 μm long on the lower surface; basal sections form papillae and rhizoids 100 μm long on the upper cut surface and rhizoids 120–200 μm long on the lower cut surface.[290] The chromatophores are polarized in this genus, generally the basin-shaped chromatophore points its rounded base to the apex of the thallus; centrifuging the thalli to invert this arrangement reduces rhizoid formation. Treatment with β-indolyl acetic acid increases rhizoid formation even in the apical sections. The orientation of the chromatophores towards the apex is maintained when the apex is lost or when light intensity is altered, and does not seem to be affected by gravity since in curled forms it is still polarized. Thus it would appear that a gradient of substances is set up early in the growth of the plant and is not easily disturbed. Extracts of apical sections suppress rhizoid formation when added to cultures of middle sections, whilst extracts of basal sections induce profuse rhizoid formation in the middle sections.

Filaments of *Chaetomorpha melagonium* require stronger solutions to plasmoylse basal cells than apical cells, thus showing a gradient of osmotic pressure and turgor pressure from apex to base.[111] In strong plasmolytic solutions, the protoplast withdraws from the side walls and then from the lower cross wall, but remains attached to the upper cross wall. This polarized contracted protoplast may lay down cell wall microfibrils in a random manner as a cap over its lower end (polarized). Small globules of cytoplasm extruded into the cavity below the main contracted mass of cytoplasm form a complete wall around themselves, i.e. are non-polarized. The cytoplasm in *Chaetomorpha* is polarized at the basal end of the cells and in cell division this lower region is cut off from the upper part where cytoplasm is sparse.[219] This polarity of *Chaetomorpha* extends back to the settling of the zoospore which attaches itself by the flagella end, the usual manner of zoospore germination in filamentous forms, although some unicells attach by their basal ends. At this early stage of spore germination the first microfibrils of the wall are randomly arranged and not composed of cellulose I or II. Immediately after this primary lamella is formed, a conspicuous band appears in the cytoplasm, orientated transversely to the long axis passing through the point of attachment. Next a second band appears, orientated along the main axis and in these two bands, the first orientated microfibrils appear.[294] Thus the polarity of the alga is established with the formation of the first orientated microfibrils; the order of formation of alternate lamellae is also laid down at this point, slow, i.e. at a small angle to the horizontal, followed by steep, i.e. at a greater angle to the horizontal. In the related genus *Spongomorpha* no cytoplasmic bands appear and the microfibrils are always unorientated.

In *Cladophora* the apex of the cell is the growing region and hence the wall of the apical cells is thinnest at the tip. Both side branches and the pores through which spores and gametes are released, are polarized just below the transverse septa, i.e. in the growing portion; in *Chaetomorpha* the pores appear most frequently in the mid region of each cell. *Oedogonium* cell division is another feature which is polarized towards the upper end of the cells in the filament.

In *Bryopsis* there is normally a polarity in the distribution of auxin into the lower half of the thallus where rhizoids are formed. If *Bryopsis* plants are inverted and indolyl acetic acid is dripped onto the cut end, rhizoid formation results at the tips of the branches, i.e. the polarity is reversed.[194]

In the unicellular, uninucleate alga *Acetabularia*, the sporangia form a whorl (the cap) at the apex of the stalk, whilst from the base of the stalk the rhizoids arise (Fig. 46M). This polarity is constant and is further exemplified by the location of the nucleus in the basal rhizoids. Fortunately *Acetabularia* possesses great powers of regeneration, combined with an ability to form interspecific grafts. With the constant occurrence of the nucleus in the

basal rhizoids, the regenerative and biochemical potentialities of the cytoplasm, distant from the nucleus, can be studied and the relationships between
nucleus and cytoplasm determined.[144, 146] The morphogenetic regenerative
power extends even to new cap formation in the stalk region, which is
polarized towards the apex; thus enucleate apical segments have a greater
regenerative power than similar enucleate portions from the base. The
regenerative capacity is related to length, and hence to the amount of morphogenetic substances present. The nucleate rhizoidal portions always possess
full regenerative powers, since here the morphogenetic substances are being
continually produced, but the nucleus has been shown in these experiments to
be only indirectly concerned. The basal ends of cut segments occasionally
form rhizoids but only incompletely; this may be due to the relative absence
of rhizoid morphogenetic substances in the stalk, possibly owing to the basal
location of the nucleus. Grafting of segments so that the cytoplasm contains
1–4 nuclei, always results in the formation of caps which are characteristic
of the species. Binucleate grafts containing one nucleus of *Acetabularia
mediterranea* and one of *A. crenulata* form caps of intermediate type growing
out from the graft. Trinucleate grafts containing two nuclei of *A. crenulata*
and one nucleus of *A. mediterranea*, produce caps which are closer in form to
A. crenulata. Grafting of a nucleate segment of *A. mediterranea* onto an
enucleate segment of *A. crenulata*, results in either pure *A. mediterranea* type
caps or intergrades; if more than one cap is formed, the second is invariably
a pure *A. mediterranea* type whatever the first one was. The amount of the
morphogenetic substances are fixed at the moment of enucleation and no
further synthesis can be detected; variation of temperature or light after
enucleation alters the rate of differentiation but not the amount. The
quantity of morphogenetic substances produced is dependent upon the size
of the nucleus, which increases throughout the life of *Acetabularia* (see p. 52).
Thus if newly regenerated stalks are cut, one from a young rhizoid and one
from an old rhizoid, i.e. having been associated with a small or large nucleus,
the portion from the old rhizoid has the greater regenerative power. The
amount of morphogenetic substance is not increased in bi- or multi-nucleate
grafts, since the energy-producing system (chloroplasts, etc.) is not increased;
in fact the more nuclei the smaller they are since the same amount of
nutrient material is divided between them. The apical/basal gradient of
regenerating capacity is present in plants grown in the dark, but if the
nucleus is removed and the plants remain in the dark, then this is equalized;
also plants grown in the light and then enucleated and placed in the dark,
equalize the gradient of morphogenetic substances. There is therefore no
asymmetrical structure to the cytoplasm. It has been shown by staining
with Azocarmine-β, that special proteins, only formed in the light, are
present in growing stalk tips of *Acetabularia* cells but not in non-growing;[411]
there is also a concentration of ribonucleic acid in the growing tips. The
degree to which intermediate caps are formed increases with the increase
in length of the enucleate portion, i.e. proportionately to the morphogenetic

substances. Thus, there is a distinct interaction between the morphogenetic substances produced by the nucleus and the morphogenetic substances in the cytoplasm which are species specific. The results show that the morphogenetic substances in the cytoplasm can be used up and are not regenerated unless a nucleus is present; hence the formation of genotype caps after intermediate caps. Cysts formed in interspecific grafts are not viable, i.e. do not form gametes, but cysts from mononucleate transplants give rise to caps of the same nuclear type, and are viable.

In *Acetabularia* the quadriflagellate zygotes are negatively phototactic and attach themselves by the flagella end. The rhizoid containing the nucleus grows from this end, and the stalk from the other. If zygotes are allowed to settle in the dark and are then illuminated the stalks grow out from the basal end of the zygote, suggesting that the polarity is established in the zygote and is not a light effect. The effect of unilateral light on polarity has not yet been studied. The rhizoid forms at the point where the nucleus lies and not vice versa, e.g. nuclei transplanted into the morphologically upper region of a segment form a rhizoid adjacent to the point of implantation and a cap at the morphologically basal end, thus reversing the polarity.[145] Two morphogenetic substances are presumed to exist, one for cap formation and one for rhizoid formation, and these are polarized in opposite directions.

Auxin increases the growth of nucleated *Acetabularia* stalks and also enhances cap formation.[397] On the other hand, 2,3,5-triiodobenzoic acid decreases both. Elongation of isolated nucleate rhizoids is inhibited by auxin, but after return to a non-auxin solution growth is greatly enhanced. Cap production is enhanced by methyl indolyl acetic acid, whilst stalk elongation is not and the optimum indolyl acetic acid concentration differs for the two processes, suggesting that two specific substances are involved. Indolyl acetic acid also increases stalk elongation and enhances cap formation in enucleated segments, suggesting that it acts without the co-operation of the nucleus. Auxins are not the morphogenetic substances or intermediates since they do not increase cap formation when applied to old plants which have begun to form caps.

Already it has been seen that auxin and other growth substances are either present in algae or have an effect if added exogenously. Some early work is suspect since it has now been shown that the ethanol in which the growth substances were dissolved may itself stimulate growth, even at the low concentrations used, e.g. a two-fold stimulation of *Chlorella* was found when CO_2 was limiting [15] and further, when glucose was limiting ethanol was respired.[383] Addition of auxin resulted in increased cell numbers but not increased cell size in *Chlorella* and *Scenedesmus* strains in the absence of alcohol.[5] In some algae no effects have been detected after addition of growth substances, but in others dramatic changes have resulted. Thus indolyl acetic acid at 3 μg dm^{-3} increases the growth of *Ulothrix subtilissima* thirteen fold, and gibberellic acid at 50 μg dm^{-3} of a 75 per cent pure compound leads to a seven-fold increase.[70] No ethanol was present in either experiment and no effect on cell shape or size could be detected, although zoospore formation was enhanced. It was suggested that the increase was due to increased cell division. Growth of germinating zygotes of *Ulva*, zoospores of *Enteromorpha* and young plants of *Fucus* and *Ascophyllum*, are all reported to be enhanced by auxin. Cell elongation in *Rhizoclonium* is stimulated by indolyl acetic acid but not by indolyl butyric acid or naphthalene acetic acid.[75] *Ulva lactuca* in pure cultures forms only small filamentous germlings which are increased in size by indolyl acetic acid, kinetin and gibberellic acid but do not form a normal blade; the latter was however produced when adenine and kinetin were present.[329] A most interesting series of results were obtained with *Vaucheria* in which tryptophane, β-indolyl acetic acid, β-indolyl proprionic acid, tryptamine, tryptophol and β-indolyl glyoxylic acid, all stimulated zoospore formation.[187] Tryptophane also caused zoosporangia to grow out laterally from beneath empty zoosporangia. These growth substances acted on the gametangia; β-indolyl acetic acid induced young antheridia to grow vegetatively, whilst β-indolyl carbonic acid stimulated gametangia, and tryptophane suppressed gametangia; treatment alternatively with these latter two compounds changed the plant from a vegetative to a sexual phase, or vice versa.

Photoperiodic responses are only rarely recorded in algae.[84a] One of the most studied is in *Porphyra tenera* in which the thallus grows during winter whilst in summer only the filamentous *Conchocelis* phase can be found growing in dead mollusc shells. The *Conchocelis* phase form spores and this formation is controlled by short day length. This is a true photoperiodic response since a light break given in the middle of the dark period inhibits the formation of sporangia.

11 Fossil algae and the deposition of calcium carbonate and silica

The majority of fossil algae have one feature in common, namely the formation of resistant skeletal material or superficial precipitations. These are either of calcium (magnesium) carbonate (Chlorophyta, Rhodophyta and the coccoliths of certain Haptophyta) or silica (Silicoflagellineae and diatoms). Under certain conditions this inorganic material is preserved, although rarely are the siliceous types found amongst the calcareous, owing to the solution of silicates at high pH values. However the exact natural conditions under which solution occurs have yet to be worked out. More rarely the cell walls of non-mineralized species are preserved, e.g. *Pediastrum* and akinetes of species of Cyanophyta, and even more rare are impressions and films of algae. Records of fossilized algae have been obtained from all ages of rocks back to the Proterozoic (Precambrian), although the greatest number of records is from the Cretaceous to the present time. Fossilization is a continual process and can be observed today in sediments forming at the bottom of lakes and oceans and this fossil material can be used to investigate the more recent changes in algal floras. Although not as obvious as some other forms of life in forming geological strata (e.g. Foraminifera and Mollusca), algae are nevertheless of considerable importance in some limestones and in the formation of diatomaceous earths both of Pleistocene and Tertiary origin.

Calcium carbonate

The calcareous Rhodophyta *Lithothamnion, Lithophyllum* and *Melobesia*, have been found in fossil bearing rocks and a similar but completely fossil group, Solenoporaceae, has been described, the main genus of which is *Solenopora*. However these, and other algae resembling modern *Lomentaria* and *Delesseria* species, are extremely difficult to fit with any accuracy into the classification of the Rhodophyta, since usually only the vegetative cells remain. Occasionally tetraspores are visible in sunken tetrasporangia. Thick beds of these fossils, which must have been formed in shallow prehistoric seas, are found in many parts of the world and in some places are used as building stone. Recent borings through coral atolls suggest that calcareous rocks, containing similar algae, have been forming in the same site throughout several geological periods. Ladd [226a] found a depth of 4500 ft. of such deposit overlying volcanic rock and representing deposits from Eocene to recent age at Eniwetok in the Marshall Islands. Deposits of calcareous Rhodophyta are also probably forming in Arctic seas today, where they occur abundantly in the benthos. In some places fragments of such algae are washed ashore and form beaches; this material is used to lime fields in a few remote regions.

Probably the best known fossil algae are some genera of the Codiaceae and Dasycladaceae. The former is best represented by fossil species of *Halimeda* from Tertiary and Quaternary deposits. Since it is an important alga of coral reef lagoons, it is not surprising to find it in reef deposits, particularly in the Indo-Pacific region. The Dasycladaceae is represented back to the Ordovician and is the only algal group in which there is evidence of more complex development in the fossil (Triassic and Jurassic), than in the present-day forms. Of 58 genera, 48 are extinct.[318] Possibly the simplest type was *Rhabdoporella* (see Fig. 67B), in which a central siphon was clothed with simple, scattered, club-shaped branches, between which calcium carbonate was deposited. In *Cyclocrinus* (Fig. 67A) the branches arise from a clavate head, whilst in *Primicorallina* (Fig. 67C) the branches are scattered along the central siphon and branch to the third degree. *Palaeodasycladus* (Fig. 67D) is more complex, the ultimate branches forming a pseudoepidermis. In many of the fossil Dasycladaceae it is also possible to recognize the gametangial branches.

An intriguing group of fossils are formed by the 'stems' and oogonia of the Charophyceae, which are recorded from as far back as the Silurian, but unfortunately give little evidence of the origin of this isolated group. The oogonium is surrounded by a wall, formed of five spiral filaments (Fig. 10E and Fig. 67E), capped by small coronal cells, one in *Chara* and *Lamprothamnium* and two in *Nitella* and *Tolypella*. Lime is deposited around the oogonium but only in the spiral threads, so it is not possible to assign the fossils to genera, since the coronal cells are lost. These reproductive structures in the fossilized state, are termed 'gyrogonites' (Fig. 67E and G). Harris [150] points out that the 'gyrogonite' is not the complete oogonium, but only the inner calcareous part which encloses the cutinized oospore membrane, which in turn encloses the egg. The oogonium wall consists of the five spiral cells; the outer surface more or less smooth and the inner strongly marked by the spirals. In the fossil genus *Clavator*, the oogonium is surrounded by a circle of elongated cells, the utricle (Fig. 67E). In the Middle Purbeck deposits, the

---

FIG. 67. SOME FOSSIL ALGAE.

A. *Cyclocrinus*; B. *Rhabdoporella*; C. *Primicorallina*; D. *Palaeodasycladus*; E. Internal view of the oogonium of *Clavator reidi* surrounded by the utricle; F. A node of *C. reidi* from six aspects; G. Gyrogonites of *C. reidi*; H. The patterns of the long and short cells of the 'corticating filaments' of *C. reidi*; I. Some fossil dinoflagellates; J. *Oocardium*. Two cells on mucilage stalk (dotted) surrounded by columns of lime; K. The same seen from above; L. *Hystrichosphaera*; M–R. Some fossil diatoms; M. *Anthodiscus*; N. *Entogonia*; O. *Bergonia*; P. *Pyrgodiscus*; Q. *Pyxidicula*; R. *Syndetocystis*.

(After Evitt, Fritsch, Harris, Magdefrau, Pia in Hirmer and Schütt.)

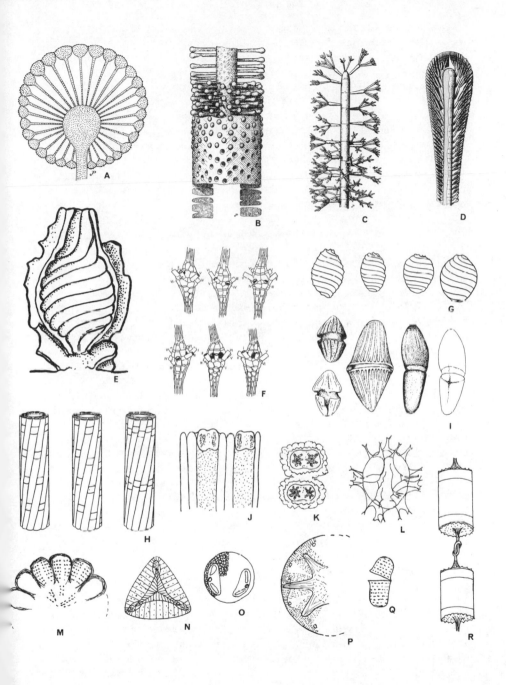

organic material has disappeared and only the calcite skeleton remains; this in turn has been replaced to varying degrees by silica.[150] Nodal structure, internodal cells and spiral corticating threads can all be detected in material of *C. reidi* (Fig. 67F and H).

Another important group of calcium-depositing fossils are the Coccolithineae usually referred to as the Chrysophyceae in geological literature but now known to be genera of the Haptophyta classified in the Prymnesiales. The calcite coccoliths, only 2–20 μm in diameter (see p. 41), are preserved in oceanic sediments and evidence suggests that they may be extremely valuable as stratigraphic indicators.[341] The earliest known records are from the Jurassic, whilst they occur in great variety and vast numbers in Cretaceous chalks. Only a small number of genera are extant but of these, some such as the genus *Coccolithus* can be traced back to the Jurassic period. According to Bramlette [341] they form an even greater part of the calcareous deep sea deposits of the Tertiary than do the Foraminifera, but are only minor components of recent calcareous ooze.

Occasional genera of other groups precipitate calcium carbonate, e.g. the desmid *Oocardium* (Fig. 67J, K), the *Cosmarium*-like cells of which secrete a basal mucilage stalk, around which calcium carbonate is deposited. The tubes form side by side and eventually give rise to tufa. The genus is restricted in occurrence, usually occurring in streams flowing from calcareous springs. Crystals of calcium carbonate are also deposited on the filaments of *Vaucheria*, and Wallner [408] records how the basal region becomes clothed with the lime-encrusted cyanophyte *Plectonema phormidioides*, which eventually grows over the *Vaucheria* strands and encloses them in a calcium carbonate jacket. The only other group depositing lime in any quantity is the Cyanophyta, of which *Plectonema* is an example. Many genera, e.g. *Gloeocapsa*, *Lyngbya*, *Petalonema*, *Schizothrix* and *Rivularia* precipitate crystals in the mucilage between the cells or filaments. In *Rivularia rufescens* these are deposited in concentric zones (Fig. 67G) and in some species the mucilage may be replaced by a mass of crystals. Cyanophyta living around thermal springs often deposit lime to form terraces (travertine) in and around the spring. The algal growth often colours the travertine. In marine habitats, however, the Cyanophyta bore into rock and shells, functioning principally as calcium carbonate decomposers. Crystals of calcium carbonate are also frequently precipitated on some diatom species but only when these are growing in base-rich water.

The biogenic deposition of calcium carbonate is considerable and undoubtedly gradually changes the geochemical balance of calcium and of carbon dioxide, however, the various processes involved are complex, e.g. at great oceanic depths there is resolution of carbonates. Calcium carbonate occurs as calcite (Cryptonemiales, Cyanophyta and Coccolithineae) and as aragonite (Chlorophyta, Phaeophyta—*Padina* is the only genus in which marked calcification occurs, and Nemaliales). The calcium carbonate of the Rhodophyta is laid down in the organic wall layers, whereas in the

Dasycladaceae it forms in the intercellular spaces; in both groups it is an integral part of the plant. The carbonate of the Charophyceae, Cyanophyta and diatoms is, however, precipitated out of a supersaturated solution due to the removal of carbon dioxide from the water during photosynthesis, and plants of these groups can be grown in culture without any encrusting carbonates being formed. However other genera not precipitating calcium carbonate grow side by side with plants which incorporate carbonate in the walls or precipitate it on the outside; it is reasonable therefore to assume that some special conditions are created by the calcareous algae which lead to this carbonate formation. The aragonite of certain Dasycladaceae and Nemaliales (*Liagora* and *Galaxaura*), has been disaggregated into aragonite needles, 2–9 μm in length, by treatment with 5·3 per cent sodium hypo-chlorite.[249] The needles form interlacing mats in the plants and, from the descriptions of the above two genera of the Nemaliales, it appears that the carbonate is laid down outside the cell walls as in the Dasycladaceae and not as in the coralline red algae. These aragonite needles of biogenic origin, may be a source of sedimentary aragonitic deposits ('drewites') in shallow seas, e.g. on the Great Bahama Bank, although other workers have also suggested that these 'drewites' may be formed by inorganic precipitation. Certainly the algal material does disaggregate in nature and Lowenstam found great concentrations of aragonite needle sediments adjacent to growths of these algae.

The Cyanophyte alga *Schizothrix calcicola* has been shown to bind sediments (siliceous or calcareous) and form layered structures known to geologists as stromatolites. The mucopolysaccharides are secreted by the alga, and rates of accumulation have been estimated at 1 mm per day.[363a]

Magnesium carbonate is also present in the carbonates deposited by algae (7–30 per cent in coralline algae) and seasonal fluctuations in the amount have been reported. Chave [59] found that the ratio of magnesium to calcium in the calcite of *Lithothamnion* was 2–4 per cent higher in winter. The aragonite-precipitating algae have a higher strontium content than the calcite-precipitating algae (1·3 per cent in *Halimeda* and up to 2·3 per cent in others as opposed to 0·35 per cent in calcitic red algae).[334] The value of 2·3 per cent is similar to that found in aragonitic sediments off the Bahamas and adds weight to the suggested biogenic origin of these. Lowenstam [249] drew attention to the fact that the algae precipitating aragonite are chiefly distributed in warm waters and those precipitating calcite in cold waters. Craig [71] reported that the aragonite of green algae was enriched in ^{13}C compared with average marine limestones, indicating that the bicarbonate of seawater is partitioned by the algae, ^{12}C being incorporated in the organic material and the heavier ^{13}C being precipitated. Theoretical estimates of the expected amounts of $CaCO_3$ precipitated during photosynthesis are much lower than those actually found, which suggests that there is also inorganic precipitation around the carbonate nuclei.

Silica

Diatoms and silicoflagellates are deposited in both marine and freshwater habitats and form either a loose or compacted greyish/white material, diatomite (Kieselguhr) (see also p. 220). This may occur as thin surface deposits as in some Saharan diatomites or may form beds up to 100 m thick, These are essentially the bottom sediments of lakes or shallow seas in which most of the organic matter has been oxidized, leaving a more or less pure siliceous deposit. Such beds of diatomite are accumulating today in most lake and ocean basins, except where conditions favour solution of silica. Since diatoms are clearly divided into marine and freshwater genera and silicoflagellates are entirely marine, it is possible to use them as indicators of marine or freshwater strata and of salinity and land level changes, e.g. in the quaternary deposits around the Baltic. According to most sources, the deposits around Antarctica and in the Arctic Pacific are extremely rich in diatoms, but this may merely be a reflection of the relative lack of terrigenous material in these parts. Almost all oceanic sediments are more or less rich in diatoms and silicoflagellates; some sediments marked on maps as terrigenous are rich in diatoms, e.g. the central region of the Gulf of California.[350a] The deposition of silica, unlike that of some biogenic calcium carbonate, is due almost entirely to incorporation of silica into the cell wall, of which it is an intrinsic part (see p. 40). Physical precipitation of silica is rare and therefore the siliceous deposits are almost entirely biogenic in origin, the exceptions being those in which silica in solution has replaced other minerals, e.g. to form cherts. The relative insolubility of silica means that biogeochemically, there is a continual loss of silica from weathering of rock fragments (which is the major origin of soluble silica) and a deposition and locking up of this in the underwater sediments, particularly in the deep seas. Fossil diatoms are occasionally found in other water lain sediments, e.g. in the London clay of Eocene age. Since the diatoms and silicoflagellates are ingested by many animals, even if incidentally, they are present in faeces and thus also in guano deposits. Reliable records of fossil diatoms extend back to the Jurassic (*Pyxidicula bollensis*, Fig. 67Q), whilst earlier Palaeozoic determinations are doubtful. In calcareous strata formed under marine conditions, the group is extremely rare, presumably not through absence in the Mesozoic seas, but through solution in the alkaline deposits. The Cretaceous is nevertheless the earliest period at which they become strikingly obvious in the fossil record. Of the approximately 190 genera of known diatoms, 70 are entirely fossil. The majority of the earliest fossil genera belong to the Centric group of diatoms which is the only group recorded in the Upper Cretaceous and only after this period do the Pennate group appear. This may indicate that the Centric group is older than the Pennate group, but it is also true that these extensive diatomite beds are marine in origin and mainly composed of plankton in which Centrales are most abundant (Fig. 67M–R). Kanaya[203] has shown that diatom assemblages can be used to recognize four subdivisions in a Californian Eocene deposit and are therefore of stratigraphic value.

Recent work has shown that the diatom remains sedimented in the North Pacific show definite distributions which are a reflection of diatoms contained in the water masses. The example given in Fig. 67a shows that *Coscinodiscus nodulifer* is an equatorial species and penetrates northward only in the current systems whilst *Denticula seminae* is a northern species with almost no extension southwards.[203a]

Since fossilization of siliceous organisms is occurring in accessible material at the present time, it is possible to compare the recent fossil flora with the recent live flora. Although many species are sedimented onto the lake or ocean bottom without too much solution or breakage of the silica walls, some delicate and weakly silicified species are not preserved. In freshwaters these are probably few and confined to certain planktonic genera, e.g. *Rhizosolenia eriensis*, *Attheya zachariasi* and possibly some *Fragilaria* spp., but by and large the deposits are a true representation of the flora except for small additions from inflows and loss by outflow. In the oceans the reverse is the case; extremely common planktonic genera such as *Rhizosolenia*. *Chaetoceros* and *Bacteriastrum* are mainly either dissolved or fragmented before reaching the oceanic sediments. Occasionally the more robust 'ends' of *Rhizosolenia* or the spores of *Chaetoceros* are found, but not in sufficient number to indicate their abundance in the original plankton. Thus for example in the Gulf of California, the sediments are dominated by *Coscinodiscus* spp., *Actinoptychus undulatus*, *Roperia tesselata*, *Thalassionema nitzschioides*, *Pseudoeunotia doliolus*, whilst the plankton is dominated by *Chaetoceros* spp., *Rhizosolenia* spp., *Bacteriastrum* spp., *Thalassiothrix longissima* and only very rarely do any of the species dominant on sediments occur in abundance in the plankton though they are always present.[350a] Inland diatomite deposits have been formed *in situ*, but oceanic deposits may represent the flora of some distant region which has been transported by ocean currents. Knowledge of the extent of this transport is important if the deposits are to be used to interpret past floras, climates, etc. Reports based on settling velocity of diatoms suggested that hundreds of years would be necessary for surface forms to reach the deep oceanic sediments and during this time would drift in ocean currents for many hundreds of miles. However more recent work suggests that sedimentation may be much more rapid, and lateral movement much less. Preliminary data suggest that cores from the Atlantic contained fewer diatoms than cores from the Pacific and Indian Oceans and they were also more corroded.[220] It is extremely rare to find freshwater remains in oceanic cores but in some Atlantic cores around the Cape Verde Islands, bands of freshwater diatoms occur deep in the marine sediments.[220] These are forms which are now common in present-day habitats and in fossil diatomites from Africa and are probably derived from windblown dust off the Sahara.[349] Indeed Hustedt (1921) in an analysis of the dust in the 'Harmattan' haze from this region, reported similar species. The absence of river forms suggests that they are not water transported.

Freshwater deposits of interglacial, late-glacial and post-glacial age have been studied more than marine sediments; this is a reflection of the comparative ease of obtaining samples. The species found in these deposits are almost all existing today and fortunately a considerable amount is known about the ecological requirements of present-day species and hence deductions can be made concerning the past ecological conditions. Hustedt (1944)

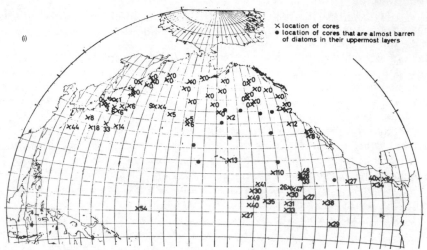

Distribution of *Coscinodiscus nodulifer* A. Schmidt in sediment samples from the surface layer of deep-sea cores from the North Pacific. Numbers indicate the frequencies of the species in a count of 200 specimens made for each sample.

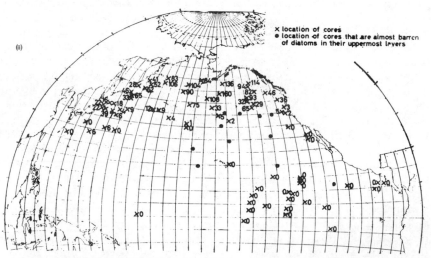

Distribution of *Denticula seminae* Simonsen and Kanaya in sediment samples from the surface layer of deep-sea cores from the North Pacific. Numbers indicate the frequencies of the species in a count of 200 specimens made for each sample.

found an alternation of *Melosira* spp. in an interglacial deposit on the Lüne-burger Heide in which a sequence *M. italica/M. ambigua/M. granulata/M. ambigua/M. granulata/M. ambigua* was recorded. This he believes reflects changes from a cold water, nutrient poor flora (*M. italica*) to warm water and a higher nutrient status (*M. ambigua*) to a less warm water but of high nutrient status (*M. granulata*).

Late-glacial and post-glacial remains of diatoms, afford an excellent means of deducing some of the changes which have occurred in the lake and drainage area, together with information on the composition of diatom communities, influx of new species, etc. In the English Lake District studies on three basins, Windermere,[317] Kentmere [340] and Esthwaite,[348] showed a similar sequence of diatoms from the late-glacial period to the present day. The dominants in the early period all indicated a higher alkalinity than exists in the waters at present. Genera such as *Gyrosigma*, *Rhopalodia*, *Cymatopleura* and *Campylodiscus* were present then, but are not common in the region today, whereas they are frequent in base-rich lakes. Other diatoms (*Cyclotella antiqua*, *Melosira arenaria*) characteristic of melt waters in semi-arctic regions were also present. The early stages of the lakes were practically devoid of planktonic species and only a small population of attached and sediment species was present. About the time of the Boreal–Atlantic transition the alkaliphilic* species begin to decline and acidophilic* species appear (e.g. species of *Eunotia*, *Anomoeoneis*, *Frustulia* and *Tabellaria*) and during the post-Atlantic period up to the present time, these increased in number and quantity (see Fig. 68). This change is related to amelioration of the climate, to the decline of Birch/Pine on the land and to a sealing off of the source of bases as the rock surfaces became leached. At the same time few new surfaces were exposed since freezing and thawing had been reduced. A similar but somewhat later change from alkaline to acid conditions was found in Gribsø in Denmark,[300] where the acidic conditions have developed further than in the English Lakes, for now Gribsø has become an acid humic lake of the dystrophic type. Numerous siliceous cysts of Chrysophyceae are also recorded in the core from Gribsø, but unfortunately it is not yet possible to relate these to the genera and species of present-day Chrysophyceae. It is rare to find several algal groups together in the sediments but in late-glacial material from N. Ireland, diatoms, *Pediastrum* spp., *Botryococcus* and desmids have all been found in the same material and therefore of similar age. All the species again indicate a base-rich period, a paucity of planktonic species whilst the desmids recorded belonged to the littoral flora. In the English Lake District the diatoms indicate a recent reversion from an acidic/oligotrophic status to a slightly less acidic/somewhat eutrophic status of the waters. This was first recognized by the appearance of *Asterionella formosa* at the top of the Windermere cores and is corroborated by evidence from Esthwaite, where

---

* Species with a distinct tendency towards distribution in alkaline or acid waters respectively.

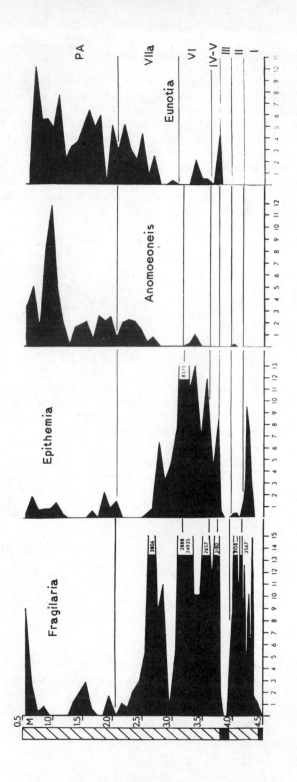

Fig. 68.

The distribution of the diatom genera *Fragilaria*, *Epithemia*, *Anomoeneis* and *Eunotia* in a core from Kentmere. Depth of core in metres on left. Diatomaceous lake mud indicated by cross hatching and clay bands by solid black. Horizontal scale, numbers of cells in hundreds in a standard wt. of sediment. Pollen analytical zones on right-hand side.

(From Round, 1957.)

Asterionella also appears at a similar point in the core. Numerous eutraphentous species, which are completely absent from the upper post-Atlantic sediment, now also grow in Esthwaite, emphasizing the recent change.

Other interesting finds of fossil algae are the Peridinians from the 'Feuerstein' of the chalk of Germany and France (Fig. 67I).[265] Also present are the once controversial group Hystrichosphaerideae (Fig. 67L), which are now placed in the Dinoflagellates since they are the empty spores of various genera of this group.[98] In 'brown coal' deposits in Germany the Chaetophoracean alga *Phycopeltis* has been found and even the gametangia and zoospores seen. The Chlorococcalean alga *Botryococcus* (see Fig. 22) has been shown to form a considerable part of 'bog-head coal' of carboniferous age. These coals contain large amounts of hydrocarbon oils, which can be distilled from them and probably had their origin in the algal material, since living *Botryococcus* is often so full of oil that cell structure is obscured. The fossil material referred to the genera *Pila* and *Reinschia* is in fact *Botryococcus*.[23] The genus also occurs in interglacial and post-glacial peat deposits often associated with *Pediastrum* and desmids.

12   Economic aspects

Algae play a small but important part in the direct economy of many countries. Four major products are derived commercially from algae: agar, carrageenin, alginic acid and diatomite. The first two products are extracted from marine Rhodophyta, the third from Phaeophyta and the fourth from either marine or freshwater diatom deposits. Other direct uses are as food, for man and cattle, and as organic or inorganic (lime) fertilizers.

It is impossible to assess the full economic importance of algal growth but even the most conservative estimates contribute 50 per cent of global carbon fixation to the algae; in aquatic habitats algae are part of the food chain leading to crustacea and fish, on agricultural land they are an important constituent of the soil flora, and in water supply reservoirs, purification plants and in sewage disposal plants, they play an important role in oxygenation and filtration.

Occasionally algal growth becomes detrimental, for example by the production of toxins poisonous to fish and by excessive growth which leads to filtration problems at water purification plants. They are important indicators of pollution in aquatic habitats, whilst under other circumstances they themselves become polluting agents, e.g. of chemical plant, fish ponds, etc. In scientific work they are used as assay organisms for vitamins, in the dating of sedimentary rocks in oil prospecting and lately as a possible source of food, absorber of carbon dioxide and provider of oxygen in space vehicles.

They are important 'tools' in the investigation of many physiological processes (e.g. photosynthesis, nitrogen fixation and ion uptake).

Alginic acid derivatives

These are extracted from Phaeophyta, e.g. from *Laminaria* and *Ascophyllum* growing on Northern coasts, from *Macrocystis* off California, from *Ecklonia* and *Eisenia* in Japan, from *Macrocystis* and *Ecklonia* off Australasia, from *Macrocystis*, *Lessonia* and *Durvillea* off S. America, and on the coast of S. Africa *Laminaria pallida* and *Ecklonia* are possible sources. The alginic acid occurs in the middle lamella and primary walls of these algae, whilst cellulose is found in the secondary walls (Andersen).[11] There is considerable variation in the alginic acid content of the cell walls, 14–40 per cent of the dry weight, and in addition, there is a seasonal variation, the values being highest in winter and lowest in summer. Alginates were first extracted in the 1880's by

PLATE 11 A: A section through the outer region of the dinoflagellate *Ceratium hirundinella* showing plates enclosed by membranes beneath the plasma membrane. B: A scanning electron micrograph of a single isolated valve of the diatom *Cyclotella meneghiniana* photographed from the outside. C: As B but a photograph of the inside of the valve. The pores through the siliceous valves are obvious, also spines on the outside and tubes beneath the spines on the outside which open at tubes on the inside ribs (arrows). Mag. A × 32 600, B & C × 6400. A kindly supplied by Dr. J. D. Dodge. B & C Original.)

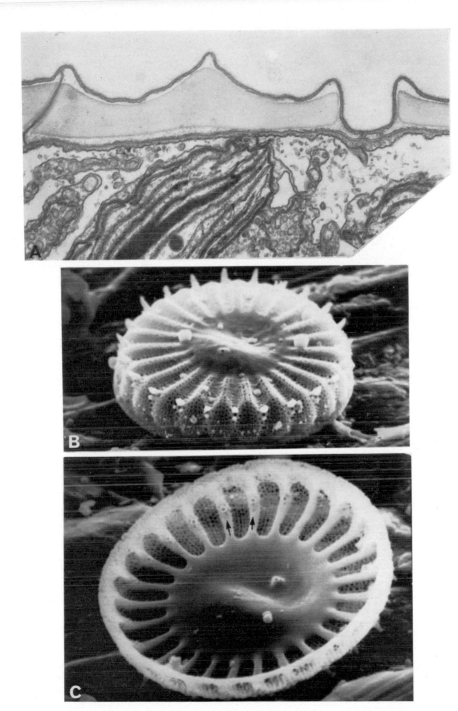

Plate 11

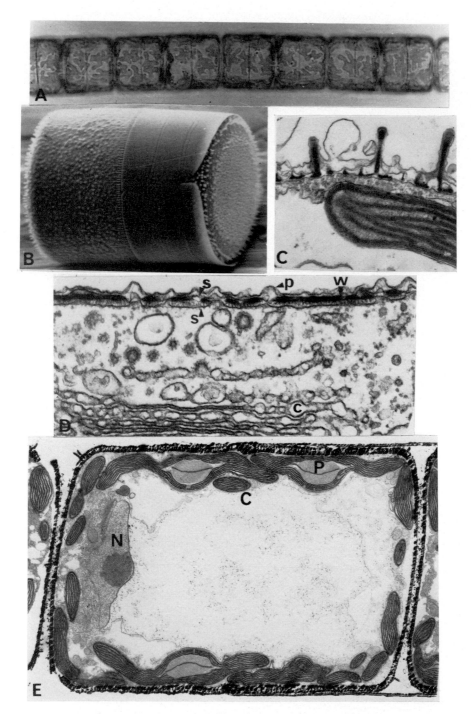

Plate 12

Stanford who named the insoluble compound, alginic acid and the soluble extract, sodium alginate. Its structure is very similar to that of cellulose and pectic acid (Fig. 69) and although still not completely worked out, it is essentially a long unbranched chain of β-d-mannuronic acid units joined by 1:4 glycosidic linkages.

The harvesting of the weed depends upon the genera used and their habitat. The most difficult weeds to harvest are the *Laminaria* spp. growing subtidally on rock surfaces. Grapples may be used, worked from boats but there is the problem of finding rich beds and the method is tedious. Likewise *Ascophyllum*, growing on rocky shores, can only be harvested by hand. Much weed is collected from material cast up on shore during storms. In California the only weed regularly harvested is *Macrocystis*. This grows attached to the sea bed by means of huge holdfasts, bearing stipes and 'leaves' trailing

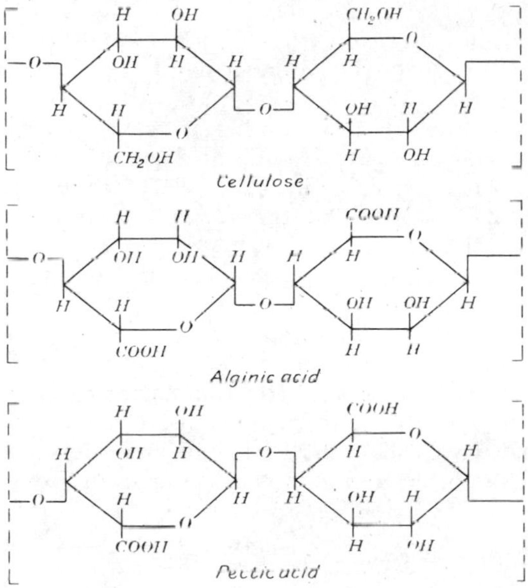

FIG. 69.

The chemical structure of cellulose alginic acid and pectic acid.

PLATE 12 **A:** Light micrograph of the filamentous freshwater diatom *Melosira varians* showing seven cells each composed of two valves and containing numbers of irregular plastids. × 500. **B:** Scanning electron micrograph of a single cell of *M. varians*. At the left is the larger valve or epivalve to which three girdle bands are attached. These enclose the smaller hypovalve on the right. × 2100 **C:** Transmission electron micrograph of a thin section of the maturing spines at the edge of the valve of *M. varians*. The siliceous wall material appears black. It is laid down within a membrane bound vesicle (see below). **D:** Thin section of developing wall of *M. varians*. The siliceous wall (W) developed within vesicles of the silicalemma (S) which is limited on the outside by the plasmalemma (P). The wall material is thought to be produced via the golgi complex, cisternae of which can be seen below (C). × 55 000. **E:** Longitudinal thin section of *M. varians* illustrating distribution of organelles. The nucleus (N) lies in the epivalve and the plastids (C) with distinct pyrenoids (P) lie around the periphery of the cell outside the large central vacuole. × 3400. (All kindly supplied by Dr. R. M. Crawford.)

up to the surface (Fig. 47E). The beds usually maintain themselves vegeta-tively as sexual reproduction is prevented by the shade under the dense canopy of fronds.[67] *Macrocystis* is subject to a bacterial disease 'Black Rot,' so even the economic exploitation of algae is not without plant pathological problems. In addition the young plants are extensively grazed by echinoderms. The upper leaves and stipe are cut by means of a mechani-cal harvester, attached to the front of a harvesting barge, and hoisted aboard by a chain elevator. Cutting of the fronds is followed by regenera-tion, and a growth rate of 3–4·5 m per week is reported;[67] this is a greater rate than that of any investigated land or sea plant. The harvested weed is desalted, shredded and digested with soda ash, yielding a crude mass of sodium alginate. Further purification involves filtering, bleaching, conversion to calcium alginate (by addition of calcium chloride), and conversion to alginic acid (by addition of hydrochloric acid), in which form it may be stored or converted into sodium or other salts (Green's cold process). Another method (Le Gloahec–Herter process) involves initial treatment with calcium chloride to remove laminarin, mannitol and other salts, followed by treatment with soda ash, clarification, conversion to alginic acid and then to sodium alginate. Alginic acid and its Ca, Al, Zn, Cu, Cr, Fe (ferric) and Ag salts are insoluble in water, whereas the Na, K, NH_4, Mg, and Fe (ferrous) are soluble. The soluble alginates behave as hydrophilic colloids. The use of alginates in industry depends on the chemical and physical properties of the compounds, e.g. they are non-toxic, highly viscous and readily form gels. They are used as thickeners in the food industry (e.g. filling creams), in cosmetics (e.g. hand creams), in the textile industry (as printing pastes) and in the rubber industry in latex production, also as emulsifiers (e.g. in ice cream, synthetic cream, processed cheese, pharma-ceutical emulsions, polishes, emulsion paints, etc.), as gelling agents in confectionery and meat jellies and as dental impression powders. Surface films in the paper industry and glazes on ceramics utilize alginates. Films of alginates may also be made into sausage casings and alginate fibres into temporary textile yarns and medically into gauze which is haemostatic and slowly absorbed in the body. It is used as a gel in the freezing of fish; antibiotics such as aureomycin being incorporated in the gel which then remain dispersed.

An enzyme, alginase, occurs in bacteria and actinomycetes which breaks down calcium alginates.[61]

Carrageenin (Carragheen)

This is extracted from the rhodophycean alga, *Chondrus crispus* ('Irish Moss') and to a lesser extent from *Gigartina* spp. *Chondrus*, growing in the intertidal zone is very abundant in the Maritime Provinces of Canada and is harvested there, using wooden rakes. The harvest of *C. crispus* in Nova Scotia has increased from 22 650 kg before 1941 to over 7·75 million kg in 1958.[262] Most of the processing is done in the United States. Carrageenin is a cell wall polysaccharide complex of D-galactose-3,6-anhydro-D-galactose and mono-esterified sulphuric acid. Two major components can be recognized, kappa carrageenin (D-galactose-4-sulphate-3,6-anhydro-D-galactose) and lambda carrageenin (D-galactose sulphate). In the presence of potassium, these compounds gel and are used like alginates to stabilize emulsions and suspend solids, etc., in the food, textile, pharmaceutical, leather and brewing industries.

Agar

This is the name now used for a dried or gel-like non-nitrogenous extract from rhodophycean algae. It is used as a medium in the culture of bacteria, fungi and algae and also in numerous industrial processes. Dry agar is insoluble in cold, but soluble in hot water, and a dilute solution (1–2 per cent) remains liquid down to a temperature varying between 35° to 58°C, according to source, purity, etc. The gel melts at 90° to 100°C. The term 'agar' has been used in various connotations; originally the Malayan word 'agar' or 'agar-agar' was used for certain East Indian edible Rhodophyceae of the genus *Eucheuma* and probably, by extension, for other seaweeds.[400] *Eucheuma* does yield an agar and this may have been used commercially, alone or mixed with agar from other sources. Until 1939 Japan was the largest producer of agar, but the actual source is difficult to determine owing to nomenclatural problems in the Rhodophyceae; it was probably manufactured mainly from a species of *Gelidium*, but *Campylaephora*, *Pterocladia* and *Gracilaria* are also used. The term 'agarophyte' was introduced by Tseng [400] for such plants. Many countries experimented during the Second World War with agar production and some are still active producers. Species of *Gracilaria* have at some time been used in Australia, Chile and S. Africa, *Ahnfeldtia* and *Pterocladia* in New Zealand, *Eucheuma* in Australia, *Gelidium* in Chile and S. Africa, *Chondrus* and *Gigartina* in the British Isles, *Furcellaria* in the Baltic countries and N. America and *Phyllophora* from the floating beds in the North-Western regions of the Black Sea. All the genera are found in the intertidal and subtidal zones. The dried and washed weed is extracted under pressure, clarified, filtered and allowed to gel. The gel is then chopped and put into freezing rooms at 14°F for about two days. It is then thawed and the water removed together with soluble impurities. The purified agar is dried into flakes and bleached.[57] Its chemical structure is similar to that of carrageenin. O'Neill and Stewart [306] showed that agar from *Gelidium cartilagineum* is a chain of alternating D-galactose and 3:6-anhydro-L-galactose residues with a half ester sulphate on about every tenth unit of the galactose. Some workers also report the presence of pyruvic and uronic acids and Japanese workers report at least two separate polysaccharides, agaropectin and agarose. Agar has also been used in the food, pharmaceutical, cosmetic, leather, textile industries, etc., in much the same way as carrageenin and alginates.

Specific enzymes (agarase and carrageeninase) have been detected in bacteria which hydrolyse agar and κ-carrageenin.

Funori

In Japan, a sizing agent and glue is made from the marine alga *Gloiopeltis furcata* and called funori. An inferior product is also made from species of

Iridaea, Grateloupia, Chondrus and *Ahnfeldtia*. From the description of its manufacture in Chapman,[57] it would appear that the crude product is composed of
compacted layers of the bleached and dried seaweed. This is then dissolved
in water to make a glue in the same way as are sheets of fish glue. Its
chemical structure is similar to that of agar except that the sulphate ester
groups are missing.

Minerals

In the nineteenth century and extending on a small scale even into this
century, the burnt ash, or kelp, of marine algae has been used for the
extraction of minerals. 'Kelp' has by extension been used as a term for the
algae themselves. The kelp was used mainly as a source of soda in the
manufacture of soap and glassware; alum and later iodine was also extracted.
It is estimated that 20 tonnes of wet weed produced five tonnes of dry weed
and one ton of ash, thus collecting must have involved considerable labour
and the discovery of mineral deposits rendered this source uneconomic.
Recovery of potash and iodine also became uneconomic.

The elements iodine and bromine were discovered in seaweed extracts
in 1812 and 1826 respectively.

Diatomite (Kieselguhr)

During Tertiary and Quaternary times, the production of diatoms has
been so great in some regions that large sedimentary deposits have been
formed. The siliceous cell walls are relatively insoluble and hence these
sediments accumulated in marine and freshwater basins and some are
relatively uncontaminated by clay, etc. The largest deposits worked commercially are of marine origin at Lompoc in California. Here the thick
deposits are scooped up with large earth-moving equipment and processed
in a modern chemical engineering plant.[185] Figures for annual sales in the
U.S.A. showed a steady increase from 95 000 tonnes per annum in 1929 to an
estimated 297 000 in 1951. In Great Britain a freshwater deposit at Kentmere
is worked. The natural deposit contains a high proportion of silica, e.g.
86 to 88 per cent in some American material and extremely low loss on
ignition, e.g. 4 per cent. When processed it is chemically inert and is
mainly used as a filtration aid, as a filler in paints, varnishes, and paper
products and in insulation materials, particularly those for use at high and
low temperatures. According to Hull *et al.*,[185] 70 per cent of diatomite is
used in industrial filtration processes. It is particularly important in the
sugar refining and brewing industries. In wine making, diatomite is added
as a filter aid, sometimes at as many as four stages in production. It is also
used as a filter in the production of antibiotics when the waste mycelium, etc.,
is removed. In many industrial processes the recovery of chemicals and
reclamation and recycling of water is aided by the addition of diatomite.
It is also used as an industrial catalyst. Alfred Nobel made use of diatomite
as an absorbent for nitro-glycerin in the manufacture of dynamite, but it

has now been replaced by other substances. Diatomaceous earth was used to make lightweight bricks in the building of the 32·6 m dome of the Cathedral of St. Sophia in Constantinople in A.D. 532.[49]

Fertilizer

In a small way algae are used as fertilizers on farmland close to the sea. The larger brown and red algae are used as organic fertilizers; these are usually richer in potassium but poorer in nitrogen and phosphorus than farm manure. The weed is usually applied direct and ploughed in, but it has also been processed into a seaweed meal for transport inland. A concentrated extract of seaweeds is sold as a liquid fertilizer. It is claimed that some seaweed products help bind sandy soil, break down clays and promote a good crumb structure. Experiments in New Zealand with *Pachymenia* meal, showed stimulation of tomato seedling growth on some soils but not on others. A similar meal from *Durvillea* depressed growth on all soils due to an induction of nitrogen deficiency, possibly caused by increased microbiological activity. Similar contradictory results are reported in experiments elsewhere.

In some coastal districts coralline algae (*Lithothamnion* and *Lithophyllum*) are ground up and used in place of lime. Similar use is made of *Chara* which becomes encrusted with calcium carbonate.

The seeding of rice fields with species of blue-green algae to increase the nitrogen content of the soil is another aspect of the use of algae as fertilizer. The economic importance of soil algae and in particular the Cyanophyta is probably considerable, especially in damp soils, but is difficult to evaluate.

Fodder

In maritime districts seaweeds have been used directly for animal fodder with beneficial effects; this effect may be related to the high vitamin and micronutrient content. The sheep on North Ronaldsay in the Orkneys live entirely on seaweed for 10 months of the year and are pastured only during the lambing season. Small industries have been developed on the west coast of Eire and in Scotland for processing weed, chiefly *Laminaria*, *Fucus* or *Ascophyllum*, into a feeding meal and in 1960 a small industry was started in Iceland for the production of *Ascophyllum* meal. The time of collection, drying, preparation and storage of the meal all affect the nutrient value, particularly the vitamin content, which can be halved in *Fucus* meals stored for five months.[163] The ascorbic acid content is at a maximum in early summer and a minimum in mid-winter (cf. the niacin content of some algae, p. 159). Eggs, from hens fed on seaweed meal, have an increased iodine content whilst increased butterfat content of milk is reported from cattle whose diet is supplemented with seaweed meal. *Sargassum* species are used as fodder (and fertilizer) in China.[63]

Many fish, both marine and freshwater, feed on planktonic or attached algae. *Tilapia* spp. in Lake Victoria ingest Cyanophyta and Chlorophyta, but only the Chlorophyta are utilized. However, other *Tilapia* species can digest blue-green algae. Diatoms are apparently easily digested by most fish, although the silica frustules are not utilized. Placing hurdles and bunches of bamboo twigs in fish ponds increases the growth of algal epiphytes and is advantageous to some *Tilapia* spp.[180] Large crops of fish were produced in Lake Kariba after the closing of the dam and this was directly related to the increased algal crops growing on the submerged vegetation. Similar growths are now occurring in the Volta Lake in Ghana where the submerged forest trees form an excellent substratum for algal growth. Young marine fish are also known to feed extensively on benthic microscopic algae particularly those attached to sand grains.

Food

Only in the Far East have algae been regularly used for human food. In the Pacific Islands the raw algae, usually species of Rhodophyta, but also Chlorophyta and Phaeophyta, are chopped and added to other dishes. Young stipes of *Laminaria* and the reproductive leaflets of *Alaria* have also been eaten without much preparation in Europe and N. America. In S. America species of *Ulva* and *Durvillea* have been collected, dried, salted and sold ('cachiyugo'). The most prolific users of seaweeds are however the coastal populations of China, Japan and of the tropical Pacific Islands, where numerous genera are used. The two commonest are species of *Porphyra* ('Amanori' which is made into purple laver, called Asakusa-Nori) and of *Laminaria* ('Kombu' or 'Konbu').[57] The former is eaten in many parts of the world and is regularly collected in S. Wales and sold in local shops. It is washed, boiled and made into a pulp (laver bread), which is then mixed with oatmeal and fried or cooked in butter. In Japan and the Philippines the alga has been cultivated on bundles of bamboo or oak brushwood fixed into the mud in shallow water, where the spores can settle. Nets made of coconut palm or hemp-palm fibre are now used since they can be moved more easily. The nets are put out in autumn to catch the spores and then placed at different levels as the plants grow. Later the young plants are transferred to water of lower salinity, often near a river mouth, where the *Porphyra* develops best. During mild winters the *Porphyra* is liable to be attacked by a fungus. The green alga *Monostroma* is cultivated in many places in Japan as a source of food ('Aonori'). *Undaria* and *Sargassum* are also used and in the Philippines *Caulerpa racimosa* is cultivated. In parts of China and S. America it is reported that terrestrial species of *Nostoc* have been used as food, but there is little doubt that this use of algae is now on a very much reduced scale.

The extensive experiments of the past two decades on mass algal culture show without doubt that if necessary, algae, particularly *Chlorella*, could be grown and processed into food. Thacker and Babcock [396] concluded that production of *Chlorella* was not an economic proposition. Under ideal conditions it has been produced at a cost of 50 cents/lb., which compares with 6 cents/lb. for whole ground soya beans. Production on a pilot scale has been shown to be quite feasible, e.g. maximum rate of 14·4 g dry *Chlorella* per sq.m per day were obtained in a closed system. The growth of algae is slow, thus *Chlorella* can produce only 7 cells from a single cell in 24 hours whereas a yeast (*Willia*) forms 10^6 cells in the same time. The following requirements need to be computed for any system: optimum exposure to light, optimum turbulence and saturation with carbon dioxide, nutrient content and temperature, constant average age of cells, and sterile conditions. Pilot scale outdoor experiments have also been conducted successfully using large concrete tanks.

Medicinal uses

The Rhodophycean alga *Digenia simplex* is made into a drug, Tse Ko-Tsoi, in S. China and is of some importance as an antihelmitic. Experimental work has been done on sodium laminarin sulphate as a blood anticoagulant, since its chemical structure is somewhat similar to heparin; fucoidin is also effective.[360]

Antibiotics

The first record of an antibacterial product from algae was of a substance, chlorellin, from *Chlorella*.[323] Extracts of marine algae have also yielded antibacterial substances, one of which, extracted from *Rhodomela larix*, was thought to be a brominated phenolic compound.[282] Vacca and Walsh [401] extracted *Ascophyllum nodosum* collected at monthly intervals and tested the antibacterial activity of the extract, finding it highest in spring and lowest in winter. These extracts were effective against both gram positive and negative bacteria. Chesters and Stott [60] found that *Halidrys, Pelvetia, Laminaria digitata* and *Polysiphonia* were active, the latter showing the widest activity. Their chromatographic separation suggested that the antibiotic effect was associated with the chlorophylls. Emeis [94] showed that cultures of *Nitzschia palea* reduced the germination of *E. coli*, being particularly effective during active growth of the diatom. Some infectious bacteria were also killed or reduced in number but others were stimulated. Water passed through a layer of *Nitzschia palea* on a filter paper, has a reduced *E. coli* count only if the algae are in the light and photosynthesizing, suggesting that the antibacterial agent is formed during photosynthesis only. Since *N. palea* and other algae are common on the sand of water works filters they probably decrease the bacterial count by antibiotic action.

Deleterious effects

Under certain circumstances and in particular during periods of mass production, algae or their toxic products may cause injury or even mortality amongst animals. Rarely are the algae found as parasites, although there are records of algal growths in and on the surface of fish leading to disease. In fish ponds and in nature, mass growth of filamentous and mucilaginous species results in a physical smothering and/or oxygen depletion leading to death of young fish fry. The most widespread harmful effects are those caused by water blooms. In the oceans, species of Dinoflagellates often cause the red discoloration known as 'red tides,' whilst in freshwaters the blooms are usually due to Cyanophyta, although some of the most detrimental are caused by minute flagellates. The algae concerned always seem to be planktonic, indeed these are probably the only ones capable of producing the necessary volume of material since they are distributed throughout a large volume of water. In the sea 'red tides' occur with greatest frequency and harm in tropical and subtropical regions, although the effects of the organisms have been detected as far north as Iceland and Norway but at such latitudes they do not cause mass mortality, merely contamination of shellfish and fish. Red tides are also correlated with regions of upwelling water, e.g. off the Pacific Coast of N. America, off Chile and off S.W. Africa. This in itself may be an incidental factor in increasing the productivity of the waters, culminating in growth of algae to the proportions of a water bloom. The greatest outbreaks of red tides occur towards the end of the summer when temperature is high and when the products of decay of previous plankton crops are at a maximum. Early workers considered that the mortality of crustacea and fish was due to the putrefaction of dead plankton, but although this may be a contributory factor, very strong poisons have been extracted from algae causing water blooms, and from shellfish feeding on the algae. It has been shown that mussels can store large amounts of these toxins, and when eaten by man, these cause paralytic shellfish poisoning. The potency of the Dinoflagellate toxins is shown by work on *Gymnodinium veneficum*,[2] but this is not the organism or the toxin involved in paralytic shellfish poisoning, which is caused by a species of *Gonyaulax*. The *Gymnodinium* toxin was lethal to *Mytilus edulis* and other shellfish. Species which can close their shells are more slowly affected, whilst species of fish and *Amphioxus* immersed in a solution of the toxin and frog and mouse injected with the toxin, are extremely susceptible (e.g. mice are killed in 2–4 mins). The only resistant group tested were the Polychaeta. Experiments suggested that the toxin acted on the nervous system causing depolarization of the nerve and muscle membranes; it probably occurred by interference with the sodium exchange mechanism, allowing rapid entry of sodium into the cells.

In freshwaters the most common deleterious algae are species of Cyanophyta (*Microcystis*, *Aphanizomenon*, *Anabaena*, etc.) killing aquatic animals, farm animals, and birds, especially those which drink the surface waters where there is the greatest concentration of plankton during a 'water bloom.' 'Blooms' of Cyanophyta are common in fish ponds in Israel, where they are enhanced by intensive fertilization. Shelubsky[364] records a 'thick viscous scum up to 10–20 cm in depth' at the water surface of such ponds. Mortality is partly caused by oxygen deficiency and partly by a toxin. Injection of suspensions of the algae into mice, rats, frogs and carp have proved lethal. Another extremely toxic alga in Israeli fish ponds (and elsewhere) is the minute flagellate *Prymnesium parvum*.[365] This alga is the most serious natural obstacle to fish cultivation in Israel. It produces an extracellular protein-like toxin. Fortunately, control of the flagellate is possible since ammonium sulphate has a lytic effect on the flagellate, which can thus be destroyed before reaching population sizes detrimental to the fish. The effect of ammonium sulphate increases with increasing temperature and pH; the ammonia enters two lateral vacuoles in the cell which swell up and burst the cell membrane.[366] Acetic acid has a similar effect but enters a large basal vacuole. It can also be controlled by addition of copper sulphate or pyridylmercuric acetate.

Sewage disposal

The disposal of sewage is an aerobic (sometimes anaerobic) process and the presence of algae greatly facilitates oxygenation. In open sewage oxidation ponds, used particularly in tropical regions, a growth of algae on and in the sewage is inevitable and an essential factor in their operation. Ostwald and Gotaas [308] studied the effects of oxygenation due to algal growth in the laboratory and in a pilot plant. Disposal of sewage in large volumes of water is possible without oxygenation, since oxygen is not completely depleted. In smaller bodies of water or in specially built ponds, it is necessary to aerate the sewage, otherwise anaerobic breakdown occurs with the production of unpleasant odours. If all the oxygen required by the bacteria for oxidative breakdown of the sewage could be obtained from algal growth, then the whole process could be achieved without extraneous aeration. The efficiency of such ponds will be affected by temperature, light and nutrient supply to the algae. Both low and high temperature strains of some of the algae have been found growing in oxidation ponds. Temperature, light and space are more adequate in tropical and subtropical countries where this type of pond is used. Many of the algae in such ponds utilize ammonia and hence benefit the system, since discharge waters containing ammonia have a high oxygen demand which is most undesirable. The only nutrient which may be limiting is carbon but since the effect of the algae in the sewage ponds is to increase the alkalinity, more rapid supply via bicarbonate ions is ensured. In this type of sewage treatment, it is necessary to remove the excess algal cells and pilot plant studies suggest that the algal yield may vary from 1–5 tonnes per acre per month, a much greater yield than that of most farm crops. Tests have shown that the algae recovered can be used as animal food and in certain regions this may be a valuable source of fodder. In the experiments *Euglena* was used as an initial inoculum but *Chlorella* and *Scenedesmus* soon replaced this and seem to be the active agents. After oxidation, *Chlorella* tends to be replaced by *Chlamydomonas*, which can actually become a nuisance in the surface scum. Silva and Papenfuss [368] listed the algal flora of some Californian oxidation ponds, finding a flora mainly composed of Volvocales, Chlorococcales and Euglenophyceae. In unstabilized ponds, a single, or at most two algae, tended to dominate, whilst in old ponds a number of algae were present. The commonest dominants were species of *Euglena, Chlamydomonas, Pyrobotrys, Micractinium, Chlorella* and *Scenedesmus*. The Volvocales tended to increase in the summer, but the others were more constant throughout the year. In some disposal plants, particularly in the tropics, the partially purified sewage from the oxidation ponds is led into fish ponds where it stimulates a large growth of algae beneficial to the fish. This has also been done in temperate climates, but the cold winter reduces the productivity.

In sewage disposal methods where the liquid sewage is sprayed on percolating filter beds, algae play an important role in the formation of a surface film also containing bacteria, fungi and protozoa. As in oxidation ponds and the filtration of drinking water, this film supplies oxygen and utilizes nutrients passing through the filter, leading to a breakdown of the sewage.

Water purification

Large growths of algae in water destined for drinking have two undesirable effects; firstly they or their decomposition products produce bad tastes in the water and secondly, and more commonly, they interfere with the filtration of the water. Small or large algal populations are present in most waters before passing into storage reservoirs; only well water is free of this algal inoculum. In reservoirs in mountainous catchment regions the algal population is often extremely small and may not delay the primary fast sand filtration. Water in lowland storage reservoirs and in reservoirs supplied with river water is usually rich in nutrients and produces large algal crops. Most of this water is filtered through fast and then slow sand filters (the water flows into large pans containing a layer of sand supported on stones, etc., and slowly percolates through into collecting channels beneath the bed) where small algal growths aid filtration by forming a micro-zone on the sand surface, which together with bacteria, fungi, etc., forms a mucilage layer in which harmful bacteria are trapped and through which the water is aerated. Large growths in the reservoirs soon clog these filters, which then have to be back-washed to remove the algae, or taken out of use whilst the surface sand is raked off and washed. Unfortunately, large algal growths develop in reservoirs, as in lakes, during spring and early summer, when water usage is reaching a maximum and hence clogging of filters can lead to a very serious shortage of water. The problem is serious enough for most large undertakings to maintain a continuous check on the development of the algal populations in their reservoirs either by direct observation of the algae or by prediction from the chemical status of the water, temperature, weather, etc. Some of the commonest organisms causing difficulties are diatoms (*Stephanodiscus, Asterionella, Fragilaria, Synedra, Melosira* and *Cyclotella* being the commonest), Cyanophyta (*Oscillatoria, Aphanizomenon, Anabaena* and *Microcystis*) and occasionally algae of other groups, e.g. *Ceratium, Dinobryon* and *Chlamydomonas*. The species involved are almost invariably planktonic and the difficulty is caused by their accumulation on the filters.

The large forms tend to block the fast filters but the small species (e.g. *Stephanodiscus* and *Cyclotella*) pass these and block the slow sand filters. There is in addition an actual flora on the sand of the filters, consisting mainly of benthic algae, e.g. Brook [37] found a spring flora dominated by *Diatoma elongatum* and *Fragilaria capucina* and an autumn flora dominated by *Melosira varians* with *F. capucina* and *Spirogyra* species. Amongst these filamentous species numerous motile diatoms were found. He also discovered that new sand filter beds supported the above filamentous and motile benthic forms, but old beds were dominated by non-motile species, e.g. *Scenedesmus quadricauda* and attached species, e.g. *Achnanthes minutissima* and *Merismopedia glauca*. Experiments showed that the primary flora was gradually removed by ciliates feeding on the algae, leaving only the more resistant attached forms.

Control of the detrimental algal growths is open to various approaches. When sufficient reservoirs are available, water may be drawn off from the unaffected, leaving those with algal blooms to subside in a natural way. Management of the reservoirs to prevent thermal stratification will tend to reduce the incidence of large algal populations. This can be achieved by various forms of pumping which tends to keep the mass of water in motion. Drawing off water from different depths can be used to avoid surface populations and drawing off bottom water of high nutrient status during periods of stratification removes a source of nutrients and may thus reduce future algal growths. Chemical treatment of the waters with algicides is regularly employed; one of the commonest treatments is with copper sulphate giving a concentration of about 1·0 p.p.m. in the reservoir waters. This is most effective when applied at the commencement of a spring or summer algal growth period. Larger doses may be applied to kill of massive algal growths, whilst continuous application at the inflow tends to kill the large algae but encourage the small which may then pass through the filters. Intermittent chlorination of the reservoir water may also be used but, as with copper sulphate, care has to be taken to avoid large doses which encourage small Chlorophyta. Undesirable tastes produced by algae or their decay can be removed by treating the water with activated carbon before filtration; the carbon is then held on the filters and continues its absorption as the water flows through the filter.

In the treatment of some river waters the undesirable chemicals, sediment and algae are partially removed by treatment with aluminium hydroxide after chlorination, which kills most of the algae.

A beneficial effect of algal growth, particularly of benthic algae, in reservoirs receiving calcareous waters is the precipitation of carbonates and subsequent reduction in hardness of the waters.

It is often necessary to remove algae from artificial ponds, industrial cooling water, open air swimming baths, etc., and the above inorganic substances can be used. An interesting application is that of copper sulphate at 5 p.p.m. added to irrigation water to control algae (*Spirogyra, Lyngbya* and *Phormidium*) which interfere with growth of rice seedlings in Australia.[44] Experiments have been conducted with organic compounds; Fitzgerald *et al.*[101] found that 2-3-dichloronaphthoquinone was toxic at 5 μg dm^{-3} to Cyanophyta producing 'blooms,' but not to other Cyanophyta, small Chlorophyta, diatoms or fish, whilst phenanthraquinone at 80 μg dm^{-3} was effective on 'bloom' species and *Chlorella*.

A method for testing the fertility of river water destined for reservoirs, has been worked out, in which *Asterionella* was used as an assay organism, inoculated into river water which had been heated to 40–45°C for one hour.[254] This showed that waters draining moorland soils were infertile, but the same water after passing through lower lying land on carboniferous limestone and shale was fertile. Further experiments adding fertilizers to the water showed increased fertility, in particular when phosphates were added, although it was concluded that fertilization of the land would probably need to be frequent before any appreciable increase in the fertility of the reservoir waters resulted. Excessive fertilization of the land is now common and is intensifying the problems arising from algal growths in reservoirs, etc.

Pollution

The effect of pollution on rivers or standing waters can be measured chemically, since it usually involves the addition of toxic substances or of organic wastes which on decomposition deplete the oxygen supply. However, the deleterious effects are on the organisms and the degree of pollution can often be measured most easily by a biological analysis, in which algae are important indicators. Algae are sensitive to the degree of reducing or oxidizing activity in the water. In the reducing zone, where oxygen is completely depleted, algae are subordinate to bacteria, sulphur bacteria and particularly the bacterium *Sphaerotilus natans*, formerly thought to be a fungus and commonly termed 'sewage fungus.' However, even in this type of water (polysaprobic) a few algae may survive, e.g. *Oscillatoria chlorina*, *Spirulina jenneri*, *Euglena* spp. and a few other flagellates. In the next zone (mesosaprobic), oxygen is not completely depleted and algae can grow; these zones succeed one another down a river from the source of pollution, or spread out in concentric zones in ponds and lakes. Two subdivisions of this zone are often used and it is only the α-mesosaprobic zone which is polluted in the common sense of the word. Here *Oscillatoria* spp., *Phormidium* spp., *Nitzschia palea*, *Gomphonema parvulum* and *Stigeoclonium tenue* appear and indicate the improvement in the water. The β-mesosaprobic zone may be still polluted on a chemical basis, but so far as the algae are concerned, it supports a rich flora comparable to that of many eutrophic waters. Further degrees of purity are found in oligosaprobic waters (i.e. in the upper reaches of streams or in oligotrophic lakes) and in katharobic waters where organic matter is at a minimum (e.g. in spring waters). The last two have a characteristic flora and in the last class, the extreme purity of the water has an effect similar to the pollution at the other end of the scale, resulting in a small and characteristic flora, indicators of which are *Lemanea* and *Batrachospermum* spp. Detailed consideration of the species distribution in waters of β-mesosaprobic status, through to waters of katharobic status, is an ecological rather than a pollution problem. The indicators of the various degrees of pollution will vary with the type of water, and Table 6 gives the relevant data slightly modified from Fjerdingstad.[102] His coprozoic zone is one of extreme pollution by unpurified sewage, supporting no algae at all, whilst more detailed subdivisions of the system are listed. In water polluted by toxic chemicals, even the bacterial flora may be killed and no breakdown of the effluents is possible. Short-term pollution of this type may be difficult to detect chemically, since the effluent may pass away rapidly but biological examination will reveal the extent to which the algal flora has suffered. Pollution with hydrogen sulphide often results in a flora in which species of *Trachelomonas* are the only common organisms. Acid mine waste causes pollution and the appearance of certain resistant algae, e.g. species of *Chlamydomonas* and *Euglena*.

The effect of slight pollution in increasing the growth and in encouraging the development of certain species has been noted elsewhere (p. 74). Järnefelt [196] shows this stimulatory effect of mild organic pollution on some planktonic lake algae, e.g. *Fragilaria crotonensis*, *Melosira islandica*, *M. granulata* and *Rhizosolenia eriensis*, which then pass into a zone of extreme pollution from sulphite discharge from a wood pulp factory, and are eliminated or reduced in number. The effect of this inorganic pollution is detrimental to many planktonic algae, which are so sensitive that they completely disappear, but their place is taken by species of the Chlorococcales, in particular *Dictyosphaerium pulchellum*, thus paralleling the effect of adding excessive copper sulphate in reservoirs.

Much discussion has centred on the method of sampling algae in polluted waters. The above results by Järnefelt were obtained by direct sampling and counting of the phytoplankton population, a method which can also be applied to the sediments (see p. 59) of ponds, lakes or running water. However, considerable studies have been made using artificial substrata, e.g. glass slides.[46] These give a perfectly workable indication of pollution and the system has been elaborated with a device, the 'Catherwood diatometer,' in which the slides are held upright in racks attached to floats which maintain the apparatus in the photic zone.[316] The claim that this method measures the entire flora is questionable; undoubtedly all species within the zone will sooner or later be noted on the slides but there is little doubt that the true flora of the various microhabitats in its quantitative aspect is not measured.

Land reclamation

Algae act as important binding agents on the surface of soils. Disturbed or burnt heath soils are rapidly covered with a growth of Chlorophyta (e.g.

Table 6. Survey of the saprobic zones and accompanying communities.
a.b.c. ... as alternative possibilities.
1.2.3. ... as graduations of pollution.

Zone	I	THE COPROZOIC ZONE Algae absent. a: the bacterial community; b: the Bodo community; c: both communities.
Zone	II	THE α-POLYSAPROBIC ZONE 1: the *Euglena* community; 2: the Rhodo-Thiobacterial community; 3: the pure Chlorobacterial community.
Zone	III	THE β-POLYSAPROBIC ZONE 1: the *Beggiatoa* community; 2: the *Thiothrix nivea* community; 3: the *Euglena* community.
Zone	IV	THE γ-POLYSAPROBIC ZONE 1: the *Oscillatoria chlorina* community; 2: the *Sphaerotilus natans* community.
Zone	V	THE α-MESOSAPROBIC ZONE a: the *Ulothrix zonata* community; b: the *Oscillatoria benthonicum* community; c: the *Stigeocloneum tenue* community.
Zone	VI	THE β-MESOSAPROBIC ZONE a: the *Cladophora fracta* community; b: the *Phormidium* community.
Zone	VII	THE γ-MESOSAPROBIC ZONE a: the Rhodophyta community (*Batrachospermum vagum* or *Lemanea fluviatilis*); b: the Chlorophyta community (*Cladophora glomerata* or *Ulothrix zonata*) (the type of pure water).
Zone	VIII	THE OLIGOSAPROBIC ZONE a: the Chlorophyta community (*Draparnaldia glomerata*); b: the pure *Meridion circulare* community; c: the Rhodophyta community (*Lemanea annulata, Batrachospermum moniliforme* or *Hildenbrandia rivularis*); d: the *Vaucheria sessilis* community; e: the *Phormidium inundatum* community.
Zone	IX	THE KATHAROBIC ZONE a: the Chlorophyta community (*Chlorotylium cataractum* and *Draparnaldia plumosa*); b: the Rhodophyta community (*Chantransia chalybea* and *Hildenbrandia rivularis*); c: the encrusting algal communities (*Chamaesiphon polonius* and different *Calothrix* species).

Hormidium, Zygogonium) and Cyanophyta (*Chroococcus, Phormidium*, etc.), which reduce the danger of erosion. Booth [26] found that coatings of Cyanophyta on prairie soils bound the soil particles, maintained a higher water content and did not reduce percolation of water into the soil. Many tropical sandy soils are bound by sheets of Cyanophyta. Singh [369] reports extensive growths of Cyanophyta on alkaline 'Usar' lands of N. India. Here *Nostoc commune* covers soil over many miles, adding much organic matter, and increasing the nitrogen content by 30–38 per cent. The soil is actually cultivated to encourage this growth prior to cropping.

13 Classification

From very early times seaweeds and filamentous pond algae (*Conferva*) were recognized as plants and variously classified as Acotyledons, Cellulares, Thallophyta, Cryptogamae, distinguishing them from cotyledonous, vascular plants. They were often confused with Bryophyta, but gradually there was a subdivision into leafy and non-leafy Thallophyta, comprising all plants without vascular systems. At this point there was more confusion, since the generally accepted term Thallophyta, first used definitively by Eichler,[91] to distinguish Algae and Fungi from Bryophyta, Pteridophyta and Spermophyta, implies a lack of leaf/stem structure, which is however a superficial feature of some complex algae. The reproduction of the Thallophyta is characterized by the fact that the cells of the reproductive structures are all fertile and the sporangia are never multicellular with sterile wall cells (but see p. 29). Additionally there is never a multicellular embryo retained within the oogonium. Eichler recognized five groups, Cyanophyceae, Diatomeae, Chlorophyceae, Phaeophyceae and Rhodophyceae, whilst earlier Harvey[153] had recognized the three main multicellular coloured groups, Chlorospermae (green algae), Melanospermae (brown algae—also termed Melanophyceae in some early classifications) and Rhodospermae (red algae) and thus from a very early stage the importance of pigmentation has been recognized.* During the nineteenth century numerous flagellates were described and placed in the class *Flagellata* of the Protozoa. The coloured Volvocalean series was recognized as an algal group over one hundred years ago and gradually other flagellates have been transferred to the algae, although even today some very obviously algal flagellates are still appearing in textbooks as Protozoa. Slowly these flagellates were allocated to the various algal phyla and finally Pascher showed how the flagellate types of organization were associated with the parallel series of flagellate, tetrasporal, coccoidal and filamentous forms in each phylum. However the taxonomic status of each and every flagellate and alga is by no means finalized and changes are continually being made. For instance there has been considerable argument over the algal or protozoal nature of the Euglenoids. Fritsch[114a] states that 'the holophytic Euglenineae (*Euglena, Trachelomonas, Phacus*, etc.) exhibit no characteristics that support their inclusion among the Protozoa and the zoological terminology suggestive of a process of holozoic nutrition is quite unwarranted and deplorable.' Strong words! However, today it is convenient to include all photosynthetic flagellates in the algae since they all have a photochemical apparatus similar

* This basic system with the addition of the blue coloured Cyanophyta is re-emphasized in a recent textbook (Christensen[64]).

to that of other plants and absent from animals. Work of the last decade shows that apart from the photochemical apparatus, the basic physiological processes and basic structure of organs, e.g. mitrochondria, flagella, nucleus, etc., are common to both plant and animal groups; the eyespot of *Euglena* contains the animal pigment astaxanthin (also in some Chlorophyceae, e.g. resting spores of *Haematococcus*[134]), whilst permanent colourless races of *Euglena* have been produced indistinguishable from Protozoa and phagotrophy has been shown in certain photosynthetic algae, e.g. Chrysomonads. Thus it is better not to be dogmatic and to allow that many of the flagellates are extremely plastic and that convenience is perhaps the only justification for some of the taxonomic positions! Other controversial points will be noted in the synopsis of the groups to follow.

The International Code of Botanical Nomenclature, Utrecht (1952), laid down the suffixes to be used for the categories of plant classification and the following are those applicable to the algae.

DIVISION (Phylum)—phyta
SUBDIVISION—phytina
CLASS—phyceae
SUBCLASS—phycidae
ORDER—ales
SUBORDER—inales
FAMILY—aceae
SUBFAMILY—oideae
TRIBE—eae
GENUS (normally a Latin name)
SPECIES (normally a Latin name)
VARIETY (a Latin name)
FORM (a Latin name)

The allocation of algal groups to these subdivisions depends somewhat on the status given them by an author, e.g. Engler [93] classes the centric diatoms as a subclass (Centricae), whereas Fott [109] gives them the standing of an order (Centrales). According to the above system used in Engler [93] the Centricae should be amended to Centriphycidae if this group is regarded as a subclass. Comparison of only these two authorities shows numerous variations in usage. The following system is based on Engler [93] with the modifications made by Fott,[109] Christensen,[64] Parke & Dixon[312a] and Round,[350c] since I regard this as the best system to date and an attempt has been made to conform with the International Code. To avoid confusion the breakdown of the phyla is taken only as far as appears necessary for the placing of genera into orders by the student who can then consult the works of Engler, Fott, Fritsch, etc., for further identification.

The characters used in the classification of the algae are diverse and combinations of characters are often necessary when considering some of the more difficult forms. Early workers relied entirely on form which resulted in a mass of filamentous species grouped as *Conferva*. Later the cytology of the cells and particularly the life history were also used. Slowly, as techniques developed, other characters such as the chemical nature of reserve products, the pigment complement, the submicroscopic wall and flagellar structure, the chromosome number and arrangement, etc., were considered and many instances can be quoted of the value of these characteristics in assigning a doubtful genus or species to a more natural position in the taxonomic system. Usually however these techniques have merely confirmed the placing, based on observation of structure, colour, etc., and illustrate how interrelated are form and physiology in the algae. The design of keys for the identification of algae is based largely on external form with the addition of obvious cytological details. Form alone can be used for many groups, e.g. diatoms, desmids, many flagellates, and large thalloid algae. Form, combined with pigmentation and chromatophore shape can lead to the identification of many algae by students who have no chance to follow the intricacies of life histories. In the Phaeophyta and Rhodophyta and to a lesser extent in the Chlorophyta, knowledge of the detailed life history is essential before the alga can be safely assigned to an order or family, even though this information may not always be necessary for a mere naming of the alga. Ecological data, e.g. marine or freshwater, may be of value in identification if used with caution; it is not a reliable taxonomic character.

The first striking point in algal taxonomy is the almost universal acceptance of the blue-green algae as algal forms though this is now beginning to be questioned again. The absence of a nucleus with typical chromosomes (see p. 52) and the dispersion of the pigments in a very primitive chromatophore structure (see p. 46) points to a close relationship with some of the bacteria. They have been variously classified as Akaryonta (on nuclear structure) or Plantae holoplastidae (on plastid structure). Vilhelm [404] regarded the Akaryonta as the most ancient plants and classified them as Archaiophyta (together with the slime moulds). Fott [109] uses the term Prokaryonta* to include the Cyanophyta and Schizomycophyta (Bacteria), thus indicating the obvious affinities of these two groups and distinguishing them from the remaining algae with typical nuclei (Eukaryonta*). For over a hundred years (Cohn [68] in 1853), the blue-green algae and bacteria (Schizophyta) have been regarded as closely related and the arguments for and against this have swayed back and forth. Stanier and Van Niel [377] use the term Monera in place of Schizophyta for these two groups and cite the following common characteristics, (*a*) absence of true nuclei, (*b*) absence of sexual reproduction, (*c*) absence of plastids. Pringsheim [325a] summarized the arguments and concluded that there is little relationship. He draws attention to the fact that motility in the bacteria is by means of simplified flagella, but in the Cyanophyta only gliding movements occur. The presence of apochlorotic Cyanophyta (*Beggiatoa, Achromatium*) is

---

* Eucaryota and Procaryota of Christensen.[64]

not necessarily a link between the two groups since apochlorotic species and genera are known in many algal groups. Since then, however, opinion seems to be veering towards the idea that there is a close relationship between the Cyanophyta and bacteria. It is perhaps best to think of both groups as primitive, being divergent in certain features (e.g. motility, fermentative activity) and convergent in others (e.g. nitrogen fixation, pigmentation), but having more mutual affinities than to other algal groups. Although exhibiting a combination of unusual morphological and physiological characteristics, nevertheless 'their life processes are based on mechanisms essentially similar to those which have been found in other organisms.'[106] The property of nitrogen fixation and the presence of α-ε-diaminopimelic acid in both Cyanophyta and bacteria is striking but this acid also occurs in minute quantities in *Chlorella ellipsoidea*. Strictly the term Myxophyceae should be used for this group since it predates the term Cyanophyta by fourteen years. However Christensen,[64] Fott,[109] Engler[93] and Drouet[87] prefer the latter term and it is used here since it indicates the pigmentation of the group and avoids confusion with the Myxomycetae (slime moulds).

PROCARYOTA

PHYLUM CYANOPHYTA (MYXOPHYCEAE)

Unicellular, colonial or filamentous. Possessing nuclear material (deoxypentose nucleic acids) and pigments (see p. 163) but neither the nuclear nor the plastid material delimited by a sharp bounding membrane. Cells blue-green, blue, olive green, yellow, red or violet according to the species and habitat conditions. Sometimes appearing black, owing to the abundance of vacuoles containing nitrogen in the cells. Cell membranes indistinct (pectin or cellulose) or thick, often striate and mucilaginous, sometimes stained with pigments. Assimilation products, glycogen and glycoproteins. Motile by means of creeping movements, possibly associated with mucilage production. In some filamentous species, heterocysts are formed and sometimes associated with these are larger cells with dense contents (akinetes). Division of cells by ingrowth of annular wall (Plate 4). Reproduction by production of endospores, exospores, encysted fragments of filaments (hormocysts), unencysted fragments of filaments (hormogonia) or variously thickened vegetative cells. No sexual stages or flagellate forms known. Occur abundantly in most freshwater environments, common in soil, hot springs, in the marine littoral zone, symbiotic with fungi to form lichens and space parasites in some plants (e.g. in *Anthoceros*, *Gunnera*, *Cycas*).

There is a single class, Cyanophyceae (Myxophyceae) divided into four orders. There is some confusion in the naming of these and so the common names in use are given as alternatives.

1. Heterocysts and hormogonia lacking. (Only rarely indistinctly filamentous.)
   a) Cells solitary or in colonies **Chroococcales**
      (*Aphanothece* = *Coccochloris*, *Aphanocapsa*, *Chroococcus*, *Coelosphaerium*, *Entophysalis*, *Eucapsis*, *Gloeocapsa*, *Gomphosphaeria*, *Holopedia*, *Merismopedia*, *Microcystis* (= *Anacystis*), *Synechococcus*, *Synechocystis*.)*
   b) Cells solitary or more often in groups, cells differentiated into base and apex, sometimes with an external sheath **Chamaesiphonales**
      or
      Dermocarpales
      (*Chamaesiphon*, *Dermocarpa*.)
   c) Plant an indistinct heterotrichous filament **Pleurocapsales**
      (*Hyella*, *Oncobyrsa*, *Pleurocapsa*, *Xenococcus*.)

2. Distinctly filamentous. Heterocysts, hormogonia and akinetes sometimes present

   Hormogonales
   or

   Oscillatoriales
   The largest group into which all simple and branched filamentous Cyanophyta fall. Two suborders.
   a) Filaments simple **Nostocinales**
      (*Anabaena*, *Aphanizomenon*, *Calothrix*, *Cylindrospermum*, *Dichothrix*, *Gleotrichia*, *Homeothrix*, *Hydrocoleum*, *Hydrocoleus*, *Lyngbya*, *Microcoleus*, *Nostoc*, *Oscillatoria*, *Petalonema*, *Phormidium*, *Plectonema*, *Rivularia*, *Schizothrix*, *Scytonema*, *Spirulina*, *Symploca*, *Tolypothrix*, *Trichodesmium*.)
   b) Filaments heterotrichous, with connecting pits
      Stigonematinales
      (*Fischerella*, *Haplosiphon*, *Mastigocoleus*, *Mastigocladus*, *Stigonema*.)

EUCARYOTA

Caryonta, Plantae euplastidae. Algae with typical nucleus and pigments localized in chromatophores. Twelve phyla.

1. Algae with green pigments
   a) Unicellular with a single obvious flagellum **EUGLENOPHYTA**
   b) Algae either unicellular, colonial, coenobial, filamentous or siphonaceous† and usually forming starch **CHLOROPHYTA**

* The algae listed are only those in this book and the keys are only intended for student use to enable the commoner algae to be determined to an order; no attempt has been made to be comprehensive.

† These have discoid chromatophores but are usually large macroscopic plants, marine, and often encrusted with lime, whereas siphonaceous Xanthophyceae are small, freshwater or brackish water forms in which calcium, if deposited at all, occurs only as isolated crystals.

c) Macroscopic algae with precise segmentation into nodal and internodal segments   CHAROPHYTA

d) Flagellate or coccoid algae. Four flagella (occasionally fewer) arising
from an apical pit and with flagella and body covered by scales
                                                    PRASINOPHYTA*

e) Algae as *b*, but usually discoid chromatophores and forming oil but
not starch   XANTHOPHYTA

f) Coccoid algae recently separated from the Xanthophyta.[171a] With
stalked pyrenoids projecting from the inner face of the chloroplasts.
Motile cells with a single emergent flagellum bearing a proximal
swelling   EUSTIGMATOPHYCEAE*

2. Algae with brown pigments
   a) Unicellular, biflagellate with flagella in two different planes[†]
                                                           DINOPHYTA
                                                    (=PYRROPHYTA)

   b) Unicellular or colonial, without flagella, with a bipartite sculptured
   silica wall   BACILLARIOPHYTA

   c) Unicellular or colonial, without flagella, or with one, or two flagella.
   Often with siliceous scales on the motile cell or cells within loricas
                                                          CHRYSOPHYTA

   d) Unicellular, coccoid or filamentous. Unicellular flagellates usually
   with a haptonema in addition to flagella and with scales on the body
   (not visible with the light microscope except for the coccoliths occurring on some genera)

   e) Simple or branched filaments or thalloid. Overwhelmingly marine and
   usually macroscopic   PHAEOPHYTA

3. Mainly marine algae with red pigments (often somewhat greyish in
   freshwaters). Unicellular, filamentous or thalloid   RHODOPHYTA

4. Algae with green, blue, red pigments. Two slightly unequal flagella
   arising laterally at the apical end   CRYPTOPHYTA

It is impossible to include the anomalous genera in a brief key but it is
hoped that the above will prove satisfactory for an initial group identification
by students.

---

* These groups are not always easy to distinguish with the light microscope. The
details have been worked out from electron microscope studies. The overwhelming
majority of green algae encountered by students will belong to the Chlorophyta. For
a more detailed discussion of the classification of the green pigmented algae see
Round, 1971 (Ref. 350c).

† Also blue and reddish pigments and numerous colourless genera and very rare
filamentous forms.

PHYLUM CHRYSOPHYTA

Flagellate, coccoid or filamentous algae with generally two golden brown chromatophores in each cell. Genera with a single emergent flagellum generally have a second reduced flagellum often associated with the eyespot. All form leucosin (see p. 180), and oil as reserve products and never starch. Siliceous scales occur on some genera; siliceous cysts are formed endogenously. One class and five orders.

CHRYSOPHYCEAE

Mainly unicellular. Some colonial and filamentous. Chromatophores brown. Cell wall often with siliceous plates. Endogenous siliceous cysts formed in some. Sexual reproduction, isogamous. Mainly freshwater. A very diverse group.

1. Unicellular, without rigid cell wall
   a) Flagellate unicells or colonies   **Chrysomonadales**
   (*Chlorodesmus, Chromulina, Chrysococcus, Chrysopyxis, Chrysosphaerella, Dinobryon, Epipyxis, Kephyrion, Mallomonas, Ochromonas, Paraphysomonas, Phaeococcus, Synura, Uroglena, Uroglenopsis.*)

   Here is found the suborder Silicoflagellineae (Dictyochineae) (*Dictyocha*).
   b) Cells rhizopodial   **Rhizochrysidales**
   (*Chrysamoeba, Heliactis, Rhizochrysis.*)
   c) Cells tetrasporal in mucilage   **Chrysocapsales**
   (*Chrysocapsa, Gloeochrysis, Hydrurus.*)

2. Cells with rigid cell wall
   a) Cells coccoidal   **Chrysosphaerales**
   (*Chrysosphaera, Stichogloea.*)
   b) Cells in filaments   **Phaeothamniales**
            (= **Chrysotrichales**)

   (*Phaeodermatium, Phaeothamnion, Thallochrysis.*)

PHYLUM XANTHOPHYTA (HETEROKONTAE)

Unicellular, colonial, filamentous or siphonaceous algae. Motile cells unequally biflagellate, rarely uniflagellate with the eyespot embedded in the plastid. Cell wall often composed of two halves, but rarely obvious without chemical treatment. Chromatophores usually disc-like, (yellow) green. Assimilation product, oil. Mainly freshwater or terrestrial. Heterokontae is the older name of the group and refers to the unequal flagella, but Xanthophyta is more descriptive and in general use. One class and six others.

Xanthophyceae

1. Unicellular, without rigid cell wall
   a) Cells motile   **Heterochloridales**
      (*Chloramoeba, Heterochloris.*)
   b) Cells amoeboid   **Rhizochloridales**
      (*Rhizochloris, Rhizolecane.*)
   c) Cells in mucilage colonies   **Heterogloeales**
                                                                  or
                                                             Heterocapsales
      (*Chlorogloea* (= *Heterogloea*), *Chlorosaccus, Gloeochloris.*)
2. Unicellular or multicellular, with rigid cell wall
   a) Unicellular or colonial   **Mischococcales**
                                                                  or
                                                             Heterococcales
      (*Characiopsis, Gloeobotrys, Goniochloris, Monodus, Ophiocytium.*)
   b) Filamentous   **Heterotrichales**
      (*Heterococcus, Heterodendron, Tribonema.*)

3. Siphonaceous   **Botrydiales**
                                                                  or
                                                             Heterosiphonales
      (*Botrydium, Vaucheria.*)

Eustigmatophyceae

A grouping of green coccoid forms which have recently been separated from the Xanthophyceae *sensu strida*. In this new class the eyespot is independent of the plastid. *Chlorobotrys* is the only genus referred to in this book which on vegetative characters needs to be transferred to this new class.

PHYLUM HAPTOPHYTA

This phylum is characterized mainly by features visible only with difficulty in the light microscope, such as the coiled or extended haptonema which can be seen between the two flagella. The organic scales coating the motile, and sometimes non-motile cells, can only be seen using the electron microscope (see Plate 3). One class and two orders.

Haptophyceae

Mainly unicellular flagellates most of which possess a haptonema and flagella. A relatively new grouping by Christensen.[61] Comprises several genera formerly in the Chrysophyceae and probably includes all the coccolithophorids. At least two orders.

1. Motile phase without an obvious haptonema   **Isochrysidales**
                                                             (*Isochrysis*)

2. Motile phases with a haptonema   **Prymnesiales**
    (*Apistonema, Chrysochromulina, Chrysonema, Chrysotila, Cyclococcolithus, Phaeocystis, Prymnesium* and the coccolithophorids, Coccolithineae of earlier authors, *Coccolithus, Cricosphaera, Cyclococcolithus, Discosphaera, Homozygosphaera, Michaelsarsia, Pontosphaera,* and *Syracosphaera.*)

PHYLUM BACILLARIOPHYTA

Unicellular or colonial algae, with numerous discoid or two plate-like brown chromatophores. Assimilatory products oil, volutin and chrysose (see p. 180). Cell wall of two distinct halves joined by hoop-like structures, all components composed of silica. Some motile with gliding movement associated with mucilage production. Cells diploid. Sexual reproduction by fusion or gametes or autogamous. Freshwater, terrestrial and marine. Commonly known as diatoms. Two classes.

CENTROBACILLARIOPHYCEAE*

Cells in valve view circular, ovoid, triradiate or polygonal. Non-motile. Often forming colonies. The subdivision into orders requires further detailed study with the electron microscope. The older classifications recognized a single order—Centrales. Silva [368a] distinguished three orders but recent work by the author and others suggests that the classification is in need of considerable re-arrangement which cannot be attempted here.

(*Actinocyclus, Actinoptychus, Anthodiscus, Asteromphalus, Astrolampra, Attheya, Bacteriastrum, Bellerochea, Bergonia, Biddulphia, Cerataulina, Chaetoceros, Climacodium, Corethron, Coscinodiscus, Cyclotella, Ditylum, Entogonia, Eucampia, Guinardia, Hemidiscus, Lauderia, Leptocylindrus, Melosira, Planktoniella, Pyrgodiscus, Pyxidicula, Rhizosolenia, Roperia, Sceletonema, Stephanodiscus, Stephanopyxis, Syndetocystis, Thalassiosira, Triceratium.*)

PENNATIBACILLARIOPHYCEAE [368a]

Cells elongate, bilaterally symmetrical in valve and girdle view. Sometimes heteropolar. Slits (raphes) present in the valves of many genera and these then motile. Others with unslit central area (pseudoraphe) and then often attached by mucilate pads formed at the one apex of the cell. A single order—Pennales—in the older classification. The sub-groupings below are based on Hustedt (1930) and are convenient in that they distinguish four major cell types but others can be recognized (see 368a).

                                                                Pennales
                                                          (Pennate diatoms)
a) Pseudoraphe present   **Araphidineae**
    (*Amphicampa, Asterionella, Campylosira, Ceratoneis, Cymatosira, Diatoma, Fragilaria, Grammatophora, Licmophora, Meridion, Peronia, Pseudoeunotia, Raphoneis, Rhabdonema, Striatella, Synedra, Tabellaria, Thalassionema, Thalassiothrix, Tetracyclus.*)

* A new class distinguished by Silva (1962) Ref. 368a.

b) Rudimentary raphe at cell ends   **Raphidioidineae**
(*Actinella, Eunotia.*)
c) Raphe on one valve and pseudoraphe on other
                                                                Monoraphidineae
(*Achnanthes, Cocconeis, Eucocconeis, Rhoicosphenia.*)
d) Raphe on both valves   **Biraphidineae**
(*Amphipleura, Amphiprora, Amphora, Anomoeoneis, Bacillaria, Caloneis,
Campylodiscus, Cylindrotheca, Cymatopleura, Cymbella, Denticula, Didymo-
sphenia, Diploneis, Epithemia, Fragilariopsis, Frustulia, Gomphonema,
Gyrosigma, Hantzschia, Mastogloia, Navicula, Neidium, Nitzschia, Phaeo-
dactylum, Pinnularia, Pleurosigma, Rhopalodia, Scoliopleura, Stauroneis,
Stenopterobia, Surirella, Tropidoneis.*)

PHYLUM CHLOROPHYTA (Isokontae)

Green pigmented algae (occasionally colourless) with true pyrenoids and
starch. Form ranges from unicellular through colonial, coenobial, filamentous, thalloid to siphonaceous. Chromatophores one or more, often complex,
but discoid in the siphonaceous genera. Flagellate stages possessing two
(four) or rarely more flagella. Asexual reproduction via zoospores, aplanospores, autospores, akinetes, palmelloid stages or fragmentation. Sexual
reproduction isogamous, anisogamous, or oogamous. Mostly haploid
vegetative plants (except Bryopsidophyceae which are diploid) and with
well developed alternation of generations in some genera. Freshwater,
terrestrial and marine, but certain groups confined to one or the other
habitat. Some genera symbiotic with fungi, forming lichens, and others
symbiotic with animals.

Although there have been changes of nomenclature and status, the
general basis of classification into orders has remained constant for many
years. The main points of argument are the status of the conjugate algae
(Conjugales or Conjugatophyceae or Akontae of the older systems), the
relationships between the Ulotrichales and Chaetophorales and finally the
position of the siphonaceous forms, including the subdivision into Siphonales
and Siphonocladales and the inclusion of the Cladophorales in the latter.
The system adopted here is a combination of Fott,[109] and Christensen[64] with
certain modifications by the author (Round[350c]). A single division is
retained for the green algae, excluding the euglenoid, charophyte and
prasinophyte series of algae (see Round[350c] for more detailed arguments to
support this view). The Chlorophyta is split into four glasses: Zygnemaphyceae[35]* (=Conjugatophyceae, cf. Fott[100]), Oedogoniophyceae,[350] Bryopsidophyceae[350] and Chlorophyceae. The Oedogoniophyceae is, I believe, a
necessary grouping since the very distinctive characters of the genera

---

* This change in name is simply due to the desirability of naming major groupings
with a 'prefix' derived from a generic name. The class is otherwise unchanged.

separate them from the filamentous Chlorophyceae to as great or greater degree than those used to separate the Zygnemaphyceae. The Bryopsidophyceae is named from Fott's Bryopsidales and includes his Siphonocladales; again the characters of this group are so distinctive (diploid, coenocytic, mainly macroscopic, often calcareous, tropical and marine, special carotenoid pigments, xylose and mannose as wall components, etc.) that they warrant raising to a class. Even then they are a complex group for which three cohorts are proposed, based on Chadefaud's [54] groups. These cohorts (i.e. groups of orders) are Hemisiphoniidae (Cladophorales, Sphaeropleales), Cystosiphoniidae (Chlorochytriales, Siphoncladales, Dasycladales) and Eusiphoniidae (Derbesiales, Codiales, Caulerpales, Dichotomosiphonales). Finally the Chlorophyceae contain a variable number of orders, possibly these could with advantage form three cohorts: (1) Volvocales, Tetrasporales, Chlorococcales, Chlorosphaerales; (2) Ulotrichales, Ulvales, Prasiolales, Microsporales; (3) Chaetophorales (or better perhaps split into Chaetophorales, Ulvellales, Trentepohliales, Coleochaetales, Pleurocapsales). The Chlorosphacrales is a new small group of soil algae not mentioned before in this book. The merging of the Ulotrichales, Ulvales, Chaetophorales and even Oedogoniales by Fott [109] produced an unwieldy, heterogeneous group which is better split into the above orders.

1. Algae macroscopic, often articulate, composed of multinucleate siphons or multinucleate cells BRYOPSIDOPHYCEAE

2. Algae microscopic or macroscopic, unicellular, colonial, filamentous or thalloid
   a) Unicellular or filamentous, with complex chromatophores, reproducing by conjugation ZYGNEMAPHYCEAE
   b) Simple or branched filaments, with a special type of cell division OEDOGONIOPHYCEAE
   c) Varied morphology but never reproducing by conjugation or with cell division as *b* CHLOROPHYCEAE

CHLOROPHYCEAE. Eight orders

1. Unicellular or colonial algae
   a) Flagellate **Volvocales***
   (*Brachiomonas, Carteria, Chlamydobotrys, Chlamydomonas, Chlorogonium, Coccomyxa, Dunaliella, Eudorina, Gonium, Haematococcus, Hyalogonium, Medusochloris, Pandorina, Phacotus, Pleodorina, Polytoma, Polytomella, Pyrobotrys, Spondylomorum, Stephanoptera, Stephanosphaera, Volvox, Volvulina.*)

* Some authorities reserve this order for the colonial genera and place the unicells in a separate order, CHLAMYDOMONADALES.

   b) Non-flagellate, cells embedded in mucilage and sometimes with
   pseudocilia and usually reproducing vegetatively by means of flagellate
   stages   **Tetrasporales**
   (*Chaetopeltis, Chlorangiopsis, Chlorangium, Elakatothrix, Palmodictyon,
   Stylosphaeridium, Tetraspora.*)
   c) Non-flagellate cells, free or in colonies, reproducing by means of
   autospores or zoospores   **Chlorococcales**
   (*Ankistrodesmus, Botryococcus, Characium* (= *Ankyra*), *Chlorella, Chlorococcum,
   Coelastrum, Dictyosphaerium, Eremosphaera, Golenkinia, Hydrodictyon, Kera-
   tococcus, Kirchneriella, Micractinium, Oocystis, Pediastrum, Protosiphon,
   Prototheca, Quadrigula, Raphidium, Reinschia*(= *Pila*), *Scenedesmus, Scotiella,
   Sphaerocystis, Tetracoccus, Tetraedron.*)

2. Filamentous or thalloid algae
   a) Filaments unbranched (rarely branched) or joined to form a pseudo-
   parenchymatous thallus
       a^1) Cells usually with interrupted band shaped chloroplast and cell
       division in one plane   **Ulotrichales**
          (*Binuclearia, Geminella, Hormidium, Raphidonema, Stichococcus, Ulothrix.*)
       a^2) Cells usually with interrupted band shaped or cup shaped chloro-
       plast and cell division in two planes   **Ulvales**
          (*Blidingia, Cylindrocapsa, Enteromorpha, Monostroma, Ulva.*)
       a^3) Cells of filament with stellate chloroplasts   **Prasiolales**
          (*Prasiola.*)
       a^4) Cell walls of filament composed of H-pieces   **Microsporales**
          (*Microspora.*)
   b) Filament heterotrichous. Either an upright or a basal system or both.
   When only the basal system is present it may be pseudoparenchymatous
   and flat   **Chaetophorales***
   (*Aphanochaete, Cephaleuros, Chaetophora, Coleochaete, Desmococcus, Drapar-
   naldia, Endoderma, Fritschiella, Gomontia, Microthamnion, Phycopeltis,
   Pleurococcus, Pringsheimia, Stigeoclonium, Stomatochroon, Trentepohlia,
   Ulvella.*)

OEDOGONIOPHYCEAE

Filaments branched or unbranched. Cells usually much longer than
broad, chloroplast perforated and an unusual type of cell division
                                                      Oedogoniales

(*Bulbochaete, Oedocladium, Oedogonium.*)

   *This is almost certainly a collection of orders which require extensive study,
e.g. *Coleochaete* is often placed in an order Coleochaetales and *Trentepohlia, Stomatochroon* and *Cephaleuros* in the Trentepohliales.

BRYOPSIDOPHYCEAE. Three cohorts

1. Thallus divided by cross walls into multinucleate portions
HEMISIPHONIIDAE

Cladophorales—(*Cladophora, Chaetomorpha, Pithophora,* and *Rhizoclonium.*)
Acrosiphoniales—(*Urospora* and *Spongomorpha.*)
Sphaeropleales—(*Sphaeroplea.*)

2. Thallus with or without segregative division* and forming cysts
CYSTOSIPHONIIDAE

Siphonocladales—(*Anadyomene, Boodlea, Cladophoropsis, Chamaedoris, Dictoysphaeria, Microdictyon, Struvea, Valonia.*)
Dasycladales—(*Acetabularia, Batophora, Cyclocrinus, Cymopolia, Dasycladus, Neomeris, Palaeodasycladus, Primicorallina, Rhabdoporella.*)

3. Lacking above characters but with special carotenoid pigments and wall compounds
EUSIPHONIIDAE

Derbesiales—(*Derbesia* (inc. *Halicystis*).)
Codiales—(*Avrainvillea, Bryopsis, Codium.*)
Caulerpales—(*Caulerpa, Halimeda, Penicillus, Udotea.*)

ZYGNEMAPHYCEAE. Four orders

1. Unicellular or occasionally filamentous. Commonly known as desmids.
   a) Cells not constricted
      a¹) Cell wall porous, of inner and outer layers, latter punctate, usually in loose filaments **Gonatozygales**
      (*Genicularia, Gonatozygon.*)
      a²) Cell wall smooth, very rarely forming filaments
      Mesotaeniales
      (*Ancylonema, Cylindrocystis, Mesotaenium, Netrium, Spirotaenia.*)
   b) Cells constricted into two semicells separated by an isthmus, cell wall of two layers, outer often striate or punctate. Cells sometimes arranged in filaments **Desmidiales**

      (*Arthrodesmus, Closterium,† Cosmarium, Cosmocladium, Desmidium, Euastrum, Gymnozygon, Hyalotheca, Micrasterias, Onychonema, Oocardium, Penium,† Pleurotaenium, Sphaerozosma, Spondylosium, Staurastrum, Staurodesmus, Tetmemorus, Xanthidium.*)

2. Filamentous, fragmenting by a special process involving growth of end walls **Zygnemales**
   (*Mougeotia, Spirogyra, Zygnema, Zygogonium.*)

* Into multinucleate units.
† In *Closterium* and *Penium* the cells are composed of two pieces but there is not always an obvious constriction between the two.

PHYLUM CHAROPHYTA

Macroscopic plants with distinct apical cells, whorled branching, long nodal and short internodal cells. Complex oogonia and antheridia produced at bases of branches. Latter often orange coloured. Rooted by means of rhizoids in the sediments at the bottom of freshwater and brackish ponds.

CHAROPHYCEAE. One order **Charales**
    (*Chara, Lamprothamnium, Nitella, Tolypella* and the fossil genera *Clavator* and *Palaeochara.*)

PHYLUM PRASINOPHYTA

A small group of algae mainly flagellate with four (occasionally 2 or 1) thick flagella arising from an apical pit surrounded by four lobes. Eyespot embedded in chloroplast. Freshwater and marine and *Platymonas* sometimes endozooic.

PRASINOPHYCEAE. Two orders.

1. Vegetative stages motile **Pyramimonadales**
        (*Micromonas, Nephroselmis, Platymonas*, and *Pyramimonas*)

2. Vegetative stages non-motile **Halosphaerales**
            (*Halosphaera*)

PHYLUM EUGLENOPHYTA

Unicellular flagellates with a long flagellum and an insignificant short one in most pigmented genera but 1, 2 or 3 in the colourless. Flagella arising in an invagination. Eyespot and contractile vacuole(s) present. Periplast soft or rigid, often striate and warty. In *Trachelomonas.* an external theca. Chromatophores, green, discoid, rod-like, ribbon-like or stellate. Assimilatory products paramylum (a β-1:3 glucose polymer) and oil. Reproduction by longitudinal fission. Sexual reproduction not substantiated. Freshwater, terrestrial, brackish and marine. One class and two orders.

EUGLENOPHYCEAE

1. Pigmented and unpigmented genera, phototrophic or saprotrophic
                Euglenales
        (*Astasia, Euglena, Eutreptia, Lepocinclis, Phacus, Trachelomonas.*)
2. Unpigmented, phagotrophic **Peranematales**
        (Best treated as Protozoa.)

PHYLUM DINOPHYTA*

Unicellular flagellates, rarely colonial or coccoid or filamentous. Two flagella differing in structure and usually in orientation. Eyespot(s) and

* An alternative name is Pyrrophyta but Dinophyta is preferable since its 'prefix' is the 'prefix' of several common genera.

contractile vacuole(s) present. With or without a cellulose wall, the latter sometimes sculptured into plates. Large central vacuole and conspicuous nucleus. Chromatophores discoid, brown, red or blue. Assimilation product starch or oil. Numerous colourless genera. Freshwater, terrestrial, brackish and marine, mainly in the latter habitat. Two classes.

1. Naked or with a cellulose wall of two watchglass-like halves
DESMOPHYCEAE

   (*Dinophysis, Exuviaella, Histioneis, Ornithocercus, Phalacroma, Prorocentrum.*)
2. Flagellate cells with transverse and longitudinal furrows, containing flagella   DINOPHYCEAE

   Two orders Peridiniales and Dinotrichales
   (*Amphidinium, Ceratium, Cystodinium, Dinoclonium, Dinamoebidium, Dinothrix, Glenodinium, Gonyaulax, Gynmodinium, Gyrodinium, Hemidinium, Massartia (=Katadinum), Oxyrrhis, Peridinium, Tetradinium.*)

PHYLUM CRYPTOPHYTA

Flagellate with two somewhat unequal flagella. Naked, dorsoventrally compressed with an anterior invagination or oblique furrow with trichocysts. Palmelloid stages occur. 1–2 chromatophores, olive green, blue, red or brown. Pyrenoid outside the chromatophore and assimilatory product starch. Division is longitudinal and sexual reproduction is lacking. One class Cryptophyceae and a single order   **Cryptomonadales**
(*Chilomonas, Chroomonas, Cryptomonas, Hemiselmis, Tetragonidium.*)

PHYLUM PHAEOPHYTA

Filamentous or thalloid algae, generally macroscopic. Pigmentation brown. Assimilatory products laminarin, mannitol and fat. Complex alternation of generations, either isomorphic or heteromorphic. Motile reproductive cells, pyriform with two lateral flagella (asexual or sexual). Unilocular (producing more than one zoospore) and/or plurilocular sporangia (producing one zoospore or gamete in each loculus). Some genera oogamous. Predominantly marine littoral forms.

One class Phaeophyceae divided into three cohorts (groups of orders).

1. Alternation of generations isomorphic   ISOGENERATAE
2. Alternation of generations heteromorphic   HETEROGENERATAE
3. Without an alternation of generations   CYCLOSPORAE

ISOGENERATAE

1. Motile zoospores formed. Isogamous or anisogamous
   a) Algae of branched filaments with intercalary growth. Some pseudo-parenchymatous   **Ectocarpales**
   (*Acrothrix, Bodanella, Ectocarpus, Lithoderma (= Heribaudiella), Mikrosyphar, Pylaiella, Ralfsia, Spongonema, Streblonema.*)

b) Filamentous but with longitudinal cell division in older parts. Growth by means of apical cells **Sphacelariales**
(*Cladostephus, Halopteris, Sphacelaria, Stypocaulon.*)

c) Thallus parenchymatous. Trichothallic intercalary meristem, or a marginal meristem present **Cutleriales**
(*Cutleria, Zanardinia.*)

2. Spores non-motile
   a) Algae filamentous. Imperfectly known group **Tilopteridales**
   (*Tilopteris.*)
   b) Algae parenchymatous. Oogamous. Tetrasporangia (unilocular sporangia) forming aplanospores on the diploid plant
   Dictyotales
   (*Dictyopteris, Dictyota, Padina, Zonaria.*)

HETEROGENERATAE

1. Subclass Haplophycidae. Sporophytic thallus composed of branching filaments, usually aggregated to form pseudoparenchyma
   a) Filamentous, often crustose, with fused cells at base or terete and differentiated into central medulla and outer photosynthetic cortex
   Chordariales
   (*Chordaria, Elachista, Leathesia, Mesogloia, Myriocladia, Myrionema, Sphlachnidium.*)
   b) Thread-like algae growing by means of an intercalary row of dome-shaped cells located at the base of hairs **Sporochnales**
   (*Carpomitra, Sporochnus.*)
   c) Terete or flat (ligulate) pinnately branched thalli attached by discoid holdfasts **Desmarestiales**
   (*Arthrocladia, Desmarestia.*)

2. Subclass Polyphycidae. Sporophytic thallus with longitudinal and transverse cell divisions forming true parenchyma
   a) Thalli solid, tubular, branched, saccate or flat and foliose but not differentiated as 2*b* **Dictyosiphonales**
   (incl. **Punctariales**)
   (*Asperococcus, Coilodesme, Dictyosiphon, Ilea, Myriotrichia, Punctaria, Scytosiphon, Stictyosiphon.*)
   b) Sporophytic thallus differentiated into holdfast, stipe and lamina (except *Chorda* which is whip-like) and growing by means of an intercalary meristem **Laminariales**
   (*Agarum, Alaria, Chorda, Ecklonia, Egregia, Eisenia, Hedophyllum, Laminaria, Lessonia, Lessoniopsis, Macrocystis, Nereocystis, Postelsia, Pterygophora, Saccorhiza, Undaria.*)

CYCLOSPORAE

The gametophytic generation is reduced to the gametes formed in the thallus of the sporophyte. Oogamous. One order.

Plants differentiated into holdfast, stipe and lamina, often much branched, growth by apical cells **Fucales**
(*Ascophyllum, Bifurcaria, Carpophyllum, Coccophora, Cystosphaera, Cystoseira, Durvillea, Fucus, Halidrys, Himanthalia, Hormosira, Pelvetia, Pelvetiopsis, Phyllospora, Sargassum, Turbinaria, Xiphophora.*)

PHYLUM RHODOPHYTA

Thallus unicellular, filamentous or most commonly thalloid based on a branching filament system. Pigmentation red except in freshwater species which tend to be greyish green. Phycochromoproteins present in addition to chlorophyll and carotenoids. No flagellate cells. Male cells (spermatia) fertilize the female organ (carpogonium) succeeded by complex post-fertilization developments. Life cycles of two main types—haplobiontic and diplobiontic (see p. 34). Mainly marine littoral in distribution but a few freshwater or terrestrial. Some partial or complete parasites on other marine algae.

One class. Rhodophyceae, divided into two subclasses.
1. Unicellular, filamentous or simple thalli with diffuse growth and no pit connections between cells. Zygote divides directly to give carpospores
BANGIOPHYCIDAE
(=Bangioideae)
2. Filamentous or pseudoparenchymatous growing from apical cell(s). Pit connections present. Zygote develops to give sporogenous threads (gonimoblast filaments) which ultimately give rise to carpospores
FLORIDEOPHYCIDAE
(=Florideae)

BANGIOPHYCIDAE

1. **Bangiales**. Variously divided into 5 or 7 families but only *Bangia* and *Porphyra* are at all common.
(*Bangia, Erythrotrichia, Porphyridium, Porphyra.*)

FLORIDEOPHYCIDAE

The classification into orders is based on the life cycle and post-fertilization changes and it is not possible to devise useful keys to the orders on vegetative characters. The following are summaries of the orders from Drew.[84]

1. **Nemaliales**. Uni- or multi-axial construction. Carpogonium simple. Auxiliary cell, if present, formed from a cell of the carpogonial branch or its derivative; sometimes more than one. Reduction division usually but not invariably occurs immediately after fertilization; some genera with

tetrasporophytes. Accessory spores present in some genera. Tetrasporangia cruciate.

(*Acrochaetium, Asparagopsis, Batrachospermum, Bonnemaisonia, Chaetangium, Galaxaura, Lemanea, Liagora, Nemalion, Rhodochorton, Scinaia, Sirodotia.*)

2. **Gelidiales.** Uniaxial; carpogonia simple but aggregated; auxiliary cells absent; three somatic phases; tetrasporangia cruciate.
   (*Gelidium, Pterocladia.*)

3. **Cryptonemiales.** Uni- or multi-axial; carpogonial branches always on special accessory branches, long, sometimes aggregated into sori, nemathecia or conceptacles. Auxiliary cells on accessory branches either adjacent to or remote from the carpogonial branch. The majority have three somatic phases, some only two. Tetrasporangia cruciate or zonate.
   (*Archaeolithothamnion, Calliarthron, Callophyllis, Corallina, Dilsea, Dudresnaya, Dumontia, Endocladia, Epilithon, Gloiopeltis, Gloiosiphonia, Goniolithon, Grateloupia, Hildenbrandia, Jania, Lithophyllum, Lithothamnion, Melobesia, Pachymenia, Peyssoniella, Polyides, Porolithon, Solenopora.*)

4. **Gigartinales.** Uni- or multi-axial; carpogonial branch formed from ordinary cells of the thallus. Auxiliary cell an intercalary cell of the thallus or the supporting cell of the carpogonial branch; either adjacent to or remote from the carpogonium. The majority have three somatic phases but diphasic types occur.
   (*Agardhiella, Ahnfeltia, Calliblepharis, Catenella, Caulacanthus, Chondrus, Cystoclonium, Eucheuma, Furcellaria, Gigartina, Gracilaria, Halarachnion, Hypnea, Iridaea, Iridophycus, Platoma, Plocamium, Phyllophora, Schizymenia.*)

5. **Rhodymeniales.** Multiaxial; carpogonial branch three or four-celled; one or two auxiliary cells in each procarp formed from the outer cell of a two-celled branch developed from the supporting cell; cut off before, but not differentiated until after fertilization. Three somatic phases with very few exceptions. Tetrasporangia or tetrahedral.
   (*Champia, Chylocladia, Gastroclonium, Lomentaria, Rhodymenia.*)

6. **Ceramiales.** Uniaxial, carpogonial branch four-celled, always borne on a pericentral cell. One or two auxiliary cells in each procarp are cut off directly from the supporting cell or from an homologous peri-central cell, after fertilization. Usually three somatic phases. Reduction division occurring at the formation of the tetraspores. Tetrasporangia usually tetrahedral, some cruciate.
   (*Acanthophora, Antithamnion, Apoglossum, Bostrychia, Brongniartella, Callithamnion, Caloglossa, Campylaeophora, Centroceras, Ceramium, Chondria, Crouaria, Cryptopleura, Dasya, Delesseria, Digenea, Griffithsia, Herposiphonia, Heterosiphonia, Hypoglossum, Laurencia, Membranoptera, Murrayella, Myriogramme, Nitophyllum, Odonthalia, Phycodrys, Plumaria, Polysiphonia, Pterosiphonia, Ptilota, Rhodomela, Spyridia.*)

References

REFERENCES

1. AACH, H. G. (1952). *Arch. Mikrobiol.*, **17**, 213.
2. ABBOTT, B. C. and BALLANTINE, D. (1957). *J. Mar. biol. Ass. U.K.*, **36**, 169.
3. ALEEM, A. A. (1950). *New Phytol.*, **49**, 174.
4. ALLEN, M. B. and ARNON, D. I. (1954). Presented before *Amer. Soc. Plant. Phys. Gainsville, Fla.*, Sept.
5. ALGÉUS, S. (1946). *Bot. Notiser*, **1946**, 129.
6. —— (1948). *Physiol. Plant*, **1**, 236.
7. —— (1950). *Physiol. Plant*, **3**, 225.
8. —— (1950). *Physiol. Plant*, **3**, 370.
9. ALLISON, R. K., SKIPPER, H. E., REID, M. R., SHORT, W. Λ. and HOGAN, G. L. (1953). *J. biol. Chem.*, **204**, 197.
10. ANAND, P. L. (1937). *J. Ecol.*, **25**, 153, 344.
11. ANDERSON, G. (1956). *Proc. 2nd Int. Seaweed Symp.*, 119.
12. ANDERSON, F. B., HIRST, E. L., MANNERS, D. J. and ROSS, A. G. (1958). *J. Chem. Soc.*, **1958**, 3233.
13. ARNON, D. I. (1959). *Nature*, **184**, 10.
14. ASMUND, B. (1955). *Dansk bot. Ark.*, **15**, No. 5.
15. BACK, M. K. and FELLIG, J. (1958). *Nature*, **182**, 1359.
16. BEATTIE, A., HIRST, E. L. and PERCIVAL, E. (1961). *Biochem. J.*, **79**, 531.
17. BELL, H. P. and McFARLANE, C. (1933). *Canad. J. Res.*, **9**, 265, 283.
17a. BELLIS, V. J. and McCARTY, D. Λ. (1967). *J. Phycol.*, **3**, 57.
18. BEHRE, K. (1956). *Ver. Inst. Meeresk. Bremerhaven*, **4**, 221.
19. BENDIX, S. W. (1960). *Bot. Rev.*, **26**, 145.
20. BENSON, A. A., BASSHAM, J. A., CALVIN, M., HALL, A. G., HIRSCH, H. E., KAGAGUCHI, S., LYNCH, V. and TOLBERT, N. E. (1952). *J. biol. Chem.*, **196**, 703.
21. BENSON, Λ. Λ. and CALVIN, M. (1950). *Annu. Rev. Pl. Physiol.*, **1**, 25.
21a. BERGE, G. (1958). *Rep. Cons. Explor. Mer.*, **144**, 85.
22. BETHGE, H. (1952–55). *Ber. dtsch. bot. Ges.*, **65**, 187: **66**, 93: **68**, 319.
23. BLACKBURN, K. B. and TEMPERLEY, B. N. (1936). *Trans. roy. Soc. Edinb.*, **58**, 841.
24. BLINKS, L. R. (1951). *Manual of Phycology*, 263. Chronica Botanica Co., Waltham, Mass.
25. —— (1954). *Autotrophic Micro-organisms*, 224. University Press, Cambridge.
26. BOOTH, W. E. (1941). *Ecology*, **22**, 38.
27. BØRGESEN, F. (1911). *Biol. Arbejder til E. Warming*, 41.
28. BOURELLY, P. (1957). *Rech. Chrysophycees. Rev. Alg. Mem.*, **1**.
29. BOURNE, E. J. (1958). *Encycl. Plant Phys.*, **6**, 345.
30. BRAARUD, T. (1951). *Physiol. Plant*, **4**, 28.
30a. BRAARUD, T., GAARDER, K. R. and GRØNTVED, J. (1953). *Rapp. Cons. Perm. Int. Explor. Mer.*, **133**, 1.
31. BRACHER, R. (1929). *J. Ecol.*, **17**, 35.
32. BRACHET, J. (1957). *Biochemical Cytology*. Academic Press, New York and London.
33. BRACHET, J., CHANTRENE, H. and VANDERHAEGE, F. (1955). *Biochim. biophys. Acta*, **18**, 544.
34. BRAMLETTE, M. N. (1958). *Bull. geol. Soc. Amer.*, **69**, 121.

35. BREIVIK, K. (1957). *Nyt Mag. Bot.*, **6**, 19.
36. BREMER, H. J. and SCHWEIGER, H. C. (1960). *Planta*, **55**, 13.
37. BROOK, A. J. (1954). *Hydrobiol*, **6**, 333.
38. BROWN, A. H. (1953). *Amer. J. Bot.*, **40**, 719.
39. BROWN, D. S. (1960). *Hydrobiol.*, **16**, 81.
40. BRUCE, V. G. and PITTENDRIGH, C. S. (1956). *Proc. Nat. Acad. Sci. Washington.* **42**, 676.
41. BUDDE, H. (1928). *Arch. Hydrobiol.*, **19**, 433.
42. BÜHNEMANN, F. (1955). *Biol. Zbl.*, **74**, 691.
43. BÜNNING, E. and SCHNEIDERHOHN, G. (1956). *Arch. Mikrobiol.*, **24**, 80.
44. BUNT, J. S. (1961). *Nature*, **192**, 479.
45. BUNTING, W. and LUND, J. W. G. (1956). Published by *The Yorkshire Naturalist Union*, 1.
46. BUTCHER, R. W. (1947). *J. Ecol.*, **35**, 186.
47. BURROWS, E. M. (1958). *J. Mar. biol. Ass. U.K.*, **37**, 687.
48. BURROWS, E. M., CONWAY, E., LODGE, S. M. and POWELL, H. T. (1954). *J. Ecol.*, **42**, 283.
49. CALVERT, R. (1930). *Amer. Chem. Soc. Monogr.*, 23.
50. CALVIN, M., BASSHAM, J. A., BENSON, A. A., LYNCH, V. H., OUELLET, C., SCHOU, L., STREPKA, W. and TOLBERT, N. E. (1951). *Symp. Soc. exp. Biol.*, **5**, 284.
51. CALVIN, M. and LYNCH, V. H. (1952). *Nature*, **169**, 455.
52. CANNON, D., LUND, J. W. G. and SIEMINSKA, J. (1961). *J. Ecol.*, **49**, 277.
53. CANTER, H. M. and LUND, J. W. G. (1948). *New Phytol.*, **47**, 235.
54. CHADEFAUD, M. and EMBERGER, L. (1960). *Traite de Botanique Systematique.* Tome I—CHADEFAUD, M. *Les vegetaux non Vasculaire.* Masson et Cie, Paris.
55. CHAPMAN, V. J. (1940). *J. Ecol.*, **28**, 118.
56. —— (1946). *Ecol.*, **27**, 91.
57. —— (1950). *Seaweeds and their Uses.* Methuen, London.
58. CHAPMAN, V. J. and RONALDSON, J. W. (1958). *Bull. N.Z. Dep. sci. industr. Res.*, **125**, 1.
59. CHAVE, K. E. (1954). *J. Geol.*, **62**, 266.
60. CHESTERS, C. G. C. and STOTT, J. A. (1955). *Proc. 2nd Int. Seaweed Symp.*, 163.
61. CHESTERS, C. G. C., TURNER, M. and APINIS, A. (1956). *Proc. 2nd Int. Seaweed Symp.*, 141.
62. CHESTERS, C. G. C., APINIS, A. and TURNER, M. (1956). *Proc. Linn. Soc. Lond.*, **166**, 87.
63. CHIU, B. T. (1956). *Proc. 2nd Int. Seaweed Symp.*, 171.
64. CHRISTENSEN, T. (1962). *Botanik. Systematisk Botanik, Bd. II, No. 2: Alger.* Munksgaard, København.
65. CHU, S. P. (1943). *J. Ecol.*, **31**, 109.
66. CLAUS, H. (1958). *Planta*, **52**, 334.
67. CLENDENNING, K. (1961). *Abst. 4th Int. Seaweed Symp.*
68. COHN, A. (1853). *Nova Acta Acad Caes. Leop.*, **24**, 103.
69. COLLYER, D. M. and FOGG, C. E. (1955). *J. exp. Bot.*, **6**, 256.
70. CONRAD, H., SALTMAN, P. and EPPLEY, R. (1959). *Nature*, **184**, 556.
71. CRAIG, H. (1954). *J. Geol.*, **62**, 115.
72. CREACH, P. V. (1952). *Proc. 1st Int. Seaweed Symp.*, 42.
73. CRONSHAW, J., MYERS, A. and PRESTON, R. D. (1958). *Biochim. biophys. Acta*, **27**, 89.

74.   CUPP, E. E. (1943). *Bull. Scripps Inst. Oceanogr.*, **5**, 1.
75.   DAVIDSON, E. F. (1952). *Amer. J. Bot.*, **39**, 700.
76.   DAVIES, E. A. (1953). *Plant Physiol.*, **28**, 539.
77.   DIXON, P. S. (1960). *J. Mar. biol. Ass. U.K.*, **39**, 331.
78.   DODGE, J. D. (1960). *Brit. Phycol. Bull.*, **2**, 14.
79.   DODGE, J. D. and GODWARD, M. B. E. (1961). *Brit. Phycol. Bull.*, **2**, 102.
80.   DOTY, M. G. (1946). *Ecology*, **27**, 315.
81.   DOTY, M. G. and OGURI, M. (1957). *Limnol. Oceanogr.*, **2**, 37.
81a. DOUGLAS, B. (1958). *J. Ecol.*, **46**, 295.
82.   DRAWERT, H. and MIX, M. (1961). *Planta*, **56**, 648.
83.   DREWS, G. (1959). *Arch. Protistenk.*, **104**, 389.
84.   DREW, K. M. (1951). Rhodophyta. In *Manual of Phycology*. Ed. G. M. SMITH.
      Chronica Botanica, Waltham, Mass.
84a. DRING, M. (1967). *J. Mar. biol. ass. (U.K.)*, **47**, 501.
85.   DROOP, M. R. (1953). *Acta bot. fenn.*, **51**, 1.
86.   —— (1957). *Nature*, **180**, 1041.
86a. —— (1967). *Br. phycol. Bull.*, **3**, 295.
87.   DROUET, F. (1951). Cyanophyta. In *Manual of Phycology*. Ed. G. M. SMITH.
      Chronica Botanica, Waltham, Mass.
88.   DUNCAN, W. A. M. and MANNERS, D. J. (1958). *Biochem. J.*, **69**, 343.
89.   DUNCAN, W. A. M., MANNERS, D. J. and ROSS, A. G. (1956). *Biochem. J.*,
      63, 44.
90.   EGLE, K. (1960). *Encycl. Plant Physiol.*, **5/1**, 440.
91.   EICHLER, A. W. (1886). *Syllabus der Vorlesungen über specielle und Medizinisch-
      pharmaceutische Botanik*, 4th Ed. Berlin.
92.   ENGELMANN, T. W. (1883). *Bot. Ztg.*, **41**, 1, 17.
93.   ENGLER, A. (1954). *Syllabus der Pflanzenfamilien*, 12th Ed., Bd. 1. Gebrüder
      Borntraeger, Berlin.
94.   EMEIS, C. C. (1955). *Desinfektion u. Gesundheitsw.*, **47**, 153.
95.   EMERSON, R. and LEWIS, C. M. (1942). *J. gen. Physiol.*, **25**, 579.
96.   ETTL, H. (1958). In *Algologische Studien*, KOMAREK, J. and ETTL, H. Tschecho-
      slowakischen Akademie der Wissenschaften, Prague.
97.   EVANS, R. G. (1949). *J. Ecol.*, **37**, 120.
98.   EVITT, W. R. (1961). *Micropaleontolgy*, **7**, 385.
99.   FAURE-FREMIET, E. (1950). *Biol. Bull., France-Belgique*, **84**, 207.
100. —— (1951). *Biol. Bull.*, **100**, 173.
101. FITZGERALD, G. P., GERLOFF, G. C. and SKOOG, F. (1952). *Sewage industr.
      Wastes*, **24**, 888.
102. FJERDINGSTAD, E. (1960). *Nord. hyg. Tidskr.*, **41**, 149.
103. FLEMING, R. H. (1940). In *The Oceans: their physics, chemistry and general
      biology*, SVERDRUP, H. V., JOHNSON, M. W. and FLEMING, R. H. Prentice-Hall,
      New York.
104. FOGG, G. E. (1952). *Proc. roy. Soc., B.*, **139**, 372.
105. —— (1953). *The Metabolism of Algae*. Methuen, London.
106. —— (1956). *Annu. Rev. Pl. Physiol.*, **7**, 51.
107. FOGG, G. E. and MILLER, J. D. A. (1958). *Verh. int. ver. Limnol.*, **13**, 892.
108. FOGG, G. E. and WOLFE, M. (1954). *Autotrophic Micro-organisms*, 99. University
      Press, Cambridge.
109. FOTT, B. (1959). *Algenkunde*. Gustav Fischer, Jena.
110. FOWDEN, L. (1954). *Ann. Bot.*, N.S. **18**, 257.

111. FREI, E. and PRESTON, R. D. (1961). *Proc. roy. Soc., B.*, **154**, 70.
112. —— (1961). *Nature*, **192**, 939.
113. FRENCH, C. S. (1960). *Encycl. Plant Phys.*, **5/1**, 252.
114. FRITSCH, F. E. (1935). *Structure and Reproduction of the Algae*, **1**. University Press, Cambridge.
114a. —— (1944). *Bot. Rev.*, **10**, 233.
115. —— (1945). *Structure and Reproduction of the Algae*, **2**. University Press, Cambridge.
116. GAFFRON, H. (1960). Energy Storage: Photosynthesis. In *Plant Physiology*. A treatise. Ed. STEWARD, F. C., Academic Press, New York and London.
117. GAFFRON, H. and RUBIN, J. (1942). *J. gen. Physiol.*, **26**, 219.
118. GEISSLER, U. (1958). *Mikroscopie*, **13**, 1.
119. GEITLER, L. (1932). *Cyanophyceae, Raberhorsts, Kryptogamen Flora*, **14**. Akademische Verlagsgesellschaft, Leipzig.
120. —— (1935). *Arch. Protistenk.*, **71**, 79.
121. GESSNER, F. (1952). *Planta*, **40**, 391.
122. —— (1955). *Hydrobotanik*, **1**. VEB Deutscher Verlag der Wissenschaften, Berlin.
123. —— (1959). *Hydrobotanik*, **2**. VEB Deutscher Verlag der Wissenschaften, Berlin.
124. —— (1957). *Arch. Hydrobiol.*, **53**, 1.
125. GESSNER, F. and PANNIER, F. (1958). *Limnol. Oceanogr.*, **3**, 478.
126. GHAZZAWI, F. M. (1933). *J. Mar. biol. Ass. U.K.*, **14**, 165.
127. GODWARD, M. B. E. (1937). *J. Ecol.*, **25**, 496.
128. —— (1953). *Ann. Bot.*, N.S. **17**, 403.
129. —— (1954). *Ann. Bot.*, N.S. **18**, 143.
130. —— (1956). *J. Linn. Soc. Lond. (Bot.)*, **55**, 532.
131. —— (1961). *Heredity*, **16**, 53.
132. GOLDBERG, E. D. (1952). *Biol. Bull.*, **102**, 243.
133. GOLDBERG, E. D., WALKER, T. J. and WHISENAND, A. (1951). *Biol. Bull.*, **101**, 274.
134. GOODWIN, T. W. (1952). *The Comparative Biochemistry of the Carotenoids*. London.
135. —— (1960). *Encycl. Plant Phys.*, **5/1**, 394.
136. GRAHAM, H. W. and BRONIKOVSKY, N. (1944). *Carnegie Inst. Wash. Publ.*, No. **565**, 1.
137. GREENWOOD, C. T. and THOMPSON, J. (1961). *J. Chem. Soc.*, **301**, 1534.
138. GRØNTVED, J. (1960). *Medd. Dan. Fisk. Havundersøg.*, N.S. **3**, 55.
139. HALLDAL, P. (1953). *Det Norsk. Vidensk. Akad., Oslo, Hvalradets Skrifter.*, No. **38**, 1.
140. —— (1957). *Nature*, **179**, 215.
141. —— (1958). *Physiol. Plant*, **11**, 118.
142. HALLDAL, P. and MARKALI, J. (1955). *Det Norsk. Vidensk. Akad., Oslo*, **1**.
143. HAMEL, G. (1931–9). *Pheophycées de France*. Wolf, Rouen.
144. HÄMMERLING, J. (1953). *Int. Rev. Cytol.*, **2**, 947.
145. —— (1955). *Biol. Zbl.*, **74**, 545.
146. HÄMMERLING, J., CLAUS, H., KECK, K. and RICHTER, G. (1958). *Exp. Cell Res.*, Suppl. **6**, 210.
147. HARDER, R. (1923). *Ber. dtsch. bot. Ges.*, **41**, 194.
148. HARRIS, K. (1953). *J. Linn. Soc. (Bot.)*, **55**, 88.
149. HARRIS, K. and BRADLEY, D. E. (1957). *J. R. micr. Soc.*, **76**, 37.
150. HARRIS, T. M. (1939). *British Purbeck Charophyta*. British Museum, London.
151. HART, T. J. (1942). *Discovery Rep.*, **21**, 263.

152. HARTSHORNE, J. N. (1953). *New Phytol.*, **52**, 292.
153. HARVEY, W. H. (1836). Algae. In *Flora Hibernica*, MACKAY, J. T. Dublin.
154. HARVEY, H. W. (1939). *J. Mar. biol. Ass. U.K.*, **22**, 499.
155. HASLE, G. R. (1950). *Oikos*, **2**, 162.
160. HASTINGS, J. W. and SWEENEY, B. M. (1957). *Proc. nat. Acad. Sci.*, **43**, 804.
161. —— (1957). *J. cell. comp. Physiol.*, **49**, 209.
162. HAUG, A. and JENSEN, A. (1956). *Proc. 2nd Int. Seaweed Symp.*, 10.
163. HAUG, A. and LARSEN, A. (1956). *Proc. 2nd Int. Seaweed Symp.*, 16.
164. HAUPT, W. (1959). *Planta*, **53**, 484.
165. HAXO, F. T. and BLINKS, L. R. (1950). *J. gen. Phys.*, **33**, 389.
166. HAXO, F. T. and CLENDENNING, K. A. (1953). *Biol. Bull.*, **105**, 103.
167. HAXO, F. T. and FORK, D. C. (1959). *Nature*, **184**, 1051.
168. HAXO, F. T. and O'EOCHA, C. (1960). *Encycl. Plant Phys.*, **5/1**, 497.
169. HENDEY, N. I. (1959). *J. Quekett micr. Cl.*, Ser. 4. **5**, 147.
170. HERDMAN, C. E. (1921). *Proc. Lpool biol. Soc.*, **35**, 59.
171. —— (1924). *Proc. Lpool biol. Soc.*, **38**, 75.
171a. HIBBERD, D. J. and LEEDALE, G. F. (1970). *Nature*, **225**, 758.
180. HICKLING, C. F. (1961). *Tropical Inlana Fisheries.* Longmans, London.
181. HIRST, E. L. (1958). *Proc. chem. Soc.*, **July,** 117.
182. HOLT, A. S. and ARNOLD, W. A. (1949). *Biol. Bull.*, **97**, 286.
183. HOLMES, R. W. (1958). *Rapp. Cons. Int. Explor. Mer.*, **144**, 109.
184. HOPWOOD, D. A. and GLAUERT, A. M. (1960). *J. Biophys. Biochem. Cytol.*, **8**, 813.
185. HULL, W. A., KEEL, H., KENNY, J. and GARSON, B. W. (1953). *Industr. Engng Chem. (Industr.)*, **45**, 256.
186. HURD, A. M. (1920). *Bot. Gaz.*, **70**, 25.
187. HUSTEDE, F. (1957). *Biol. Zbl.*, **76**, 555.
188. HUSTEDT, F. (1921). Quoted in KOLBE, R. W. (1955). *Rep. Swedish Deep-Sea Exped.*, **6**, 1.
189. —— (1954). *Abh. naturw. Ver. Bremen*, **33**, 3.
190. HUTCHINSON, G. E. (1957). *A Treatise on Limnology.* Wiley, New York and London.
191. HUTNER, S. H. (1948). *Trans. N.Y. Acad. Sci.*, **10**, 136.
192. ISAAC, W. E. (1937). *Trans. roy. Soc. S. Afr.*, **25**, 115.
193. JACOBI, G. (1957). *Planta*, **49**, 561.
194. JACOBS, W. P. (1951). *Biol. Bull.*, **101**, 300.
195. JACQUES, A. G. and OSTERHOUT, W. J. V. (1938). *J. gen. Phys.*, **21**, 687.
196. JÄRNEFELT, H. (1961). *Verh. int. ver. Limnol.*, **14**, 1057.
197. JENKIN, P. M. (1937). *J. Mar. biol. Assoc. U.K.*, **22**, 301.
198. JENSEN, A. (1956). *Norsk Inst. Tang og Tareforsk*, Rep. No. **9**, 1.
199. —— (1961). *Abst. 4th Int. Seaweed Symp.*
200. JØNNSON, H. (1912). *Botany of Iceland.* Part 1. Copenhagen.
201. JØRGENSEN, E. G. (1957). *Dansk bot. Ark.*, **18**, 1.
202. KAIN, J. M. (1960). *J. Mar. biol. Assoc.*, **39**, 609.
203. KANAYA, T. (1957). *Sci. Rep. Tohoku Univ. Sendai.*, 2nd Ser. Geol., **28**, 27.
203a. KANAYA, T. and KOIZUMI, I. (1966). *Sci. Rep. (2nd Ser. Geol.) Tohoku Univ.*, **37**, 89.
204. KANN, E. (1959). *Arch. Hydrobiol.*, **55**, 129.
204a. KEMPNER, E. S. (not dated). *The Upper Temperature Limit of Life.* Nat. Inst. Arthritis & Metabolic Diseases, Bethesda, Maryland.

205. KESSLER, E. (1952). *Z. Natur.*, **7b**, 280.
206. —— (1955). *Planta*, **45**, 94.
207. KETCHUM, B. H. (1954). *Annu. Rev. Pl. Physiol.*, **5**, 55.
208. KETCHUM, B. H. and REDFIELD, A. C. (1949). *J. cell. comp. Physiol.*, **33**, 281.
209. KING, G. C. (1954). *Nature*, **172**, 592.
210. —— (1959). *New Phytol*, **58**, 20.
211. —— (1960). *New Phytol.*, **59**, 65.
212. KITCHING, J. A., MACAN, T. T. and GILSON, H. C. (1934). *J. Mar. biol. Assoc.*, N.S. **19**, 677.
213. KJELLMAN. F. R. (1877). *Köngl. Ges. d. Wissensch. Uppsala.*
214. KNAPP, E. (1931). *Planta*, **14**, 731.
215. KNUDSEN, B. M. (1954). *J. Ecol.*, **42**, 345.
216. —— (1955). *Proc. int. Assoc. Limnol.*, **12**, 216.
217. —— (1957). *J. Ecol.*, **45**, 93.
218. KOL, E. (1944). *Arch. Hydrobiol.*, **52**, 574.
219. KÖHLER, K. (1956). *Arch. Protistenk.*, **101**, 223.
220. KOLBE, R. W. (1955). *Rep. Swedish Deep-Sea Exped.*, **6**, 1.
221. KRAUSS, R. W. (1953). In *Algal Culture, From Laboratory to Pilot Plant.* Carnegie Inst. Wash. Publ. No. **600**, 85.
222. KRAUSS, R. W. and GALLOWAY, R. A. (1960). *Caribbean Beach Studies*, Rep. No. **9**, Louisiana State Univ.
223. KRATZ, W. A. and MYERS, J. (1955). *Amer. J. Bot.*, **42**, 282.
224. KRUMHOLTZ, L. A. (1954). *U.S. Atomic Energy Comm. Inform. Serv.*, **ORO–132**, 1.
225. KYLIN, H. (1917). *Ber. dtsch. bot. Ges.*, **35**, 376.
226. —— (1956). *Die Gattungen der Rhodophyceen.* Gleerups, Lund.
226a. LADD, H. S. (1953). *Am. Assoc. Petr. Geol. Bull.*, **37**, 2257.
227. LARSEN, B. (1958). *Norsk inst. Tang og Tareforskning*, Rep. No. **19**.
228. LARSEN, B. and HAUG, A. (1958). *Norsk inst. Tang og Tareforskning*, Rep. No. **20**, 25.
229. LAUB, W., KIERMAYER, V. W., DISKUS, A. and HILMBAUER, K. (1954). *Öst. Akad. Wiss. Math-natur.*, **163**, 447.
230. LAWSON, G. W. (1956). *J. Ecol.*, **44**, 153.
231. —— (1957). *J. Ecol.*, **45**, 831.
232. LEEDALE, G. F. (1958). *Nature*, **181**, 502.
233. —— (1959). *Biol. Bull.*, **116**, 162.
233a. —— (1959). *J. Protozool.*, **6**, Abstr. in Suppl. 26.
234. LEVINE, R. P. and EBERSOLD, W. T. (1958). *Cold Spr. Harb. Symp. quant. Biol.*, **23**, 101.
235. —— (1960). *Annu. Rev. Microbiol.*, **14**, 197.
236. LEWIN, J. C. (1950). *Science*, **112**, 652.
237. —— (1954). *J. gen. Physiol.*, **37**, 589.
238. —— (1955). *J. gen. Physiol.*, **39**, 1.
239. LEWIN, R. A. (1954). *J. gen. Microbiol.*, **11**, 358.
240. —— (1956). *Canad. J. Microbiol.*, **2**, 665.
241. —— (1961). *Encycl. Plant Phys.*, **14**, 401.
242. LEWIN, J. C. and LEWIN, R. A. (1960). *Canad. J. Microbiol.*, **6**, 127.
243. LEWIN, J. C., LEWIN, R. A. and PHILPOT, D. E. (1958). *J. gen. Microbiol.*, **18**, 418.
244. LEWIN, R. A. and MEINERT, J. O. (1953). *Canad. J. Bot.*, **31**, 711.
245. LEWIS, J. R. (1953). *Proc. Zool. Soc. (Lond.)*, **123**, 481.

246. —— (1957). *Trans. roy. Soc. Edinb.*, **63**, 185.
247. LEYON, H. (1954). *Exp. Cell Res.*, **6**, 497.
248. LINDBERG, B. (1956). *2nd Int. Seaweed Symp.*, 33.
249. LOWENSTAM, H. A. (1955). *J. sediment. Petrol.*, **25**, 270.
249a. LUND, J. W. G. (1945). *New Phytol.*, **44**, 196.
250. —— (1949). *J. Ecol.*, **37**, 389.
251. —— (1950). *J. Ecol.*, **38**, 1, 15.
252. —— (1952). *Naturalist*, **1952**, 163.
253. —— (1954). *J. Ecol.*, **42**, 151.
254. —— (1959). *J. Instn Water Engrs*, **13**, 527.
255. —— (1959). *Brit. Phycol. Bull.*, No. **7**, 1.
256. —— (1959). *Limnol. Oceanogr.*, **4**, 57.
260. LUTHER, H. (1954). *Acta bot. fenn.*, **55**, 1.
261. LUCAS, C. E. (1944). *Hull Bull. Mar. Ecol.*, **1**, 73.
262. MACFARLANE, C. (1961). *Abst. 4th Int. Seaweed Symp.*
263. McDOWELL, R. H. (1957). *Properties of Alginates*. Alginate Indust., Ltd., London.
264. McLAUGHLIN, J. J. A. and ZAHL, P. A. (1959). *Ann. N.Y. Acad. Sci.*, **77**, 55.
265. MAGDEFRAU, K. (1953). *Paläobiologie der Pflanzen.* 2 Aufl. Gustav Fischer, Jena.
266. MANTEN, A. (1948). Phototaxis, phototropism, and photosynthesis in purple bacteria and blue-green algae. *Diss. Utrecht.* Quoted in Haupt, W. (1959), see above.
270. MANTON, I. (1955). *Proc. Leeds phil. Soc.*, **6**, 306.
271. —— (1956). *J. exp. Bot.*, **7**, 416.
271a. —— (1955). Plant Cilia and Associated Organelles. In symposium on *Cellular Mechanisms in Differentiation and Growth*, ed. RUDNICK, D. Univ. Press, Princeton.
272. —— (1959). *J. exp. Bot.*, **10**, 448.
273. —— (1959). *J. Mar. biol. Ass. U.K.*, **38**, 319.
274. MANTON, I. and CLARKE, B. (1956). *J. exp. Bot.*, **7**, 416.
275. MANTON, I., CLARKE, B. and GREENWOOD, A. D. (1953). *J. exp. Bot.*, **4**, 319.
276. MANTON, I. and LEEDALE, G. F. (1961). *J. Mar. biol. Ass. U.K.*, **41**, 145.
277. —— (1961). *Phycologia*, **1**, 37.
277a. —— (1969). *J. Mar. biol. Ass. U.K.*, **49**, 1.
277b. MANTON, I., OATES, K. and PARKE, M. (1963). *J. Mar. biol. Ass. U.K.*, **43**, 255.
278. MANTON, J. and PARKE, M. (1960). *J. Mar. biol. Ass. U.K.*, **39**, 275.
279. MARSHALL, W. (1960). *Brit. Phycol. Bull.*, **2**, 18.
280. MAST, S. O. (1927). *Arch. Protistenk.*, **60**, 197.
281. MATSUDAIRA, T. (1942). *Proc. imp. Acad. Japan*, **17**, 107.
282. MAUTNER, H. C., GARDNER, G. R. and PRATT, R. (1953). *J. Amer. Pharm. Ass.*, **42**, 294.
283. MEEUSE, B. J. D. (1956). *Biochim. biophys. Acta*, **19**, 372.
284. MENKE, W. (1961). *Z. Naturf.*, **16B**, 543.
285. MILLBANK, J. W. (1957). *Ann. Bot.*, N.S. **21**, 23.
286. MILLER, J. D. A. and FOGG, G. E. (1958). *Arch. Microbiol.*, **28**, 1.
286a. MOESTRUP, Q. (1970). *Planta*, **93**, 295.
287. MONER, J. G. (1955). *Amer. J. Bot.*, **42**, 802.
288. MOTHES, K. and SAGROMSKY, H. (1941). *Naturwissenschaften*, **29**, 271.
290. MÜLLER-STOLL, W. R. (1952). *Flora*, **139**, 148.

291. NAYLOR, M. (1958). *Brit. Phycol. Bull.*, No. **6**, 34.
292. NEWTON, L. (1931). *Handbook of the British Seaweeds.* British Museum (N.H.), London.
293. NICOLAI, E. and PRESTON, R. D. (1952). *Proc. roy. Soc., B.*, **140**, 244.
294. —— (1960). *Proc. roy. Soc., B.*, **151**, 224.
295. NIELSEN, E. S. (1934). *Dana Reports*, **4**, 1.
296. NULTSCH, W. (1956). *Arch. Protistenk.*, **101**, 1.
297. —— (1961). *Planta*, **56**, 632.
298. NYGAARD, G. (1945). *Dansk Plante Plankton.* Gyldendal, Copenhagen.
299. —— (1955). *Verh. int. ver. Limnol.*, **12**, 123.
300. —— (1956). *Folia limnol. scand.*, No. **8**, 1956.
301. ODUM, E. P. (1954). *Fundamentals of Ecology.* Saunders, Philadelphia.
302. ODUM, H. T. and ODUM, E. P. (1955). *Ecol. Monogr.*, **25**, 291.
303. OLSEN, R. A. and DU BUY, H. G. (1937). *Amer. J. Bot.*, **24**, 611.
304. OLSEN, R. A. and ENGEL, E. R. (1959). In *The Photochemical Apparatus; Its Structure and Function.* Brookhaven Symp. in Biology, 1958. Upton, New York.
305. OLTMANNS, Fr. (1922). *Morphologie und Biologie der Algen*, 1 and 2. G. Fischer, Jena.
306. O'NEIL, A. N. and STEWART, D. K. R. (1956). *Canad. J. Chem.*, **34**, 256.
307. OSTERLIND, S. (1950). *Physiol. Plant.*, **3**, 353.
308. OSTVALD, W. J. and GOTAAS, H. B. (1955). *Proc. Amer. Soc. civ. Engrs*, **81**, 1.
308a. PALMER, J. D. and ROUND, F. E. (1965). *J. Mar. biol. Ass. U.K.*, **45**, 567.
308b. —— (1967). *Biol. Bull.*, **132**, 44.
309. PARKE, M. (1961). *Brit. Phycol. Bull.*, **2**, 47.
310. PARKE, M. and ADAMS, I. (1960). *J. Mar. biol. Ass. U.K.*, **39**, 263.
311. PARKE, M., MANTON, I. and CLARKE, B. (1958). *J. Mar. biol. Ass. U.K.* **37**, 209.
312. —— (1959). *J. Mar. biol. Ass. U.K.*, **38**, 169.
312a. PARKE, M. and DIXON, P. S. (1968). *J. Mar. biol. Ass. U.K.*, **48**, 783. An earlier edition in Vol. 44 (1964).
312b. PARKE, M. and MANTON, I. (1967). *J. Mar. biol. Ass. U.K.*, **47**, 445.
313. PARR, A. E. (1939). *Bull. Bingham oceanogr. Coll.*, 6.
314. PASCHER, A. (1914). *Ber. dtsch. bot. Ges.*, **32**, 136.
315. —— (1939). *Kryptogamenflora*, **11**.
316. PATRICK, R., HOHN, M. H. and WALLACE, J. H. (1954). *Notul. nat. Acad. Philad.*, No. **259**, 1.
317. PENNINGTON, W. (1942). *New Phytol.*, **42**, 1.
318. PIA, J. (1927). In *Handbuch der Paläobotanik*, Band 1, HIRMER, M. Oldenburg, Munich and Berlin.
319. PIRSON, A. and BERGMAN, L. (1955). *Nature*, **176**, 209.
320. PIRSON, A. and SCHÖN, W. J. (1957). *Flora*, **144**, 447.
321. POCHMANN, A. (1953). *Planta*, **47**, 478.
322. POHL, R. (1948). *Z. Naturf.*, **3B**, 367.
323. PRATT, R. *et al.* (1944). *Science*, **99**, 351.
324. PRINGSHEIM, E. G. (1927). *Beitr. Biol. Pfl.*, **14**, 283.
325. —— (1946). *Pure cultures of algae.* Univ. Press, Cambridge.
325a. —— (1949). *Bact. Rev.*, **13**, 51.
326. —— (1951). In *Manual of Phycology*, SMITH, G. M. Chronica Botanica, Waltham, Mass.

327. PRINGSHEIM, E. G. and PRINGSHEIM, O. (1959). *Biol. Zbl.*, **78**, 987.
328. PRINGSHEIM, E. G. and WIESNER, W. (1960). *Arch. Mikrobiol.*, **40**, 231.
329. PROVASOLI, L. (1958). *Ann. Rev. Microbiol.*, **12**, 279.
330. PROVASOLI, L., McLAUGHLIN, J. J. A. and DROOP, M. R. (1957). *Arch. Mikrobiol.*, **25**, 392.
330a. QUENNERSTEDT, N. (1955). *Acta phytogeogr. suec.*, **36**, 1.
331. RABINOWITCH, F. T. (1945). *Photosynthesis*, Vol. 1. Interscience, New York.
332. REAZIN, G. H. (1954). *Amer. J. Bot.*, **41**, 771.
333. —— (1956). *Plant Physiol.*, **31**, 299.
334. REVELLE, R. and FAIRBRIDGE, R. (1957). *Geol. Soc. Am. Mem.* No. **67**, 239.
335. RILEY, G. A. (1957). *Limnol. Oceanogr.*, **2**, 252.
336. RODHE, W. (1958). *Verh. int. ver. Limnol.*, **13**, 121.
336a. ROELOFS, T. D. and OGLESBY, R. T. (1970). *Limnol. Oceanogr.*, **15**, 224.
337. ROUND, F. E. (1953). *J. Ecol.*, **41**, 174.
338. —— (1955). *Arch. Hydrobiol.*, **50**, 111.
339. —— (1956). *Arch. Hydrobiol.*, **52**, 457.
340. —— (1957). *New Phytol.*, **56**, 98.
341. —— (1957). *J. Ecol.*, **45**, 133, 343, and 649.
342. —— (1959). *Soc. Sci. Fenn. Comment. Biol.*, **21/1**, 1.
343. —— (1959). *Soc. Sci. Fenn. Comment. Biol.*, **21/2**, 1.
343a. —— (1959). *Proc. R. Irish. Acad.*, **60B**, 193.
344. —— (1960). *Arch. Protistenk.*, **104**, 524.
345. —— (1960). *J. Ecol.*, **48**, 529.
346. —— (1960). *New Phytol.*, **591**, 332.
347. —— (1961). *J. Ecol.*, **49**, 31, 245.
348. —— (1961). *New Phytol.*, **60**, 43.
349. —— (1961). *J. R. micr. Soc.*, **80**, 59.
350. —— (1963). *Brit. Phycol. Bull.*, **2**.
350a. —— (1967–8). *J. Exp. mar. biol. ecol.*, **1**, 76, **2**, 64.
350b. —— (1970). *Ann. Bot.*, **34**, 75.
350c. —— (1971). *Brit. Phyc. J.*, **3**, 235–264.
350d. —— (1972). *Phycologia*, **2**, 109–17.
351. ROUND, F. E. and BROOK, A. J. (1959). *Proc. R. Irish Acad.*, **60B**, 167.
351a. ROUND, F. E. and HAPPEY, C. M. (1965). *Br. Phycol. Bull.*, **2**, 463.
352. RUTTNER, F. (1952). *Fundamentals of Limnology.* Univ. Toronto Press, Toronto.
353. RZÓSKA, J., BROOK, A. J. and PROWSE, G. A. (1955). *Proc. Int. Ass. Limnol.*, **12**, 327.
354. SAGER, R. and PALADE, G. E. (1954). *Exp. Cell Res.*, **7**, 584.
355. —— (1957). *J. Biophys. Biochem. Cytol.*, **3**, 463.
356. SARMA, Y. S. R. K. (1958). *Brit. Phycol. Bull.*, No. **6**, 22.
357. SCHILLER, J. (1937). *Dinoflagellatae. Rabenhorsts Kryptogamen Flora*, **10**.
358. SCHLECHTER, V. (1934). *J. gen. Physiol.*, **18**, 1.
359. SCHÖN, W. J. (1955). *Flora*, **142**, 347.
360. SCHULER, W. and SPRINGER, G. E. (1957). *Naturwissenschaften*, **44**, 265.
361. SCHUSSNIG, B. (1960). *Handbuch der Protophytenkunde*, Bd. II. G. Fischer, Jena.
362. SCHÜTT, F. (1900). In *Die Naturlichen Pflanzenfamilien*, 1 Ab. b.1, ENGLER, A. Engelmann, Leipzig.
363. SCOTT, G. T. (1943). *J. Cellular Comp. Phys.*, **21**, 327.
363a. SHARPE, J. H. (1969). *Limnol. Oceanogr.*, **14**, 568.
364. SHELUBSKY, M. (1951). *Verh. int. ver. Limnol*, **11**, 362.

365. SHILO, M. and SHILO M. (1955). *Verh. int. ver. Limnol*, **12**, 233.
366. —— (1961). *Verh. int. ver. Limnol*, **14**, 905.
367. SHIVIROFF, P. and FEDOROV, E. (1938). *Nature*, **141**, 629.
368. SILVA, P. C. and PAPENFUSS, G. E. (1953). *S. W. P. C. B. Public.* No. 7.
368a. SILVA, P. C. (1962). Classification in *Physiology and biochemistry of algae*. Ed.
      R. A. Lewin, Academic Press.
369. SINGH, R. N. (1950). *Nature*, **165**, 325.
370. SKUJA, H. (1956). *Nova Acta Soc. upsal.*, Ser. 4, **16**, No. 3. 1.
371. SMAYDA, T. J. (1958). *Oikos*, **9**, 158.
372. SMITH, G. M. (1955). *Cryptogamic Botany*, Vol. 1. McGraw-Hill, New York
      and Maidenhead.
373. SMYTH, J. C. (1955). *J. Ecol.*, **43**, 149.
374. SOROKIN, C. (1957/8). *Physiol. Plant*, **10**, 659, **11**, 275.
375. SOROKIN, C. and KRAUSS, R. W. (1958). *Plant Physiol.*, **33**, 109.
376. SPOEHR, H. A. and MILNER, H. W. (1949). *Plant Physiol.*, **24**, 120.
377. STANIER, R. Y. and VAN NIEL, C. B. (1941). *J. Bact.*, **42**, 437.
378. STEEMAN-NIELSEN, E. and JENSEN, A. (1957). *Galathea Report*, **1**, 49.
378a. STEPHENSON, T. A. and STEPHENSON, A. (1949). *J. Ecol.* **37**, 289.
379. STEPHENSON, T. A. and STEPHENSON, A. (1950). *J. Ecol.*, **38**, 354.
380. —— (1952). *J. Ecol.*, **40**, 1.
381. —— (1954). *J. Ecol.*, **42**, 14, 46.
382. STRAIN, H. H. (1958). *32nd Annual Priestley Lectures*, Penn. State Univ.
      Pennsylvania.
383. STREET, H. E., GRIFFITHS, D. J., THRESHER, C. L. and OWENS, M. (1958).
      Nature, **182**, 1360.
384. SWEENEY, B. M. and HASTINGS, J. W. (1957). *J. cell. comp. Physiol.*, **49**,
      115.
384a. SWEENEY, B. M. and HAXO, F. T. (1961). *Science*, **134**, 1361–1363.
385. SWEENEY, B. M. (1963). Rhythms. In *Physiology and Biochemistry of Algae*.
      Ed. LEWIN, R. A. Academic Press, New York and London.
386. SYMOENS, J. J. (1957). *Bull Soc. Bot. Belg.*, **89**, 111.
387. SYRETT, P. J. (1953). *Ann. Bot.*, N.S. **17**, 1.
387a. SZCZEPANSKI, A. (1966). *Verh. int. ver. Limnol*, **16**, 364.
388. TALLING, J. F. (1955). *Ann. Bot.*, N.S. **19**, 329.
389. —— (1957). *New Phytol.*, **56**, 133.
390. —— (1960). *Limnol. Oceanogr.*, **5**, 62.
391. TAMIYA, H. (1957). *Annu. Rev. Pl. Physiol.*, **8**, 309.
392. TANADA, T. (1951). *Amer. J. Bot.*, **38**, 276.
393. TAYLOR, W. R. (1957). *Marine Algae of the North-eastern Coast of North America*.
      Univ. of Michigan Press, Ann Arbor.
394. —— (1960). *Marine Algae of the Eastern and Subtropical Coasts of America*. Univ.
      of Michigan Press, Ann Arbor.
395. TCHAKHOTINE, S. (1936). *C. R. Soc. Biol.*, **121**, 1162.
396. THACKER, D. R. and BABCOCK, H. (1957). *J. Solar Energy Sci. Eng.*, **1**, 37.
397. THIMAN, K. V. and BETH, K. (1959). *Nature*, **183**, 946.
398. THOMAS, J. B., VAN DER LEEN, A. A. J. and KONING, J. (1957). *Biochim.
      biophys. Acta*, **23**, 443.
399. TIFFANY, L. H. and BRITTON, M. E. (1952). *The Algae of Illinois*. Univ. of
      Chicago Press, Chicago.
400. TSENG, C. K. (1944). *Sci. Monthly*, New York, **59**, 37.

401. VACCA, D. D. and WALSH, P. A. (1954). *J. Amer. pharm. Ass.*, **43**, 24.
402. VAN NIEL, C. B., ALLEN, M. B. and WRIGHT, B. E. (1953). *Biochim. biophys. Acta*, **12**, 67.
403. VERDUIN, J. (1951). *Amer. J. Bot.*, **38**, 5.
404. VILHELM, J. (1931). *Archaeophyta und Algophyta.* Prague.
405. VINOGRADOV, A. P. (1953). *Mem. Sears Found. Marine Res.*, **11**, 1.
406. VON STOSCH, H. A. (1961). *Abst. 4th Int. Seaweed Symp.*
407. WAERN, M. (1952). *Acta phytogeogr. suec.*, **30**, 1.
408. WALLNER, J. (1934). *Zbl. Bakt. Parasitenk.*, **2**, Abt. 90, 150.
409. WARBURG, O. and NEGELEIN, E. (1920). *Biochem. Z.*, **110**, 66.
410. WATANABE, A. (1951). *Arch. Biochem. Biophys.*, **34**, 56.
411. WERZ, G. (1959). *Planta*, **53**, 502.
412. WERZ, G. and HÄMMERLING, J. (1959). *Planta*, **53**, 145.
413. WEST, W. and WEST, G. S. (1906). *Proc. R. Irish Acad.*, **32B**, 77.
414. WHITTAKER, D. M. (1931). *Biol. Bull.*, **61**, 294.
415. —— (1936). *Biol. Bull.*, **70**, 100.
416. —— (1937). *Biol. Bull.*, **73**, 249.
417. WHITTAKER, D. M. and LOWRANCE, E. W. (1936). *J. cell. comp. Phys.*, **17**, 417.
418. WHITTINGHAM, C. P. (1960). *Encycl. Plant Phys.*, **12/2**, 447.
419. WILSON, P. W. (1952). *Advanc. Enzymol.*, **13**, 345.
420. WOLFE, M. (1954). *Ann. Bot.*, N.S. **18**, 299.
421. WOLKEN, J. J. (1959). In *The Photochemical Apparatus; Its Structure and Function.* Brookhaven Symp. Biol. No. **11**, 87.
422. —— (1961). *Euglena. An Experimental Organism for Biochemical and Biophysical Studies.* Rutgers U. P., New Brunswick, N.J.
423. WOLKEN, J. J. and PALADE, G. E. (1953). *Ann. N.Y. Acad. Sci.*, **56**, 873.
424. WOLKEN, J. J. and SHIN, E. (1958). *J. Protozool.*, **5**, 39.
425. WOMERSLEY, H. B. S. (1959). *Bot. Rev.*, **25**, 543.
426. WOOD, R. D. (1952). *Bot. Rev.*, **18**, 317.
427. YOCUM, C. S. (1951). Some experiments on photosynthesis in marine algae. *Diss. Stanford Univ.* Quoted in BLINKS, L. R. (1954), see above.
428. YOUNG, C. M. and NICHOLS, A. G. (1931). *Sci. Rep. Great Barrier Reef Exped.*, 135.

Index

Index

Bold type indicates reference to figures; italic type indicates references to taxonomy.

265